IDEAS AND INVESTIGATIONS IN SCIENCE — LIFE SCIENCE

iiS

Ideas and Investigations in Science

Second Edition

LIFE SCIENCE

HARRY K. WONG
Las Lomitas School District
Menlo Park, California

LEONARD BERNSTEIN
Intermediate School 201
New York, New York

EDWARD SHEVICK
Portola Junior High School
Tarzana, California

PRENTICE-HALL, INC., ENGLEWOOD CLIFFS, NEW JERSEY

IDEAS AND INVESTIGATIONS IN SCIENCE

LIFE SCIENCE, Second Edition

Laboratory Data Book
Teacher's Manual
Laboratory Equipment

Design and graphics by Lee Ames & Zak Ltd.,
with Mel Erikson, Andre LeBlanc, Frank Schwarz,
Lorraine Loomer, Anthony D'Adamo,
Holly Moylan, Geraldine Russell, Robert Frank,
and Valerie P. Kasper.

Title page and cover photo, Austing/National Audubon Society

Cover design by James Walsh

IDEAS AND INVESTIGATIONS IN SCIENCE — LIFE SCIENCE

Second Edition

Harry K. Wong, Leonard Bernstein, and Edward Shevick

ISBN 0-13-450064-4   10 9 8 7 6 5 4 3 2 1

Prentice-Hall International, Inc., **London**
Prentice-Hall of Australia, Pty, Ltd., **Sydney**
Prentice-Hall of Canada, Ltd., **Toronto**
Prentice-Hall of India Private Ltd., **New Delhi**
Prentice-Hall of Japan, Inc., **Tokyo**
Prentice-Hall of Southeast Asia Pte. Ltd., **Singapore**
Whitehall Books Limited, Wellington, **New Zealand**

Welcome:

Welcome is a friendly word. You find it on invitations to parties. It means you have been invited. Someone is thinking about you. You are wanted.

Consider this an invitation to learn about life, its properties, structures, functions, and relationships.

Your invitation to learn will be rewarding. You are about to learn 66 basic concepts. These concepts represent the content or subject matter of this program. These concepts have not been handed down from some high source. The knowledge of science has been discovered by scientists. This is what scientists do: they observe the world around them, they ask questions, make hypotheses, construct models, solve problems, and make discoveries. In IIS you will learn the basic concepts of life science by discovering them on your own.

This year you will be studying about life, its characteristics, and the relationships that take place among living things. You will study the properties and organization of living things. You will study metabolism and energy requirements. You will find out where living things come from, how they reproduce, and why they live where they do. You will make slides, use microscopes, balances, and burners. You will look into the windows of the world through the eyes of a scientist. You will do all of these things right in your science classroom. Get yourself ready; the window will open in just a while.

We hope you will accept our invitation. That's why we invited you. We'll see you again soon.

Harry Wong
Len Bernstein
Ed Shevick

CONTENTS

Idea 1

SCIENTIFIC METHOD

Investigation		Topic
1	YOU'RE THE SCIENTIST 1	Observation
2	HOW DO YOU MEASURE UP? 9	Measurement
3	A METRIC MASS 17	Prediction
4	EXPERIMENTS UNDER CONTROL 23	Control
5	LET'S GET ORGANIZED 29	Data Tables
6	WHAT'S YOUR GAME PLAN? 33	Problem Solving

Idea 2

CHARACTERISTICS

Investigation		Topic
1	IS IT ALIVE? 39	Size and Shape
2	GROWING FOR A CHANGE 45	Growth and Change
3	IT IS A STIMULATING LIFE 51	Stimulus—Response
4	THE NEED FOR WATER 57	Water Requirements
5	TAKE A DEEP BREATH 61	Air Requirements
6	FOOD AND LIFE 67	Food Requirements

Idea 3

CELLS

Investigation		Topic
1	LEARNING TO USE THE MICROSCOPE 73	Microscopes
2	EARLY MICROSCOPES 79	Cell Study
3	CELLS COME IN MANY SHAPES AND SIZES 85	Shape and Function
4	THE CELL DOES IT ALL 91	Cell Structures
5	THE WONDERFUL WORLD OF THE CELL 95	Permeability
6	CELL ORGANIZATION 99	Organization

Idea 4

PHOTOSYNTHESIS

Investigation	Topic
1 ROOTS AND CONDUCTION TISSUES 107	Conduction
2 STOMATES AND GAS EXCHANGE 113	Gas Exchange I
3 GREEN POWER 119	Chlorophyll
4 SOME LIGHT ON THE SUBJECT 123	Light Energy
5 A PLANT FEEDS ITSELF 127	Carbohydrate Production
6 THE BIGGEST RECIPE OF ALL 131	Food Energy

Idea 5

RESPIRATION

Investigation	Topic
1 THE BREATH OF LIFE 137	Oxygen Intake
2 SOMETHING IN, SOMETHING OUT 143	Carbon Dioxide Release
3 FISH RESPIRATION 147	Gas Exchange II
4 SUGAR AND RESPIRATION 153	Sugar Breakdown
5 YOU NEED ENERGY 157	Energy Release
6 FOODS FOR ENERGY 161	Energy Storage

Idea 6

HUMAN SYSTEMS

Investigation	Topic
1 WHAT HAPPENS WHEN YOU EAT? 167	Digestive System
2 BREATHING AND SMOKING 173	Respiratory System
3 THE CIRCULATION OF BLOOD 179	Circulatory System
4 GETTING IT THROUGH TO YOU 185	Diffusion
5 HOW TALL WILL YOU BE? 193	Endocrine System
6 CREATING CONCEPTS CAN CAUSE CONSTERNATION 199	Nervous System
7 THE LATEST TEEN DRUG 205	Drugs and Alcohol

Idea 7

REPRODUCTION

Investigation	Topic
1 THE GOOSE TREE 213	Biogenesis
2 ONE FORM OF REPRODUCTION 217	Asexual Reproduction
3 A SPECIAL KIND OF REPRODUCTION 221	Regeneration
4 GETTING TOGETHER 225	Sexual Reproduction
5 GENES ARE THE THING 231	Genetics

Idea 8
ENVIRONMENT

Investigation	Topic
1 WATER AND THE ENVIRONMENT 237	Water Conditions
2 ENVIRONMENTAL TEMPERATURE 243	Temperature Conditions
3 LIGHT AND SURVIVAL 247	Light Conditions
4 THE FOOD SUPPLY 253	Food Supply
5 CHANGE IN THE ENVIRONMENT 259	Environmental Change
6 WHERE ON EARTH IS LIFE? 263	Biosphere

Idea 9
ADAPTATION

Investigation	Topic
1 THINGS CHANGE 269	Adjustment
2 A SELF-REGULATING MACHINE 273	Homeostasis I
3 SEEING IS BELIEVING 277	Homeostasis II
4 FOOTPRINTS IN THE SANDS OF TIME 283	Fossils
5 THE MYSTERY OF CHANGE 289	Survival

Idea 10
RELATIONSHIPS

Investigation	Topic
1 COUNT, KIND, PLACE, AND TIME 297	Population
2 TYPES OF COMMUNITIES 303	Community
3 PREDATOR AND PREY 309	Predator—Prey
4 SYMBIOTIC RELATIONSHIPS 315	Symbiosis
5 FOOD RELATIONSHIPS 321	Food Chain
6 COMBINING FOOD CHAINS 327	Food Web
7 THIS IS OUR WORLD 333	Ecosystem

Idea 11
BALANCE

Investigation	Topic
1 OVER AND OVER AGAIN 339	Water Cycle
2 DO WE DRINK THIS? 343	Water Pollution
3 LIVING DANGEROUSLY 349	Air Pollution
4 THE CYCLE GOES ON 355	Nutrient Cycle
5 OUR GREATEST RESOURCE 361	Resources

INDEX 369

You're the Scientist

Marlene Franklin is a scientist. When she goes to work, she spends most of her time reading.

She works with other people. In her work, she listens, talks, and discusses. It is important that she know what others are doing. She learns from others.

Ricardo Vasquez was in a science class. These pictures were taken when he took IIS. He had to read, but there was much more.

He interacted with his classmates. Much of the time he spent working and learning in a group.

Much of her time, Marlene asks questions, finds answers to questions, and looks for new questions. She is an inquiring person.

She often works in a laboratory. She may do experiments, because experiments provide answers to questions.

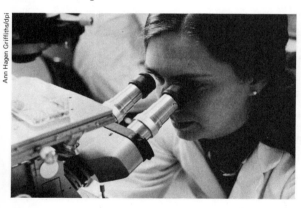

The experiments frequently require that she make measurements. Answers are easier to understand if they are in numbers.

Ricardo asked a lot of questions. In IIS, he did not have to listen to lectures all the time. Instead, he learned how to solve problems. He became an inquiring person.

He enjoyed the daily activities. He did experiments, played games, solved puzzles, and talked with his classmates. Science is doing.

He learned to use numbers. He used measuring devices that had numbers on them. Numbers made his answers more accurate.

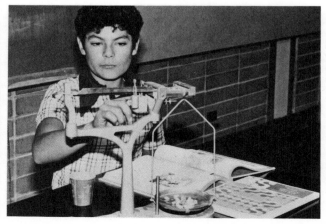

Finally, Marlene thinks. This is what science is all about. It is a way of thinking. It is a method used to solve problems.

Ricardo learned by reading, by doing, and by questioning. He learned how to think out a problem logically. That's what science is all about.

You will be like Marlene and Ricardo this year. You will explore science the way a scientist does. You will be responsible for your own learning. To help you succeed in IIS, you'll have a lot of help. Here are some features that will help you.

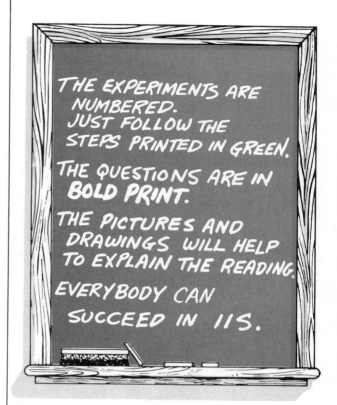

THE EXPERIMENTS ARE NUMBERED. JUST FOLLOW THE STEPS PRINTED IN GREEN.

THE QUESTIONS ARE IN BOLD PRINT.

THE PICTURES AND DRAWINGS WILL HELP TO EXPLAIN THE READING.

EVERYBODY CAN SUCCEED IN IIS.

Your teacher will also be a helper. He or she will supply the materials, explain some of the reading, and ask questions. Your teacher will not tell you all the answers, but rather will challenge you. You have to find the answers. To find the answers, each Investigation requires that you do these four things: read, do the activities, discuss the results, and answer the questions.

Each INVESTIGATION consists of:

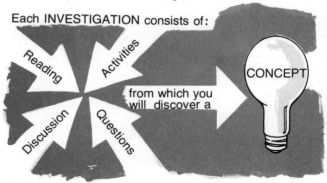

Reading   Activities   Discussion   Questions   from which you will discover a   CONCEPT

The purpose of each Investigation is to teach you one concept. The concept that you will study in this Investigation is a skill all scientists use.

A. MANY PEOPLE SEE, BUT DO NOT OBSERVE

An important skill of the scientist is **observation**. Observation means many things. It may mean *seeing* a flower's color or *listening* to a bird's song. It may mean *smelling* a polluted pond or *touching* a furry animal. It may also mean *tasting* some cheese. Scientists use most of their senses to observe. Careful observations help scientists solve problems.

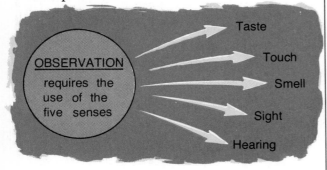

Heron/Monkmeyer

You will do many things in this class. To help you keep track, blanks have been left after the Step numbers on your data sheets. Check off each Step as you do it.

1. Touch the index fingers of your two hands together.

2. Place the two fingers about a book's length in front of your eyes.

3. Stare at the two fingers as you slowly bring them toward your eyes.

4. **Describe what you observe as your fingers approach your eyes.**

5. Roll a sheet of paper into a tube. Make the tube opening about the width of your thumb.

6. Look through the tube with your right eye. Bring your left hand up against the side of the tube. Keep both eyes open.

7. **What appears to be in your left hand?**

8. Look at the three boys in the drawing.

9. **Which boy is the tallest?**

10. **Check your answer by measuring each boy with the length of your pencil.**

What you have just observed are ***optical illusions***. Optical illusions can fool your eyes. It is important that the skill of observation be practiced with great care. Let's see how carefully you can observe.

11. **Observe the drawing of the scissors.**

12. **What is wrong with these scissors?**

13. **Observe the words in the triangle.**

PARIS
IN THE
THE SPRING

14. **What is wrong with the sentence?**

15. **Observe the sentence in the box. Read it only once. Count the number of ''F's'' in the sentence.**

FIFTY FRIENDLY FARMERS FINISHED FIFTEEN HARD YEARS OF SCIENTIFIC FARMING OF FIELDS PLANTED IN LOADS OF SOFT PERFUMED FLOWERS.

16. **How many ''F's'' did you count?**

17. **Check with your teacher to see if you counted correctly.**

It's not too difficult to fool your eyes or your other four senses. It is also possible for you to learn to make more accurate observations. Taking care to observe carefully can help you succeed in the activities in this book. Science starts with accurate observations.

18. **Which one of your five senses have you been using?**

19. **What are your other four senses?**

20. **What skill have you been practicing?**

21. **What is one important skill of a scientist?**

B. YOU DON'T HAVE TO SEE TO OBSERVE

Helen Keller

Culver Pictures, Inc.

Helen Keller was a famous woman who couldn't see or hear. Yet she was able to accomplish much with her life by using the senses she still had. She used mainly her sense of touch to learn about her world.

Here is a chance for you to develop your sense of touch. You will be given a set of letters. Can you identify them by your sense of touch only?

22. Sit down, close your eyes, and hold both hands behind your back.

23. Your partner will hand you letters, one at a time. Tell your partner what you think each letter is.

24. Switch places with your partner and repeat Steps 22 and 23.

25. How many letters did you recognize?

26. How many letters did your partner recognize?

27. What sense did you use to observe the letters?

28. Explain why scientists need to make careful observations to solve their problems.

C. THE WATER FOUNTAIN PROBLEM

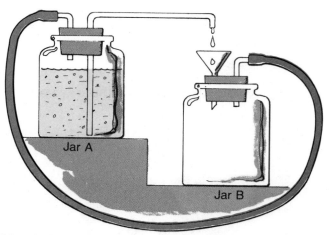

Jar A

Jar B

29. Carefully observe the drawing. Your teacher will have a similar set-up on display.

30. **What is in Jar A?**

31. **What is in Jar B?**

32. **Which jar is higher?**

33. **What is the only thing that connects Jar A to Jar B?**

Your teacher will now pour some water in the funnel on top of Jar B.

34. **Describe what happened.**

35. **On the basis of your observations, explain why you think it happened.**

Share your solution to the water fountain problem with your classmates. After the class discussion, answer Question 36.

36. **What is the best explanation of the water fountain problem?**

37. **What is the first step in solving scientific problems? (Hint: What did you have to do to answer Questions 30-33?)**

38. **Why is it important for scientists to make careful observations?**

D. PUTTING IT ALL TOGETHER

This Investigation has given you a chance to practice a science skill. You've worked with optical illusions, letters, and a water fountain. Each activity has asked you to solve a problem.

39. **To solve each problem, what did you have to do?**

40. **What must scientists do to solve a problem?**

41. **What is one important skill of a scientist?**

In this course you will discover one concept in each Investigation. A concept is an idea. In other words, what concept did you learn in this Investigation?

Re-read your answers to Questions 39-41. Then write your concept in a complete sentence on your data sheet.

CONCEPT

ENRICHMENT

1. Observe this optical illusion. Try to copy it on a sheet of paper. Do not trace it.

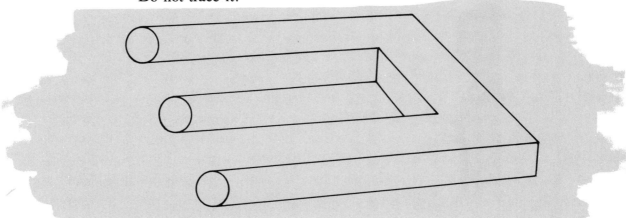

2. Look in the library for books on optical illusions. Share your findings with the class.

3. Check the class for their ability to observe sounds. See if they can recognize various sounds. Their eyes should be closed.

4. How do blind people read by using their sense of touch? Look up Braille in a reference book to find the answer.

5. Observe both hands of a classmate. Try to find differences between the two hands.

6. The following inscription appears on a gravestone. Can you observe an obvious error?

In Memory of
HERMAN JOHNSON
Born June 20, 1751
Died December 21, 1826
Age 75

In Memory Also
Of His Widow
HILDA JOHNSON
Born August 29, 1755
Died October 24, 1825
Age 70

Investigation 2

How Do You Measure Up?

Ewing Galloway, N.Y.

Culver Pictures, Inc.

Dr. Edward Jenner discovered how to prevent the disease called smallpox. His discovery was a result of careful observation. Dr. Jenner observed that people who milked cows came down with a mild disease called cowpox. They never caught the more serious smallpox disease that could cause death. By deliberately giving people cowpox, he prevented them from catching smallpox.

Sir Alexander Fleming received the Nobel prize in medicine for his accurate observations. He observed that mold growing in one of his experiments killed bacteria. The mold contained a bacteria-killing substance which Dr. Fleming called *penicillin*. Penicillin and substances like it help cure many diseases.

Drs. Jenner and Fleming needed more than observation skills in order to succeed. Let's investigate another skill they must have used.

A. ARE YOU ALL THUMBS?

This dog house failed because each part was measured differently. One person used a ruler marked in inches. Another used a metric ruler. The third couldn't find a ruler and used his thumb for measuring.

You will make a ruler just like the third person did. Remember to check off each Step on your data sheet as you do it.

1. Your teacher will give you a piece of cardboard.

2. Mark off spaces the width of your thumb.

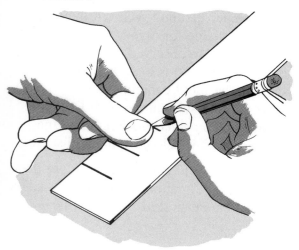

3. Number the lines as shown.

4. Measure the width of your table using your thumb ruler.

5. How many thumbs wide is your table?

6. Check with some of your classmates who measured the same size table. How many thumb widths did they measure?

You have a problem. The tables seem to be different sizes.

7. Explain why this might be.

8. What's the problem with using thumbs for measurement?

In the last Investigation, you learned that a scientist must observe accurately.

9. What else must scientists do accurately?

B. IT'S A METRIC WORLD

Our old system of measuring was originally based on human measurements. The length from the king's nose to the end of his thumb became our yard. The length of the king's foot became our foot. Our inch was the length of the last bone of a man's thumb. Even the mile was equal to 1000 steps of a Roman soldier. Can you see some of the problems that could be caused by using people measurements? To build dog houses or buildings you need a better standard to measure length. There is a better and easier standard, based upon a unit called the **_meter_**. You will use a **_metric ruler_**. The metric ruler is the most widely used ruler in the world. It's very easy to use. All you have to do is count by 1's and 10's. You don't use fractions.

This is an enlarged drawing of a section of a metric ruler. The distance between two lines is a **_millimeter_**, or _mm_.

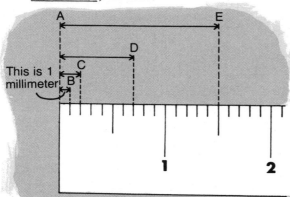

There is 1 millimeter between A and B.
There are 2 millimeters between A and C.
There are 7 millimeters between A and D.
There are 15 millimeters between A and E.

To make it easier to read, every 5th and 10th line is longer.

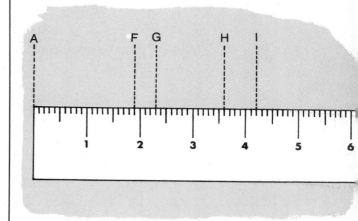

10. **How many millimeters are between A and F?**

11. **How many millimeters are between A and G?**

12. **How many millimeters are between A and H?**

13. **How many millimeters are between A and I?**

14. **Get a metric ruler. Study it carefully.**

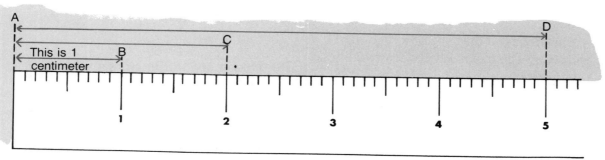

15. How many millimeters long is line J?

16. How many millimeters long is line K?

17. How many millimeters long is line L?

18. Measure the length of a playing card. How many millimeters long is it? Remember to place *mm* after your answer.

19. Measure the width of a playing card. How many millimeters wide is it?

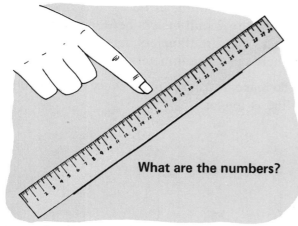

What are the numbers?

That's a good question. The numbers are **_centimeters_**. Each centimeter is equal to 10 millimeters. A centimeter is called *cm*.

This student is measuring a book. On the metric ruler, the edge of the book falls between two numbers. Write down the *smaller* number. For this book it is 22. Then put a decimal point after the 22. Count the lines after 22. Then write that number after the decimal point. The book is about 22.7 centimeters long.

There are 10 millimeters or 1 centimeter between A and B.

There are 2 centimeters between A and C.

There are 5 centimeters between A and D.

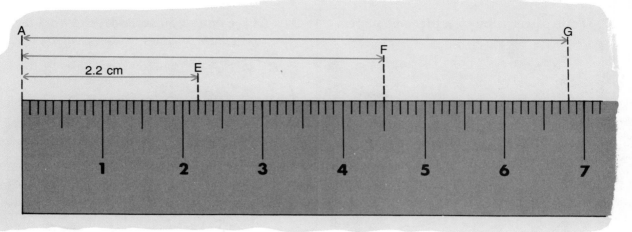

There are 22 millimeters or 2.2 centimeters between A and E.
There are 4.5 centimeters between A and F.
There are 6.8 centimeters between A and G.

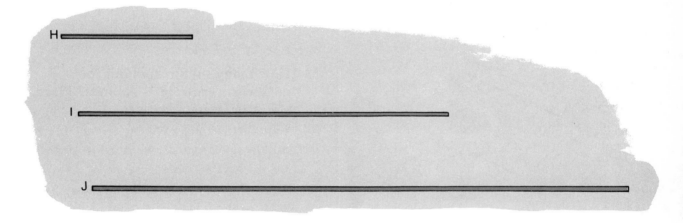

20. **How many centimeters long is line H? Place *cm* after your answer.**

21. **How many centimeters long is line I?**

22. **How many centimeters long is line J?**

23. **Measure the length of this book's cover. How many centimeters long is it? Remember to place *cm* after your answer.**

24. **Measure the width of this book's cover. How many centimeters wide is it?**

25. **What system of measurement have you been using?**

26. **What must a scientist be able to do accurately?**

C. A METRIC MEALWORM RACE

Walter Dawn

27. Tape a test tube to a piece of paper.

28. Draw a line next to the open end of the test tube.

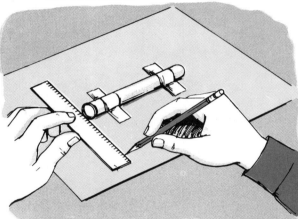

29. Place a mealworm at the opening of the test tube.

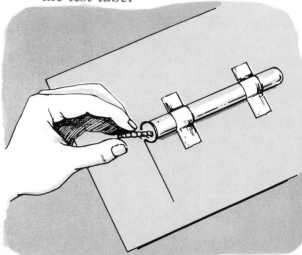

30. Observe the mealworm for 30 seconds.

31. At the end of 30 seconds, draw a line next to the *tail* end of the mealworm.

32. Measure the distance between the lines in *millimeters*.

33. **How many millimeters did the mealworm crawl in 30 seconds? Place *mm* after your answer.**

34. Find 2 classmates willing to race their mealworms against yours. Give each mealworm a name.

35. Place the test tubes and papers next to each other.

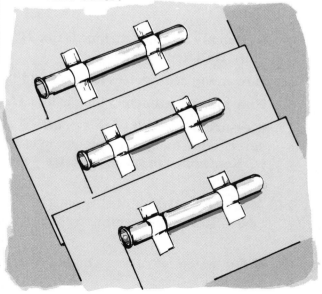

36. Repeat Steps 29-31. Be sure to start each mealworm at the same time.

37. Measure the distances between each set of lines in *centimeters*.

38. How many centimeters did each mealworm travel? List each mealworm's name and distance. Be sure to write *cm* after each distance.

39. Mealworm races are only for fun. What might happen in drag races if distances were not measured accurately?

40. Explain why it is important to measure accurately.

UPI

D. THE METRIC END

"You'd never get to the moon. You'd need two hundred of those things."

© 1976 Universal Press Syndicate

To measure the distance to the moon you would need units larger than meters or ladders. The metric unit used for long measurements is called a *__kilometer__.* The *kilo* in kilometer means thousand, so the kilometer is equal to 1000 meters. Imagine 1000 meter sticks lined up end to end. That's a distance of one kilometer.

41. What system of measurement have you been using?

42. Besides observing, what skill must you have to solve problems?

Re-read your answers to Questions 40 and 42. Then write the concept.

CONCEPT

ENRICHMENT

1. Want to get tall fast? Measure your height in centimeters. Want to get even taller? Measure your height in millimeters.

2. Measure the width and length of your thumb in centimeters. Check to see if your right and left thumbs are exactly the same.

3. How long is your shoe? Compare your shoe length with those of other students in your class.

4. What are the diameters of a penny, nickel, dime, and quarter? How could you measure the distance around a quarter?

5. Find the length, width, and height of your classroom in centimeters. You may want to borrow a meter stick from your teacher.

Investigation 3

A Metric Mass

You're doing fine. You've studied two scientific skills. You know the importance of accurate observations and measurements.

THE WIZARD OF ID by Brant parker and Johnny hart

Johnny Hart/Field Enterprises, Inc.

But there's much more to science. Science is being curious about how birds fly and how fish swim. Science means asking a lot of questions about why and how things work. Scientists try to solve problems in an orderly manner. They attempt to use a logical method to obtain more knowledge about the world in which we live.

Your five senses need help to pry loose the secrets of nature. You can't even measure a book without a ruler. Scientists use many instruments to obtain measurements that couldn't be obtained with the unaided senses. Measurement instruments make science more detailed and precise.

This is a _**balance**_ used by the ancient Egyptians. In this Investigation you will learn to use a balance. Your classroom balances work in much the same way as the Egyptian balance.

A. ARE YOU WELL BALANCED?

The amount of matter in an object is called its **mass**. You can measure the mass of solids, liquids, and gases. The metric unit of mass is the **gram**. The symbol for gram is g. A paper clip has a mass of about 1 gram.

One thousand grams equal a **kilogram**. The symbol for kilogram is kg. Your body may have a mass of 45 kilograms, which is equal to 45,000 grams.

You will be using a balance to measure mass. The balance is like a see-saw. If two students of the same mass are on a see-saw, it will balance. A laboratory balance works the same way. You put an object in one pan. Then you add known masses to the other pan until it balances.

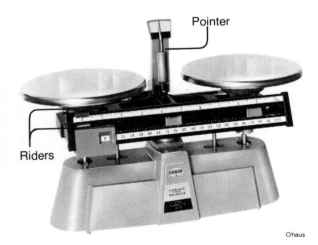

Pointer

Riders

Ohaus

There are many kinds of balances. Your teacher will demonstrate how to use your classroom balances. Here are some general rules that apply to all balances.

1. Carry the balance with both hands.

2. Keep the balance pans clean.

3. Always place your balance on a level surface.

4. Place all riders completely to the left before each use.

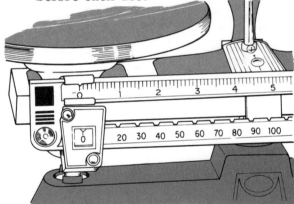

5. Zero the balance before each use. Your teacher will point out the knob that zeroes your particular balance. The pointer can be at zero. Or, the pointer can swing the same number of lines on each side of zero.

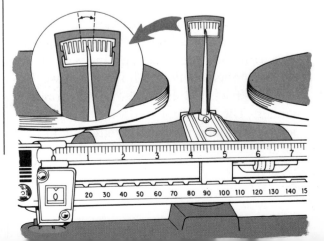

6. Place the object being measured on the *left* pan.

7. Move the riders to the right so that the pointer is at zero. The pointer can also swing the same number of lines on each side of zero.

8. Add extra masses as needed to the right pan.

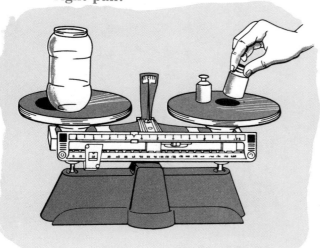

9. After each use, set all riders back to the left and re-zero the balance.

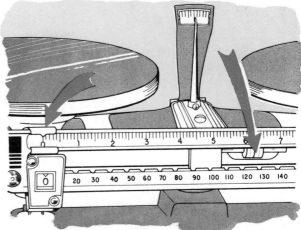

Now for some practice in measuring masses. Your teacher will give you a set of five objects.

10. Measure the mass of the rubber stopper. Record its mass in grams on your data sheet.

11. Repeat Step 10 using a nail, beaker, ruler, and a glass microscope slide.

12. Compare your results with those of your classmates to see how well you did. If time permits, find some other objects around the room to measure.

13. **What instrument is used to measure the mass of objects?**

14. **Length can be measured in centimeters and millimeters. What units are used to measure mass?**

B. PREDICTION TIME

Seaver/March of Dimes

Scientists make guesses. They make guesses all the time. And, they are often right. This is because many things in nature happen over and over the same way.

A *prediction* is an educated guess. Predicting helps a scientist solve problems. If you have a problem and don't know the answer, a prediction will help. The prediction helps you to see where you are going.

Let's use our metric skills to make some predictions.

15. Find the mass of a jar.

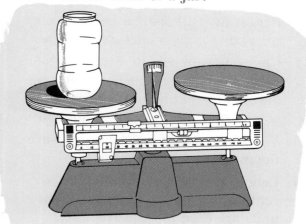

16. What is the mass of the jar?

17. Use a grease pencil to mark a line 2 centimeters from the bottom of the jar.

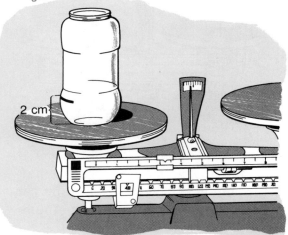

2 cm

18. Add water to the jar exactly up to the 2-centimeter mark.

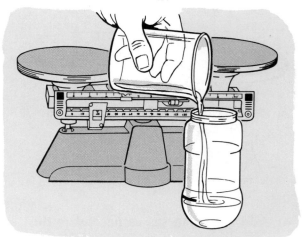

19. Find the mass of the jar plus water.

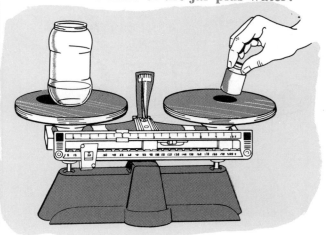

20. What is the mass of the jar plus water?

21. What is the mass of the water alone? (Hint: Subtract your answer to Question 16 from your answer to Question 20.)

You now have enough information to make an educated guess. You know the mass of the jar, and you know the mass of two centimeters of water. *Without measuring,* can you predict the total mass of the jar and four centimeters of water?

22. What is your prediction for the total mass of the jar plus four centimeters of water?

23. Mark a line 4 centimeters from the bottom of the jar.

24. Add water to the jar to the 4-centimeter mark.

25. Find the mass of the jar plus water.

26. What is the mass of the jar plus four centimeters of water?

27. Compare your prediction from Question 22 with your measured answer to Question 26. Was your prediction just right, too high, or too low?

28. How can you account for any difference between your predicted and measured answers?

Your prediction may not have been exactly right. Neither are the predictions of scientists always right. Predictions are used to point out possible ways to solve problems. They are based upon accurate observations and some previous knowledge. Predictions must be tested. Tests often show you that the prediction is wrong. Then you must change your prediction and try new tests.

29. What do scientists call their guesses?

30. How do scientists use predictions?

C. A FLOATING PREDICTION

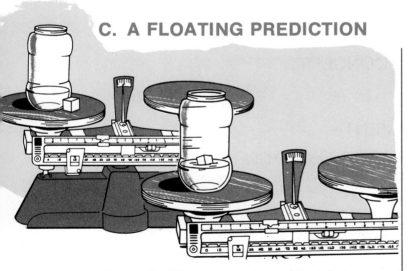

Study the illustration above. Both balances have the *same* objects on the left pan. In the left balance, the wood block and the jar of water are separate. In the right balance, the wood block is floating on the water. Your problem is to decide if there would be any difference in total mass.

Would the right balance show *more* mass, *less* mass, or the *same* mass as the left balance?

31. What is your prediction? Will the right balance show more, less, or the same mass as the left balance?

32. Get a wood block, jar of water, and a balance.

33. Find the mass as shown in the left illustration.

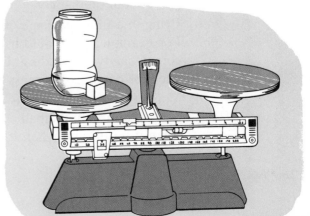

21

34. **What is the total mass of the separated jar of water and wood block?**

35. **Find the mass when the block is floating in the jar of water.**

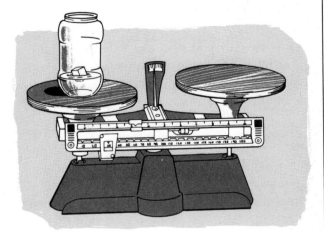

36. **What is the total mass of the block floating in the jar?**

37. **Compare your answers to Questions 34 and 36. What have you discovered?**

38. **How do your results compare with your predictions?**

At the top of the page is a photograph of a precision balance that can measure the mass of a speck of dust. It can be used to test

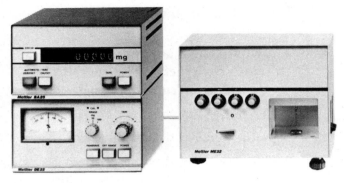

Mettler Instrument Corp.

predictions about small quantities of matter. You could use this balance to measure how much mass a fly gains after eating.

You've learned to use the balance in this Investigation. Measurements with balances are only part of how scientists solve their problems.

39. **What are guesses in science called?**

40. **Why shouldn't you expect predictions always to be right?**

41. **Explain why scientists use predictions to help solve their problems.**

Re-read Questions 39, 40, and 41 and write the concept.

CONCEPT

ENRICHMENT

1. Would you like to know your metric mass? Multiply your weight in pounds by 454. This will give you your approximate mass in grams.

2. Check the labels on food products. Notice how many tell the mass of the contents in grams. Collect some metric labels and place them on display.

3. Bring in a small package of food that gives the mass in grams. For example, you could use a small package of potato chips, cereal, candy, or pudding. Use your class balance to check if the package contains the mass it says it does.

4. You've measured the mass of water in a jar. Try to measure the mass of air in a basketball. Hint: Measure the basketball's mass when it is full and when it is empty.

Investigation 4

Experiments Under Control

The Bettmann Archive, Inc.

Thomas Jefferson was one of America's greatest presidents. He also was a scientist and an inventor. He disliked the system of measuring length that was used in his time. This system included inches, feet, hands, spans, links, leagues, fathoms, furlongs, and rods. Way back in 1790 Jefferson proposed a system of measurement based upon units of 10. His proposal was turned down by Congress.

Suva/dpi

Ohio Dept. of Transportation

Our present measurement system is used by very few of the world's countries. Slowly, but surely, we are switching over to the metric system. You will find the metric system used throughout this book. You have already learned to measure mass and length in metric units. In this Investigation you will learn how to measure volume in metric units. And you will use the skill to discover how scientists set up their experiments.

A. POUR IT ON

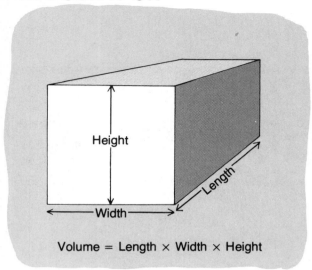

Volume = Length × Width × Height

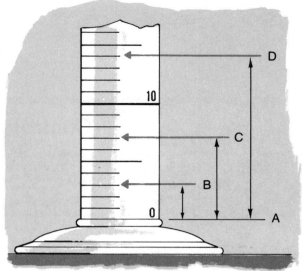

Volume is the amount of space something takes up. You, a rock, and a glass of water all have a certain volume.

You will use a graduated cylinder to measure volume. The graduated cylinder is a scientific measuring cup. It is called a **graduate** for short. There are lines on the graduate. The lines show the volume of what is being measured. Your graduate measures in **milliliters,** or *ml*. The milliliter is a metric unit of volume. It takes only 5 milliliters of water to fill a teaspoon.

When scientists work with large volumes, they use a unit called a **liter**. One liter equals 1000 milliliters. A liter is slightly bigger than a quart.

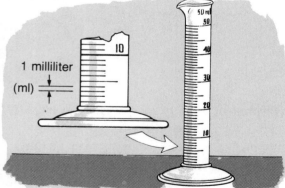

Look at the picture of the 50 ml graduate. There are 10 spaces between 0 and 10. Therefore, each line stands for 1 milliliter. To help you, every 5th and 10th line is longer.

1. **What is the volume between A and B? Write *ml* after your number.**
2. **What is the volume between A and C?**
3. **What is the volume between A and D?**
4. Get a graduate. Examine it.
5. Carefully pour water into the graduate. Stop when the water *nears* the 50 ml line.

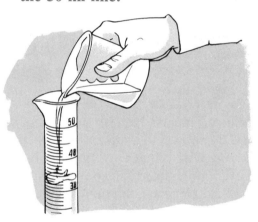

6. Observe the surface of the water. It curves downward. Volume measurements are always taken at the *bottom* of the curve.

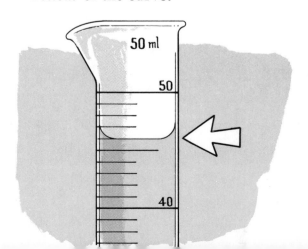

7. **How many milliliters of water are in the graduate? Remember to read the _bottom_ of the curve.**

8. **Obtain a set of objects from your teacher. Fill the smaller test tube to the brim with water.**

9. **Carefully pour the water from the test tube into your graduate. Measure the amount of water in milliliters and record on your data sheet.**

10. **Fill the larger test tube with water and repeat Step 9.**

11. **Fill the smaller jar with water and repeat Step 9.**

12. **Fill the larger jar with water and repeat Step 9.**

Your graduate may be too small to handle all the water in the larger jar. Try filling the graduate to its top number. Let's assume this is 50 milliliters. Jot down 50 ml on your data sheet. Pour the 50 milliliters of water into the sink. Now pour the remaining water from the jar into the graduate. Let's assume it measures 43 milliliters. Therefore, the volume of water in the jar was 50 plus 43, or 93 milliliters.

13. **Fill a small milk carton with water and repeat Step 9.**

14. **If time permits, find the volume of some other containers.**

You've now learned to measure three things with metric tools. Let's review to help you remember them.

15. **What instrument is used to measure length?**

16. **In what units have you learned to measure length?**

17. **What instrument is used to measure mass?**

18. **In what units have you measured mass?**

19. **What instrument is used to measure volume?**

20. **What units are used to measure volume?**

B. WHAT EVERY GOOD EXPERIMENT SHOULD HAVE

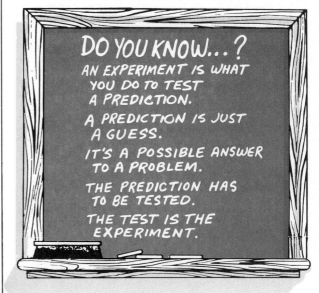

DO YOU KNOW...?

AN EXPERIMENT IS WHAT YOU DO TO TEST A PREDICTION.

A PREDICTION IS JUST A GUESS.

IT'S A POSSIBLE ANSWER TO A PROBLEM.

THE PREDICTION HAS TO BE TESTED.

THE TEST IS THE EXPERIMENT.

It's not enough for scientists just to do experiments. Their experiments must provide a comparison. The comparison is called the **_control_**. In a controlled experiment you change only the *one* thing you are testing. Everything else must be as alike as possible. Otherwise, you cannot trust the results of the experiment.

A student read a magazine which predicted that aspirins would help plants grow faster. She decided to test this prediction with a controlled experiment. Here's what she did.

She found two geranium plants the *same* size and shape.
She placed them in the *same* soil.
She placed them where they got the *same* amount of sunlight.
She kept them at the *same* temperature.
She gave them the *same* amount of water.

There was only one difference in how the plants were treated. One plant had aspirins placed in its soil.

21. What were some of the conditions that the student controlled?

22. What was the *only* difference in how she treated the plants?

23. Suppose there was a difference in how the plants grew. What must have caused the difference?

24. Suppose the student had also watered one plant more than the other. What *two* things may then have caused any difference in growth?

25. How many things should vary in a controlled experiment?

26. Explain why scientists use controlled experiments to test their predictions.

C. CONTROLLING SUGAR AND SALT

What happens when you add sugar or salt to water? Does the volume increase? Suppose you added the *same* amount of sugar and salt to *equal* volumes of water. Would sugar and water have the same, less, or equal volume as salt and water? What's your prediction?

27. **Read the last paragraph carefully and then make your own prediction. Will the sugar water have the same, less, or equal volume as the salt water?**

28. **Fill two graduates with exactly 30 milliliters of water. Mark one graduate "Sugar" and the other "Salt."**

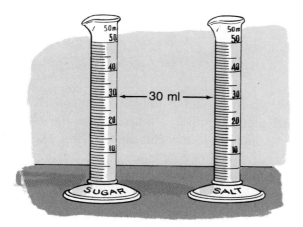

29. **Cut two paper circles roughly the size of the pan of your balance. They should both be exactly the same size.**

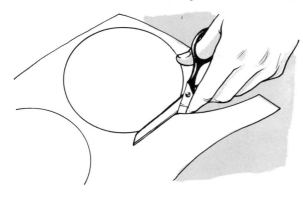

30. **Place one paper on the left pan of your balance. Add sugar until the sugar and paper together have a mass of 15 grams.**

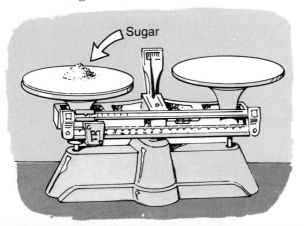

Sugar

31. **Pour the sugar into the graduate marked "Sugar."**

32. **Place the second paper on the balance. Add salt until the salt and paper together have a mass of 15 grams.**

Salt

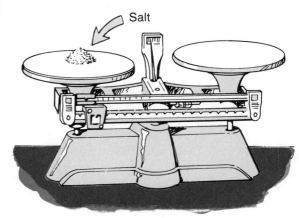

33. **Pour the salt into the graduate marked "Salt."**

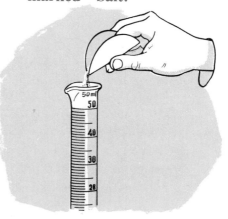

34. **Read the volume of each graduate. Remember to measure from the bottom of the curve.**

35. What is the volume in milliliters of the sugar and water?

36. What is the volume in milliliters of the salt and water?

37. Which one increased more in volume?

38. Why were you able to ignore the mass of the paper used to handle the sugar and salt?

39. This was a controlled experiment. What was kept the *same* in both graduates?

40. What was the *only difference* between the graduates?

41. Why is this considered a controlled experiment?

42. Why are predictions tested with controlled experiments?

D. YOU ARE NOW IN CONTROL

American Cancer Society

This is a cigarette smoking machine. Scientists are measuring the amount of tar in different brands of cigarettes. Each brand must be smoked in *exactly the same way*.

Otherwise this would not be a controlled experiment. The only thing that will vary is the amount of tar in each brand. That's what the experiment is designed to test.

43. Suppose the machine smoked brand "X" for three minutes and brand "Y" for five minutes. Explain why you wouldn't consider the results accurate.

44. How many things should vary in a controlled experiment?

45. What should scientists use to test their predictions?

Re-read your answers to Questions 44 and 45. Then write the concept.

CONCEPT

ENRICHMENT

1. Check the labels on liquid products such as milk and soda pop. Notice how many give the volume in milliliters. Collect some for display.

2. Convert a tall, slim olive jar into a graduate. Place a strip of tape along the outside, running from top to bottom. Use a graduate to add 5, 10, 15, etc. ml of water. Mark each amount on the tape.

3. Find an object that does not fit into a graduate. Design an experiment to find its volume.

4. Carry out the controlled experiment with aspirin. Report your results to the class.

Investigation 5

Let's Get Organized

Culver Pictures, Inc.

A. A DIFFERENT KIND OF TABLE

Wide World Photos

In many ways, Columbus was a scientist. He had to make careful observations and accurate measurements. He predicted the world was round. His trip across the Atlantic was his way of testing his prediction.

In testing predictions, scientists collect **_data_**. Data are facts and information discovered during observations and experiments. Scientists organize this information into **_data tables_**. A well organized data table can help a scientist draw conclusions from his or her experiments. Data tables can sometimes point the way to new predictions and new experiments.

So far you have collected data on length, mass, and volume. In this Investigation you are going to collect and organize more data. Let's start out by looking at some baseball data tables.

BABE RUTH'S RECORD
Regular Season

Year	Club	No.	Year	Club	No.
1914	Boston (AL)	0	1926	New York (AL)	47
1915	Boston (AL)	4	1927	New York (AL)	60
1916	Boston (AL)	3	1928	New York (AL)	54
1917	Boston (AL)	2	1929	New York (AL)	46
1918	Boston (AL)	11	1930	New York (AL)	49
1919	Boston (AL)	29	1931	New York (AL)	46
1920	New York (AL)	54	1932	New York (AL)	41
1921	New York (AL)	59	1933	New York (AL)	34
1922	New York (AL)	35	1934	New York (AL)	22
1923	New York (AL)	41	1935	Boston (NL)	6
1924	New York (AL)	46			
1925	New York (AL)	25		Total 714	

Until 1974, Babe Ruth held the world's record for the most career home runs. His yearly record is shown in the data table on page 29. The table organizes the data about his home runs. It's easy to find information organized in a data table.

1. **In what year did Babe Ruth hit 60 home runs?**

2. **When was the last year that Babe Ruth played baseball? How many homers did he hit that year?**

3. **In what two years did Babe Ruth hit 54 home runs?**

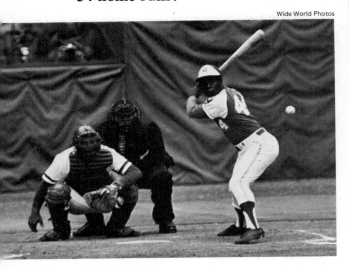
Wide World Photos

HENRY AARON'S RECORD
Regular Season

Year	Club	No.	Year	Club	No.
1954	Milwaukee (NL)	13	1966	Atlanta (NL)	44
1955	Milwaukee (NL)	27	1967	Atlanta (NL)	39
1956	Milwaukee (NL)	26	1968	Atlanta (NL)	29
1957	Milwaukee (NL)	44	1969	Atlanta (NL)	44
1958	Milwaukee (NL)	30	1970	Atlanta (NL)	38
1959	Milwaukee (NL)	39	1971	Atlanta (NL)	47
1960	Milwaukee (NL)	40	1972	Atlanta (NL)	34
1961	Milwaukee (NL)	34	1973	Atlanta (NL)	40
1962	Milwaukee (NL)	45	1974	Atlanta (NL)	20
1963	Milwaukee (NL)	44	1975	Milwaukee (AL)	12
1964	Milwaukee (NL)	24			
1965	Milwaukee (NL)	32		Total	745

Babe Ruth hit 714 home runs in his regular season career. Hank Aaron broke Babe Ruth's record by hitting 745 regular season homers before retiring.

4. **What was the most home runs that Hank Aaron hit in one year?**

5. **In what years did Hank Aaron hit 44 homers?**

6. **In how many years did Hank Aaron hit 20 or fewer homers?**

Here's a more complicated baseball data table. It is called the box score. It organizes the data of a game played by the Atlanta Braves and the Pittsburgh Pirates. The heading "ab" means times at bat; "r" means runs; "h" means hits; and "bi" stands for runs batted in.

Pirates 9, Braves 7

PITTSBURGH	ab	r	h	bi	ATLANTA	ab	r	h	bi
Taveras ss	3	2	2	2	Office cf	5	0	0	0
Stennett 2b	5	0	3	2	Gilbreath 2b	4	2	1	0
A. Oliver cf	5	0	0	0	Wynn lf	4	2	3	2
Stargell 1b	1	0	0	0	Montanez 1b	5	2	1	1
Kirkpatrick 1b	4	1	1	0	Paciorek rf	4	1	4	2
D. Parker rf	5	1	1	0	Henderson ph	1	0	0	0
Zisk lf	4	1	1	1	E. Williams c	4	0	1	1
B. Robinson 3b	4	2	2	1	Royster 3b	3	0	1	1
Helms 3b	0	0	0	0	Chaney ss	2	0	0	0
Sanguillin c	3	2	2	2	Ruthven p	2	0	0	0
Reuss p	2	0	0	1	Correll ph	1	0	0	0
Demery p	0	0	0	0	Beard p	0	0	0	0
Hernandez p	0	0	0	0	Del Canton ph	1	0	0	0
Moose p	0	0	0	0	Marshall p	0	0	0	0
	36	9	12	9		36	7	11	7

Pittsburgh	100 403 010 — 9
Atlanta	200 002 030 — 7

7. **What Pittsburgh player got the most hits?**

8. **What four players scored for Atlanta? (Look under "r.")**

9. **How many players were at bat five times for Pittsburgh?**

10. **How many players batted in two runs for Atlanta?**

11. **What is information called in both baseball and science?**

12. **What is the best way to organize data?**

B. DON'T DROP THIS

Can you react fast when riding your bike? Let's collect data on how fast you and your classmates react.

13. Study Table 1 on your data sheet.

14. Place your name plus the names of three other classmates under "Student." Notice the John Doe example.

15. Have student number 1 place his or her arm on a table as shown. The hand should extend over the edge.

16. Have the student hold his or her thumb and index finger 3 centimeters apart.

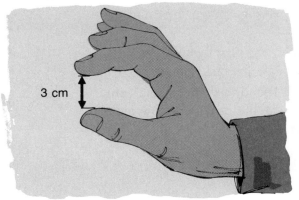

17. Hold a metric ruler over the student's fingers. The "O" end of the ruler should be between the finger and thumb.

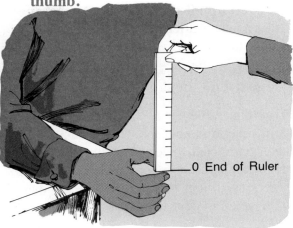

18. Have the student try to grab the ruler between the finger and thumb as it is dropped. Practice a few times to improve the reactions.

19. Now start the first trial. Read the number of centimeters where the student's finger and thumb grab the ruler. Read the number to the *nearest whole centimeter*.

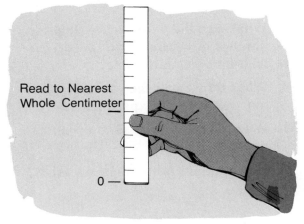

20. Repeat the first trial if the ruler is completely missed. Missing doesn't count.

21. Record the number of centimeters next to the student's name under the "First Trial" on the data table.

22. Repeat Steps 15-20 with the *same* student. Record under "Second Trial."

23. Repeat Steps 15-20 with the *same* student. Record under "Third Trial."

24. Add up all three trials. Record the answer under "Total Score" on the data table. (See the example.)

25. Repeat Steps 15-24 for each student listed on the data table.

Your data table has all the measurements of your reaction experiment. The data have been organized for easy reading. Your data table can be used to compare each student's reactions. It can be used to compare data with other student teams.

26. Which student had the best reaction speed? (Hint: Look at the "Total Score." The lowest score is the best in this test.)

27. How many centimeters difference was there between the largest and smallest total score?

28. What was the best score (lowest number of centimeters) for any *one* trial on your data table?

29. What was the worst score (highest number of centimeters) for any *one* trial on your data table?

30. What do we call the measurements that result from experiments?

31. What do scientists use to organize data?

32. How do data tables help scientists?

C. THERE'S NO END TO DATA

NASA

Not all experiments give simple data. Sometimes scientists store complex data in computers. Computers can store and organize millions of experimental measurements. Your classroom is probably not equipped with a computer. Therefore, you'll be using data tables to organize the results of your experiments.

33. What do you call the results of an experiment?

34. Where should your data be recorded?

35. Explain the purpose of a data table.

36. Why do scientists use data tables?

CONCEPT

ENRICHMENT

1. Collect data tables from newspapers and magazines. Display them.

2. Collect data on age, height, weight, etc. from your classmates. Organize the figures into a data table for class display.

3. Collect data on the kinds of trash found in certain trash cans. Organize the data into a table. The table can show how many valuable items are being thrown away.

Investigation 6

What's Your Game Plan?

and data collection. It also must include curiosity and imagination.

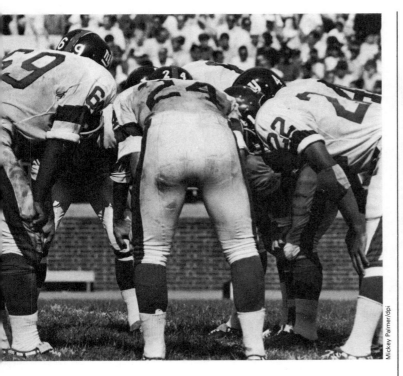

Mickey Palmer/dpi

United Nations

Ann Hagen Griffiths/dpi

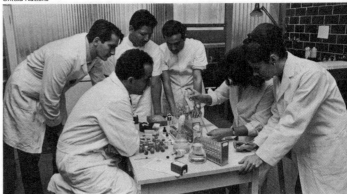

We all need a game plan, whether it's for football, science, or our lives. This Idea has been about a game plan that scientists use, called the *scientific method*. The scientific method is used by all kinds of scientists in all parts of the world. It is a general guide that enables science to proceed along a logical path. It is not a step by step procedure that can guarantee success in solving problems. The scientific method includes observation, measurement, prediction, experimenting,

Some scientists do most of their work using math and a chalkboard. Some scientists work mainly in a laboratory using controlled experiments. Whether working on the chalkboard or in the lab, their math language is metric.

A. HOW HOT IS IT?

The time has come for you to put the game plan of science into use. You're going to solve some problems on your own. To solve these problems, you will need to learn how to use a **_thermometer_**. A thermometer measures temperature.

CAUTION
THE TIP OF THE THERMOMETER BREAKS EASILY.
DO NOT TAP THE END. NEVER <u>STIR</u> WITH A THERMOMETER. USE A STIRRING ROD INSTEAD.

1. **Get a thermometer from your teacher.**

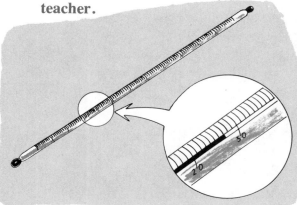

2. **Look for the colored liquid inside the thermometer.**

The colored liquid moves up or down, depending on the temperature. Find the letter "C" on your thermometer. This shows that your thermometer measures in degrees

Celsius. There are 100 spaces between 0 and 100. The freezing point of water is 0°C. The boiling point of water is 100°C.

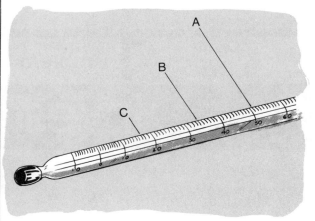

Study the drawing of the thermometer. Every 10 degrees is marked. Between each two numbers are 10 spaces marked by lines. Each line is equal to 1°C. Every fifth line is longer to help you read temperatures more accurately.

3. **Suppose the liquid were up to arrow A. What would the temperature be?**

4. **What would the temperature be if the liquid were at arrow B?**

5. **What would the temperature be if the liquid were at arrow C?**

6. **What temperature is shown in the drawing under Step 1?**

7. **What instrument is used to measure temperature?**

8. **Every line on your Celsius thermometer equals how many degrees?**

B. KEEPING IT COOL

Here's a science problem for you. How does hot water lose its heat? Is heat lost rapidly in the first few minutes? Or is heat lost slowly at a steady rate?

9. **Re-read the problem. Think back to your experience drinking hot liquids. What is your prediction? Does hot water lose its heat rapidly or slowly?**

Now let's follow the science game plan. To test your prediction, you'll need to observe, measure, collect data, and experiment.

10. Your teacher will give you a jar of hot water. Be careful handling the jar.

11. Measure the temperature of the water in the jar. Allow a few seconds for the thermometer to reach the highest temperature. Leave the thermometer in the jar.

12. Record the starting temperature in Table 1 on your data sheet.

13. Record the starting time in the data table.

14. Wait 4 minutes. Again measure the water temperature. Record it in the data sheet under "After 4 Minutes."

15. Wait 4 more minutes. Record the temperature under "After 8 Minutes."

16. Wait 4 more minutes. Record the temperature under "After 12 Minutes."

Your data table now has the information you need to check your prediction.

17. How much did the temperature drop in the first four minutes? (Subtract the "After 4 Minutes" temperature from the "Starting Temperature.")

18. How much did the temperature drop in the last four minutes? (Subtract the "After 12 Minutes" temperature from the "After 8 Minutes" temperature.)

You now have collected enough data to solve the problem. Study the data table and compare your answers to Questions 17 and 18. Then answer Question 19.

19. Does hot water lose its heat rapidly or slowly?

20. Besides observing, what else did you have to do to solve this science problem?

21. What are scientists always trying to solve?

C. LET'S TAKE A THINKING BREAK

Some schools give their students a break in the morning. It may be called "nutrition" or "recess." Adults usually call it a "coffee break."

There's your problem. Which way will cool a cup of hot chocolate faster? Should you add milk or blow on it?

22. What do you predict the answer will be?

23. How can you test your prediction? On your data sheet, write out your game plan.

Here is one way to test your prediction. Does it look like your game plan?

24. Get 3 cups of hot water from your teacher. All 3 cups have the *same* amount of hot water in them.

25. Label the cups A, B, and C.

26. Measure the temperature of water in any one of the cups.

27. Record the starting temperature in Table 2 on your data sheet. Record the *same* temperature for A, B, and C, since all started out the same.

28. Measure out 25 ml of cold water in a graduate.

29. Note the time. Mark it next to "Starting Time" on the data table.

30. Add the cold water to Cup A.

31. Blow on Cup B for 2 minutes. Take turns with your partner.

32. Do not disturb Cup C.

33. After 2 minutes, measure the temperature in each cup.

34. Record the final temperatures in Table 2.

35. For each cup, subtract the final temperature from the starting temperature. Write your answers in the last row.

36. Which cup was the control?

37. Which cup cooled faster?

38. Which is the better method of cooling hot chocolate quickly?

39. What would happen if you added more cold water to Cup A?

40. What would happen if you blew faster on Cup B?

41. Explain how scientists solve their problems.

D. ANOTHER PROBLEM SOLVED!

Congratulations! You've used your science skill to solve some practical problems. You can solve many other problems, too. All you need is to think of a game plan. For science is a way of solving problems. All you have to do is:

Observe.

Predict.

Experiment.

Measure.

Organize your data.

42. What do scientists try to solve?

43. Explain how the skills you've learned help a scientist.

44. What is science?

Re-read Questions 42, 43, and 44.

CONCEPT

WORDS TO KNOW

The following words have been used in this Idea. Carefully review the Idea and define each of them on your data sheet.

Balance	Mass
Celsius	Meter
Centimeter	Metric ruler
Control	Milliliter
Data	Millimeter
Data table	Observation
Graduate	Optical illusion
Gram	Prediction
Kilogram	Scientific method
Kilometer	Thermometer
Liter	Volume

SUMMARY OF THE IDEA: THE SCIENTIFIC METHOD

You have completed your first Idea. This Idea has been about the scientific method.

How can we discover more about our natural world?

Observing, measuring, predicting, and experimenting are all part of the scientific method. Yet the scientific method is not like a cake recipe. You don't just follow each step and "discover" a new cake. Unlike a recipe, the scientific method involves curiosity, creativity, and imagination. Plus a lot of hard work, and sometimes pure luck.

The scientific method is a way of solving problems. It starts with the identification of the problem. Problems result from a curiosity about the natural world. Observations are made that depend on the skill of the observer. These observations are often made with measuring tools such as thermometers and balances.

Predictions are possible solutions to the problems being solved. They are creative, educated guesses that lead to experiments. Experiments are actually tests of predictions. Good experiments allow only one thing to vary. Experiments should have a control. Experiments provide facts and data. Organizing the information discovered is essential to the scientific method. By studying the organized data, scientists may find the answers to their questions. The data may even give rise to new predictions and new experiments.

The world you live in has been greatly changed by scientific discoveries. Knowing the scientific method may not cause you to make any great discoveries. However, it can help you discover more about the world.

In this Idea on the methods of science, you studied six concepts.

1. **State these six concepts.**
2. **What science skills have you studied in this Idea?**
3. **What tools have you used to make accurate measurements?**
4. **Which come first in the scientific method — predictions or experiments?**
5. **Should experiments have a control? Explain your answer.**
6. **What method helps scientists make discoveries about the natural world?**

Each Idea will be like this one, You will study one concept at a time. Then you will put all the concepts together to form a bigger Idea.

Re-read the six concepts and Question 6. Then write on your data sheet what this Idea has been about.

IDEA SUMMARY

ENRICHMENT

1. Do research in the library to learn more about the discoveries of some great scientists.
2. Measure the temperature of some hot and cold liquids served in the cafeteria.
3. Grasp the bulb end of a thermometer *gently* in your closed fist. See how high you can make the liquid rise. Try various students.
4. Are light clothes or dark clothes cooler on a hot day? Devise a game plan and experiment to find the answer.

Investigation 1

Is It Alive?

You should be very proud of yourself. You've just finished the first Idea, which had to do with science. Science is a way of thinking. Everyone likes to think. Everyone likes to ask questions and solve problems. This is why you may like science. Science is a method used to discover more about the world.

People want to find out more about the world, especially about themselves. And that is what this course is all about. It is about living things, especially you.

Below is a photo of the surface of the planet Mars. It was taken by a Viking landing craft. These photos, plus some experiments, will help determine if there is life on Mars.

Determining if life exists on Mars is not an easy problem to solve. Even deciding what is living or non-living on Earth is not always easy. It is not enough to say that living things move and non-living things do not. Being alive is very complicated and is determined by many characteristics. You will investigate some of the characteristics of life in this Idea.

NASA

A. THERE IS NO SUCH THING AS A LIVING ROCK

1. Your teacher will give you a rock. Observe it carefully.

2. **Would you say your rock is alive or not alive?**

3. **What reasons can you give for your answer to Question 2?**

4. Your teacher will give you an insect in a container. Observe it carefully, but don't touch or harm it.

5. **Would you say your insect is alive or not alive?**

6. **What reasons can you give for your answer to Question 5?**

7. Your teacher will give you a leaf. Observe it carefully.

Your leaf may not seem to be alive. Yet, while on a plant, it may move to face the sun. A small leaf can grow into a big leaf. Your leaf even has veins to carry plant liquids. Leaf veins look like the veins that carry blood through your body.

8. Observe the blood veins in your wrist.

9. Observe the veins of your leaf.

10. **Would you say your leaf is alive or not alive?**

11. **What reasons can you give for your answer to Question 10?**

12. Place the leaf, vein side up, on your table.

13. Cover it with a blank piece of paper.

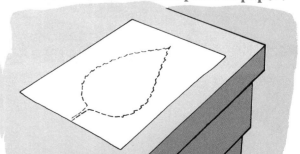

14. Rub a crayon on the paper right above the leaf. Use the side of the crayon.

You've now made a print of your leaf. It has the size and shape you would expect of a leaf. Any time you see that size and shape, you think of a leaf.

Most living things have a definite size and shape. A mouse has a size and shape you recognize. An elephant has a size and shape you recognize. Most animals have the same size and shape as their parents.

15. **You've observed rocks, insects, and leaves. Which one doesn't have a definite size and shape?**

16. **Why wouldn't you expect a rock to have a definite size and shape?**

B. SIZE AND SHAPE

A ten foot cat is hard to imagine. A dog the size of an ant is hard to imagine. Each living thing, within limits, has a definite size.

The illustration above shows how some animals compare in size. Knowing their size helps you identify living things.

Alvin Adams is taller than most people. There are midgets less than half his size. Yet most people have an average size. Like other living things, people have a definite size.

17. What living things could fit inside a coffee cup?

18. What living things could *not* fit into a Volkswagen?

Living things also have a definite shape. You can easily imagine the shape of a starfish or a butterfly. It's not easy to imagine the shape of a rock. A rock does not have a definite shape.

Even parts of living things have shapes you recognize. Can you identify these animals?

19. What is animal A?

20. What is animal B?

21. What is animal C?

22. What is animal D?

23. Get a metric ruler. It will help you to make some guesses.

24. Imagine a fly sitting on your ruler. Guess how many centimeters long it might be.

25. Imagine an average size goldfish on your ruler. Guess how many centimeters long it might be.

26. Imagine a pet mouse sitting on your ruler. Think of its length from the tip of the tail to the nose. Guess how many centimeters long it might be.

27. Snakes have their own unique shape. Describe a snake's shape in words.

28. Human beings can be tall or short. They differ in size more than shape. What is the *same* about the shapes of tall and short people?

29. Imagine a box filled with living and non-living objects. None are moving. What two things about their appearance might help you identify the living ones?

C. SORTING LIFE BY SIZE AND SHAPE

Joel Shine

Maria Elena Pereya works in a museum. Her job is to take a close look at living things. She specializes in identifying birds. She tries to place each bird with its proper group, which is not easy. There are about 9,000 different kinds of birds in the world.

Placing living things in groups is called **classification**. Scientists who do this work are called **taxonomers**. It takes skill to classify living things. Classification is based upon careful observation of differences.

Maria Elena classifies birds by differences in their size, shape, and color. She notes differences in feet, wings, beaks, and even eggs.

Your classroom is probably a little short on birds to classify. Let's classify leaves instead.

Leaves are only one part of a living plant. Yet their size and shape can identify the plant. An elm leaf comes from an elm tree. A maple leaf identifies a maple tree.

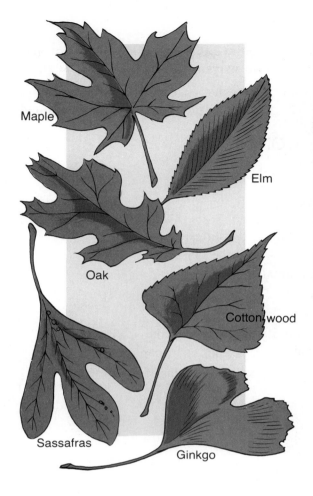

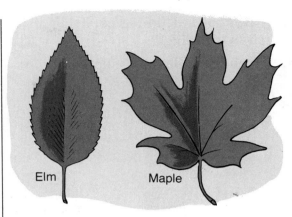

Notice the shapes of your leaves. Some are irregular around the edge, like the maple leaf. Some have a regular edge, like the elm leaf.

32. **Observe your group of smaller leaves. Divide it into two piles. Place regular-shaped leaves in one pile. Place irregular-shaped leaves in another pile.**

33. **Repeat Step 32 with your larger leaves.**

You now have classified your leaves into four separate groups. They were grouped by size and shape. Size and shape can be used to classify all living things.

34. **You used size and shape to classify leaves. What other leaf differences might you have used?**

35. **How do you know that leaves are parts of living things?**

30. **Obtain a set of leaves from your teacher. You will have one of each kind of leaf. They may or may not be the same as in the drawing.**

31. **Measure each leaf. Place all leaves over ten centimeters long in one group. Place leaves less than ten centimeters in another group.**

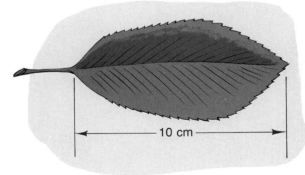

You've done the first step in classification. You have separated leaves into two groups by size. Now let's break *each* group up into two more groups by shape.

D. SHAPING UP THE CONCEPT

A leaf's size and shape depend upon what tree it came from. Your size and shape depend upon your parents.

A penny has a definite size and shape. But it is made by a machine. A penny doesn't have parents. It is not alive.

36. **A Cadillac has a definite size and shape. It even moves. Why is a Cadillac considered non-living?**

37. **Which has a definite size, living or non-living things?**

38. **Which has a definite shape, living or non-living things?**

39. **You are observing a leaf. What are two ways of knowing that it is alive?**

40. **What are two ways in which living things differ from non-living things?**

CONCEPT

ENRICHMENT

1. Look up the size of the tallest human, the tallest tree, and the largest animal. Share your findings with the class.
2. Display photos or drawings of animals with interesting shapes.
3. Make sketches of parts of animals. See if your classmates can recognize the animals.
4. Collect pictures of cars. Try to classify the cars into groups. You could start by grouping them into foreign and American cars.
5. Collect many kinds of stamps. How would you classify them into groups?

Investigation 2

Growing For a Change

Living things differ in many ways from non-living things. In the last Investigation you learned that each living thing has a certain size and shape. But that size and shape may change greatly as living things mature.

A giant redwood tree can reach 100 meters in height. That is longer than a football field;

yet the tree starts as a seed smaller than two millimeters. A whale can reach a length of 30 meters and a mass of 70,000 kilograms. Yet you would need a microscope to observe a whale's egg.

Not all living things change as drastically as redwood trees and whales. Change, however, is one of the characteristics of life.

A. DO YOUR CLOTHES STILL FIT?

Babies are very much alive. They have a certain size and shape. You were once the size of this baby. Most babies have a mass of about 3½ kilograms at birth. They are about 50 centimeters long.

1. **Find your mass on a bathroom scale.**

2. **How many kilograms are you?**

3. **How much more is your mass than that of a newborn baby? (Hint: Subtract the baby mass from your mass.)**

4. **Measure your height in centimeters. Have a friend help you.**

5. How many centimeters tall are you?

6. How much taller are you than the newborn baby?

7. What have you been doing since birth?

8. Look at your fingernails. What do they do every day?

9. What does your hair do every day?

10. What do living things do that non-living things do not?

B. CARS DO NOT GROW LIKE TREES

Cars do not grow. But trees grow. Every tree keeps a record of its growth. Each spring and summer a tree adds a new layer of wood to its trunk. The wood formed in the spring grows fast and is lighter. In summer the growth is slower and the wood is darker.

The rings are like a data table. A thick ring means the tree grew rapidly that year. A thin ring means the tree did not grow much. By counting the number of rings, you can tell how old a tree is.

St. Regis Paper Co.

11. How many rings are shown in the photo of the cut tree?

12. How many years had this tree been growing?

13. Obtain a magnifying glass and a cut tree branch.

14. Count the yearly growth rings from the inside out.

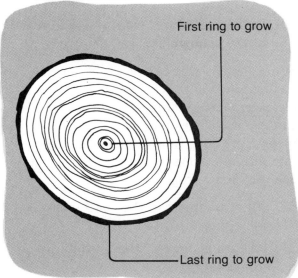

First ring to grow

Last ring to grow

15. How many rings did you count?

16. How old is the branch?

17. In what years did the branch grow the most?

18. In what years did the branch grow the least?

19. What do the rings show us the branch is doing?

Trees are not the only living things that record growth. Many living things carry a record of their age and growth. The wing feathers of a quail tell the story of the bird's growth. You can tell the age of a horse by studying its teeth. Fish have growth rings on their scales. Sheep have growth rings on their horns.

20. Sheep horns and fish scales both have rings. What do these rings tell us that fish and sheep are doing?

21. What are all living things doing?

C. YOU HAVE CHANGED

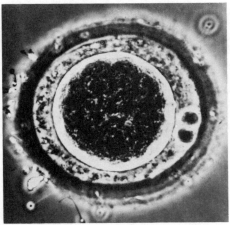

Picture A

Courtesy of Rugh and Shettles
"From Conception to Birth:
The Drama of Life's Beginnings"

Picture B

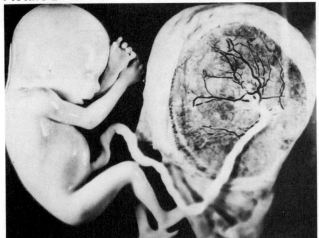

Mt. Sinai Hospital

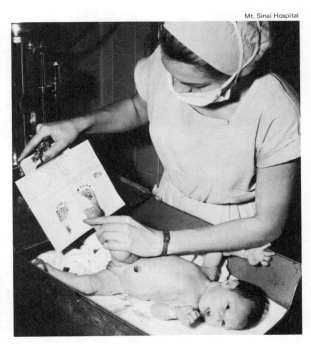

Picture C

Do you recognize these pictures? You should. They are pictures of you. Picture A is a human egg. Picture B shows it five months later. Picture C is a newborn baby.

In Parts A and B, you learned that living things grow. As living things grow, they may also do something else.

22. Look again at the pictures on the last page. Besides growing, what else happened to the egg?

Here are three more pictures. The top picture is a caterpillar. The next is the cocoon the caterpillar spins. And the last is the butterfly that comes out of the cocoon. All three are the same animal.

23. Besides growing, what else happened to the caterpillar?

Some animals change completely as they mature into adults. This is called *metamorphosis*. During metamorphosis, a caterpillar changes into a butterfly. A maggot crawling in a garbage can changes into a fly. A tadpole swimming in a pond changes into a frog.

24. What happens to flies and frogs as they grow up?

25. Besides growing, what else do living things do?

Plants also change as they grow. An acorn grows and changes into an oak tree. A common pea seed can grow and change into a pea plant.

26. Obtain a pea seed. Draw it in Space A on your data sheet.

27. You will be given a soaked pea seed that is three days old. Draw the pea seed in Space B on your data sheet.

28. You will be given a pea plant that is 7-10 days old. Draw the pea plant in Space C on your data sheet.

29. In what way has your pea seed grown?

30. In what ways has your pea seed changed?

31. What do pea seeds and acorns do as they get older?

32. What is it called when a caterpillar grows and changes into a butterfly?

33. A puppy is very much alive. What will happen to it as it gets older?

D. SUMMING IT UP

34. Why can't a small rock grow and change into a big boulder?

35. Why can't a Chevrolet grow and change into a Cadillac?

36. What two things happen to people as they mature from babies into adults?

37. What two things are living things able to do?

CONCEPT

ENRICHMENT

1. Bring in your baby pictures to show how you have grown and changed.

2. How long will a corn seed become in two weeks? Grow corn seeds in a milk carton filled with a mixture of soil and sawdust. At the end of two weeks, compare your plant length with those of your classmates.

3. Measure the growth of one fingernail over a one week period.

4. Measure the growth of your hair over a one week period.

5. Obtain a branch from a local tree, preferably one that has fallen off naturally. Try to figure out its age.

6. Try to bring in insects in various stages of metamorphosis. Provide a home, food, and water for them. Observe their changes.

Investigation 3

It Is a Stimulating Life

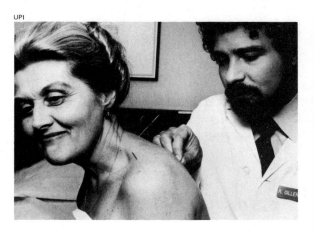

This patient is having acupuncture treatment. Acupuncture has been used in China for thousands of years. Only recently have

Americans begun to use it to relieve pain and to cure certain ailments. We still have much to learn about acupuncture and how to use it.

Acupuncture treatment begins with needles inserted at certain points on the human body. The theory is that the needles can stop pain in a different part of the body. In some cases, patients undergo surgery with only acupuncture needles to prevent pain. They are awake during the entire operation.

How would you react to a needle in your arm? The way you would react is another characteristic of life.

A. MORE LIVELY MEALWORMS

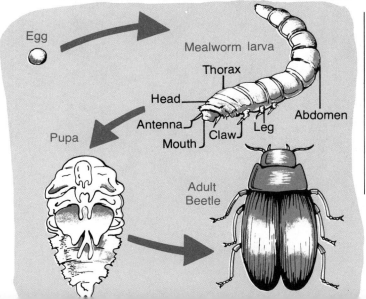

Egg

Mealworm larva

Thorax

Head

Antenna

Mouth · Claw · Leg

Abdomen

Pupa

Adult Beetle

Mealworms and butterflies are both insects. They both go through metamorphosis. Mealworms are like caterpillars. Mealworms grow and change into beetles.

Mealworms are grown by the millions as food for such pets as fish and lizards. They are kept in the dark in a container of bran for their entire life cycle. Inside the container they hatch, go through metamorphosis, and reproduce.

51

1. **Put a mealworm in one of the halves of a small petri dish. Use a magnifying glass to identify its parts.**

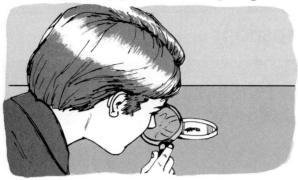

2. **Touch the mealworm *gently* several times with a pencil.**

3. **What did the mealworm do?**

4. **Blow *gently* at the head end with a straw.**

5. **What did the mealworm do?**

6. **If you had poked or blown at a rock, what would it have done? Why?**

You expect a worm to react differently than a rock. Why did the mealworm move? Let's add two new words to your vocabulary. A change in the world around a living thing is called a ***stimulus***. When a living thing receives a stimulus, a reaction takes place. A reaction to a stimulus is called a ***response***. A cat receives a stimulus when it smells food. It responds by running toward the food. A cricket senses someone approaching. It responds by stopping its chirping.

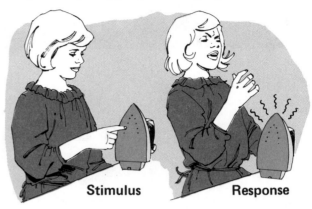

Stimulus   Response

7. **Cover half of an open petri dish with aluminum foil.**

8. **Place the mealworm in the middle of the dish.**

9. Place the dish under a lamp.

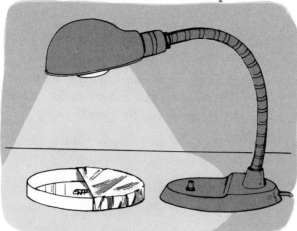

10. **What did the mealworm do? (Repeat the experiment a few times before answering.)**

11. **What was the stimulus?**

12. **What was the mealworm's response?**

13. **Suppose you had used a rock instead of a mealworm. Why wouldn't you expect the rock to respond to the light stimulus?**

14. **Use the words stimulus and response (or respond) in your next sentence. What can living things do that non-living things cannot do?**

B. PUPIL RESPONSE

You have already been told never to look at the sun. It can blind you.

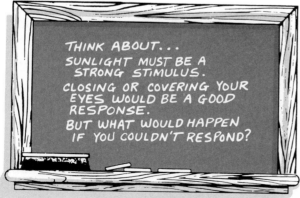

THINK ABOUT...
SUNLIGHT MUST BE A STRONG STIMULUS.
CLOSING OR COVERING YOUR EYES WOULD BE A GOOD RESPONSE.
BUT WHAT WOULD HAPPEN IF YOU COULDN'T RESPOND?

That's a good question. Responding has to do with staying alive. Living things that respond have a better chance of staying alive. Your eyes show a good example of how you respond.

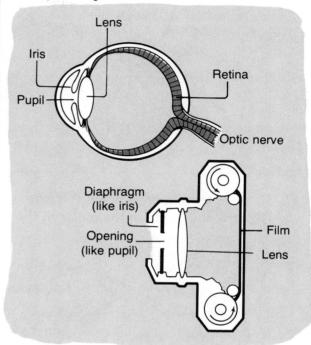

Your eye is like a camera. Light enters the opening in the center. This opening is called the *pupil*. The *iris* of the eye controls the amount of light coming in. The light is focused by the *lens* to form a picture at the back of the eye. This picture is focused on the *retina*, which corresponds to the film in a camera. From the retina, the *optic nerve* carries the light messages to the brain.

15. **Stand in front of your partner's chair.**

16. Ask your partner to close and cover his or her eyes for one minute.

17. Remove the hands or open the eyes. Observe the pupils in the center of the eyes.

18. What happened to the size of the pupils as the eyes opened?

19. Shine a small light into your partner's eyes.

20. What happened to the size of the pupils?

21. What was the stimulus?

22. What was the response?

23. Bright lights can be harmful to the eyes. If the iris did not respond, what might happen to the eyes?

This boy is being checked for marijuana. If he is on pot, his eyes will not respond to light. Smoking pot slows your ability to respond in many ways.

24. What might happen to a person who can't respond to a stimulus?

The eye has another response to protect you from injury. Your eyelids blink when an object gets too close. It is natural for you to blink. Do you think you can keep yourself from blinking? Here's your chance to find out.

25. Hold a sheet of plastic in front of your eyes.

26. Another student will toss a cotton ball at the plastic. It will be thrown at you five times from a distance of one meter.

27. How many times out of five could you prevent yourself from blinking?

28. What was the stimulus to your eyes?

29. What was your response?

It is natural for your pupil to respond to a light stimulus. It is natural to blink in response to a ball coming at you. You were born with both responses.

Ivan Pavlov was a Russian scientist who studied a different kind of response. He was interested in responses that animals learn. He trained dogs so that they responded to a bell as if it were food.

30. How do you respond when you smell a juicy hamburger?

31. Why doesn't a hamburger respond to you?

32. What else do you respond to besides light and odors?

33. What must living things do to stay alive?

C. WE ALL RESPOND

Maybe plants don't respond to music. But do they respond to other kinds of stimuli?

34. Observe the large box your teacher has. There is a plant inside the box. The plant has been there a few days.

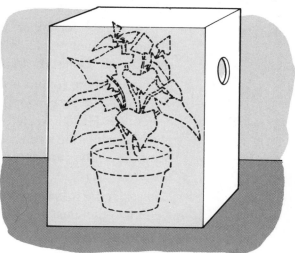

35. **What do you see on one side of the box?**

36. **What is reaching the plant through this opening?**

37. **How do you predict the plant will respond to this stimulus?**

Your teacher will remove the box. Observe the plant and check your prediction.

38. **How did the plant respond to the stimulus?**

Plants are very much alive. They can respond to many kinds of stimuli. A plant's response to a stimulus is called a *tropism*. The response of the boxed plant to light is called *phototropism*. Can you guess what a plant's response to water might be called?

39. **What might happen to a plant that didn't bend toward the light?**

40. **What can a plant do that a rock cannot do?**

41. **What might happen to living things that couldn't respond to a stimulus?**

D. PUTTING IT ALL TOGETHER

Let's review what you have learned.

42. **Dust gets in your nose and you sneeze. What is the stimulus and what is your response?**

43. **What stimulus caused this student to wake up?**

44. **Why wouldn't you expect the bed to react to the alarm clock?**

45. **What can living things do that non-living things cannot?**

46. **What must living things do to stay alive?**

CONCEPT

ENRICHMENT

1. Find out how mealworms respond to various sounds, odors, and foods. Check how they respond to water or lack of water. Place a damp paper towel on one side of the petri dish and a dry towel on the other.

2. Check how plants respond to gravity. Place a young plant on its side for a few days and find out how it responds.

3. Check plants for other tropisms. Obtain a plant, such as Mimosa, which responds to touch. Get an insect-eating plant such as the Venus fly trap.

4. Knowing where sounds come from can sometimes mean survival. Find out how people respond to sounds from different directions. Have a seated student close his or her eyes. Snap your fingers or tap a ruler in different places around the subject. See if he or she can respond by pointing out the location of the sound.

5. Look up more information on Ivan Pavlov and his experiments. Report to the class.

Investigation 4

The Need For Water

Living things have a definite size and shape. They grow and change. They respond to stimuli. But is that all there is to being alive?

There is much more to being alive. For example, living things not only grow, but they can repair themselves. You get a cut or bruise and your body repairs itself like new. A car with a dented fender could never straighten itself out.

This starfish has lost one of its arms. It will soon begin to grow a new arm as a replacement. Crabs and lobsters can grow new claws to replace ones that have broken off. Some lizards give up their tails when attacked by an enemy. They can grow a new tail to replace the old one.

Living things also have certain needs. Let's study one of these needs.

A. WATER AND SEEDS

Your teacher will give you two beakers, five lima bean seeds, and five pebbles.

1. **Label both beakers with your name and section.**

2. **Find the mass of the 5 lima bean seeds. Enter this mass in Table 1 on your data sheet.**

3. **Place the seeds in one beaker.**

4. **Find the mass of the 5 pebbles. Enter this mass in Table 1.**

5. **Place the pebbles in the second beaker.**

6. **Fill both beakers nearly full with water.**

7. Store your experiment for 1 day. Do not disturb.

8. After 1 day, remove the seeds from the beaker.

9. Carefully dry the seeds with paper towels.

10. Find the mass of the dry seeds. Enter this mass in Table 1.

11. **What was the mass of the seeds at the start of the experiment?**

12. **What is the mass of the seeds now?**

13. **What happened to the mass of the seeds?**

14. **What do you think caused this change?**

15. **What do you think got into the seeds?**

16. Remove the pebbles from the beaker.

17. Dry the pebbles with paper towels.

18. Find the mass of the dry pebbles. Enter this mass in Table 1.

19. **What was the mass of the pebbles at the start of the experiment?**

20. **What is the mass of the pebbles now?**

21. **What happened to the mass of the pebbles?**

22. **What did the seeds do that the pebbles did not?**

23. **What did the seeds take in?**

B. WHY SEEDS NEED WATER

You've learned that living things grow and change. Without water, seeds would not grow and change into plants. Let's investigate a lima bean seed after its big drink.

24. Open up a new, dry lima bean seed.

25. Open up one of your soaked seeds.

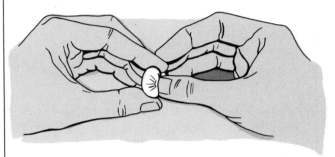

26. **Compare the dry and soaked seeds. Describe the differences between them.**

27. Use a magnifying glass to observe and identify the seed parts.

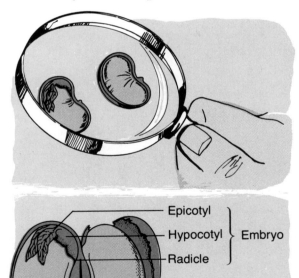

Your soaked seed contains an **_embryo_** and a **_cotyledon_**. The embryo is an undeveloped plant. It will grow and change into a bean plant. The cotyledon stores food to help the plant start growing. The *radicle* will become the root. The *hypocotyl* will become the plant stem. The *epicotyl* will become the first leaves.

The *seed coat* protects the seed from drying out. When the seed gets enough water, the seed coat softens. It then splits and lets the embryo out.

28. **What part of the seed stores food?**

29. **What part of the seed will become a plant?**

30. **How does the seed coat help the seed?**

31. **What must seeds take in to start their growth?**

32. **What must all living things take stay alive?**

C. THE BREATH OF LIFE

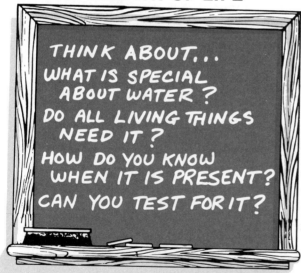

THINK ABOUT...
WHAT IS SPECIAL ABOUT WATER?
DO ALL LIVING THINGS NEED IT?
HOW DO YOU KNOW WHEN IT IS PRESENT?
CAN YOU TEST FOR IT?

Your teacher will give you a covered jar. It contains some strips of test paper.

33. **Use your forceps. Remove one of the paper strips from the jar.**

34. **What color is the dry test paper?**

35. **Wet one end of the paper.**

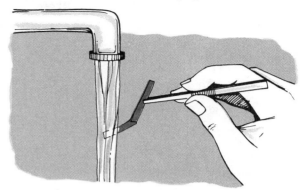

36. **What color is the wet test paper?**

37. **What caused the paper to change color?**

This paper is used to test for water. If water is present, the paper will always turn pink. If there is no water, the paper remains blue.

You have learned that living things take in water. Your body takes in about 2½ liters of water each day. The test paper can show where some of this water goes.

38. **Use your forceps. Dry 2 strips of paper near a light bulb.**

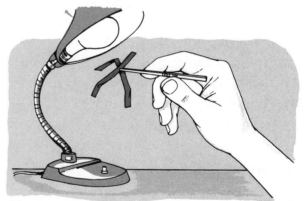

39. **Place one of the strips in a plastic bag.**

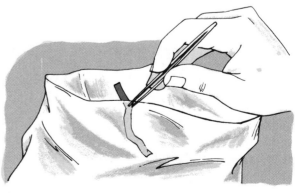

40. Twist the bag closed. Tie it with a rubber band.

41. Place the second paper strip in another plastic bag.

42. Hold the bag to your mouth. Blow into it several times.

43. Twist the bag closed. Tie it with a rubber band.

44. **Look at the test paper in the bag you breathed into. What color is it?**

45. **Look at the test paper in the bag you didn't breathe into. What color is it?**

46. **What is the only difference between the two bags?**

47. **Which bag contains water?**

48. **How do you think the water got there?**

49. **What is in the air you breathe out?**

50. **What might be in the air other animals breathe out?**

D. WATER AND LIFE

Launois/Black Star

The world wouldn't be much fun without water. But living things need water for more than fun.

Without water there would be no life. Finding enough water is a matter of life or death for all plants and animals. Your own body mass is 2/3 water. You couldn't cry or blink your eyes without water. Your muscles couldn't move if they were dry. Without water, you couldn't dissolve the solid food you eat. Water in your bloodstream carries food, air, and heat to all parts of your body. You are kept cool on hot days by water perspiring from your body.

51. **Why is water important to seeds?**

52. **You drink many fluids to get most of the water you need. Name some solid foods you eat that also provide your body with water.**

53. **Besides air, what do you breathe out?**

54. **What do living things take in?**

55. **What do living things give off?**

CONCEPT

ENRICHMENT

1. Use the test paper to check for water in perspiration. Place your hand and a test paper inside a plastic bag. Close the bag tightly.

2. Is water given off by plants? Place a test paper and a small plant in a plastic bag.

3. Find if insects give off water. Place a test paper and an insect inside a covered petri dish.

Investigation 5

Take a Deep Breath

You've learned that living things take in and give off water. Yet people have lived over a week without taking in water. And some have gone over a month without eating. The only thing you can't do without for more than a few minutes is air.

Air itself has no color, smell, or taste. Yet, without air, no life could exist on earth. Living things find the air they need on the highest mountains and in the deepest soils. Air dissolved in water makes life in the oceans possible.

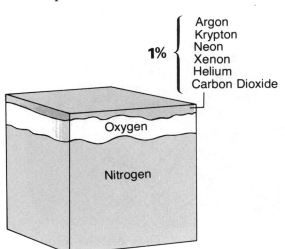

1% {
Argon
Krypton
Neon
Xenon
Helium
Carbon Dioxide
}

Oxygen

Nitrogen

This diagram shows what makes up the air. About 78% of the air consists of nitrogen gas. Your body breathes nitrogen in and out without really using it. Some living things,

though, need the nitrogen for their life activities. Oxygen makes up about 21% of the air. How living things use oxygen will be investigated in later Ideas.

The remaining 1% of the air consists of such strange sounding gases as argon, krypton, neon, xenon, and helium. A very small part of the air is carbon dioxide, which plays a major role in life activities. Water in a gas form, called water vapor, is also important to life.

A. HOW LIVING THINGS BREATHE

You breathe. Cats, dogs, and birds also breathe. So do fish, insects, and plants. All living things breathe. They don't all breathe the same way, but they breathe.

A person breathes through his or her nose and mouth.

Shackman/Monkmeyer

61

Cats, dogs, and birds breathe the same way.

Block/Monkmeyer

Block/Monkmeyer

Monroe/dpi

Walter Chandoha

Fish breathe through the mouth and gills. That is how they obtain air from the water they live in.

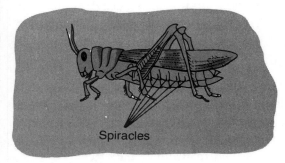

Spiracles

Insects breathe through tiny slits on the sides of their bodies. The slits are called *spiracles*.

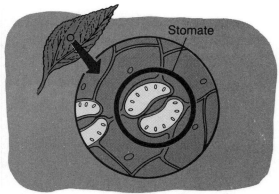

Stomate

Plants also breathe. They breathe through tiny openings in their leaves. These openings are called *stomates*. There may be 10,000 stomates per square centimeter of leaf. Polluted air can kill plants by clogging these stomates.

B. HUFFING AND PUFFING

UPI

1. Sit quietly and relax.

2. Count the number of times you breathe in one minute. Count in and out as one breath.

3. The number of times you breathe in one minute is called your breathing rate. How many times did you breathe in one minute?

4. Compare your breathing rate with those of your classmates. How does your breathing rate compare with theirs?

5. What are you and your classmates taking into your body?

6. Stand up and run in place near your desk for one minute.

7. Sit down. Count the number of times you breathe in one minute.

8. How many times did you breathe in one minute after exercising?

9. Compare your breathing rate after exercising with those of your classmates.

10. What does your body need more of while exercising?

You normally take in one half liter of air with every breath. When you exercise you need more air. On a deep breath, you can take in about four liters of air.

John Walker won the 1500 meter race in the 1976 Olympics. During his 3½ minute run, his body took in over 250 liters of air.

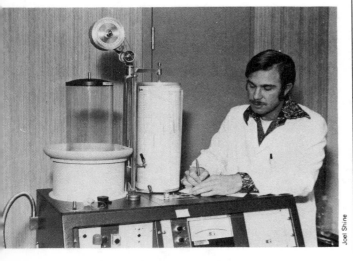

Walt Plus knows a lot about breathing. He works in a hospital as a ***respiratory therapy technician***. Respiratory means breathing; therapy means treatment. Walt helps people who have breathing problems. Some of his patients may have diseased lungs. Other patients may have heart conditions. By helping them breathe, Walt reduces the strain on their hearts. Patients recovering from operations need his help to keep their lungs clear. Walt is well paid and enjoys his work. Perhaps someday you would like to join him as a health technician.

11. What do respiratory therapy technicians do?

12. What do runners need more of during a race?

13. Name the part that fish use for breathing.

14. Name the part that insects use for breathing.

15. Name the part that plants use for breathing.

16. Besides water, what do living things take in and give off?

17. What do living things need to stay alive?

C. BUBBLES IN THE BREAD

18. Fill two test tubes ½ full with warm water.

19. Add a yeast mixture to one test tube. The mixture contains living yeast plants plus something to help them grow.

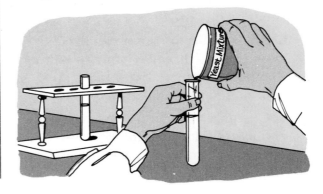

20. Add a few pebbles to the other tube.

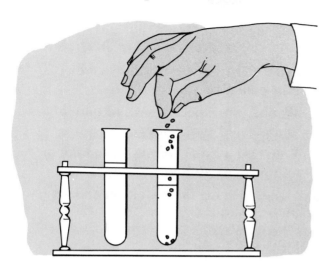

21. Shake both tubes gently.

22. Wait a few minutes.

23. Which of the two tubes contains something living?

24. What do you observe in the tube containing yeast?

25. What do you observe in the tube containing pebbles?

26. What do living yeast plants give off that pebbles do not?

27. What do living things give off that non-living things do not?

D. THE LAST BREATH

Statile/dpi

Whales live in water, but they are not fish. They have lungs just like you and dogs and birds.

28. Why must whales keep coming up to the surface?

NASA

29. What do you think this astronaut is breathing in?

30. Why must astronauts carry their own air in space?

Bahamas Tourist News Bureau

31. **What do you think this scuba diver is breathing in?**

32. **Notice the bubbles. What does this tell you the diver is giving off?**

33. **What do living yeast plants give off that pebbles do not?**

34. **Would you expect a desk to take in and give off air? Why?**

35. **Would you expect an insect to take in and give off air? Why?**

36. **What do living things take in and give off?**

CONCEPT

ENRICHMENT

1. Collect data on the normal breathing rates of boys and girls. Construct a data table on the board.

2. Check the normal breathing rate of a pet such as a dog or cat.

3. Find out how to help people who have stopped breathing. This is called artificial respiration. Teach your classmates how it is done.

4. Look up the lung disease called emphysema. Share what you learn with the class.

Food And Life

You are really making progress. You've learned to identify living things by their size and shape. You've investigated how living things grow and change and respond to stimuli. You know that living things must take in air and water.

Besides air and water, living things must find a supply of food. It is food that provides the material for growth and repair. It is food that provides the energy needed to respond to a stimulus. The need of living things for food is another characteristic of life.

The chemicals in food are needed to build a substance called **_protoplasm_**. Protoplasm is a colorless, jellylike material found in the living matter of all plants and animals. The most important chemicals found in protoplasm are carbon, hydrogen, oxygen, and nitrogen. These and other chemicals must be in the food supplied to all animal and plant life.

Scientists know all the chemicals needed to make protoplasm. They can even mix these chemicals in a test tube in the same proportions as real protoplasm. Yet there is no life in the test tube. Only when these chemicals react in a certain way do they take on the characteristics of living protoplasm. As of now, these reactions take place only in living organisms.

A. A FEAST FOR YEAST

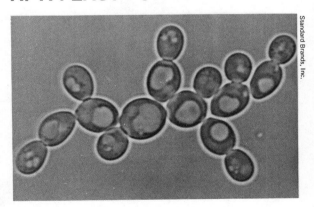

Standard Brands, Inc.

The yeast plants you worked with look like this. They are microscopic in size and oval in shape. When conditions are right, they grow and change. You saw yeast plants giving off air bubbles as they grew. Yeast plants can help us discover something else that living things must take in.

National Dairy Council

1. Get two test tubes. Label one "Control" and the other "Experiment."

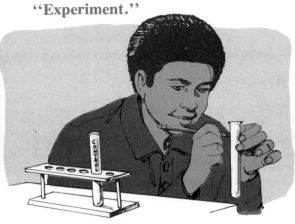

2. Fill both tubes 3/4-full with warm yeast mixture.

3. Add a level teaspoon of sugar to the Experiment tube only.

4. Place a stopper with rigid tubing in each test tube. Be sure the stoppers are in tight.

5. Shake both tubes gently. Hold the stoppers on tightly as you shake the tubes.

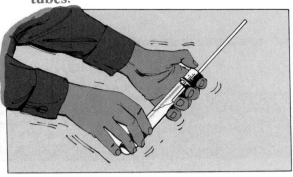

6. Place both tubes flat on the table. Wait a few minutes.

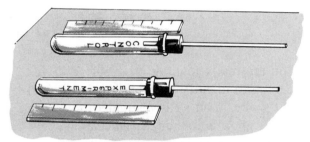

7. What is the only difference between the two test tubes?

8. What do you observe in the tube without sugar?

9. What do you observe in the tube with sugar?

10. Which yeast plants are more active?

11. In order to be active and grow, what must yeast plants take in?

Sugar is only one kind of food. The yeast plants could have grown on molasses, fruit, or any kind of sugary food.

Sharks also must take in food to live. They mainly eat all kinds of fish. Animals like sharks that eat other animals are called _carnivores_.

John Gajda/dpi

Cows eat only grass and other plants. Animals that eat only plants are called _herbivores_.

Ann Hagen Griffiths/dpi

Most people eat both plant and animal food. Animals that eat plants and animals are called _omnivores_.

12. **What is a carnivore?**

13. **What is a herbivore?**

14. **What is an omnivore?**

Most plants make their own food using air, water, and sunlight. Some plants are carnivorous and digest insects. This sundew plant can trap flies on its sticky tentacles.

Carolina Biological Supply Co.

15. **What provides food for carnivorous plants?**

16. **Why don't most plants have to take in food?**

17. **Besides air and water, what must you take in to stay alive?**

18. **Besides air and water, what do all living things need?**

B. DO YOU HAVE A BALANCED DIET?

You've learned that living things need food to stay alive. What kinds of food have you been taking in?

19. **What foods did you eat for breakfast?**

20. **What foods did you eat for your most recent lunch?**

21. **What foods did you eat for your most recent dinner?**

22. **What snacks have you eaten between meals in the last 24 hours?**

A Guide to Good Eating

Use Daily:

Milk Group
3 or more glasses milk — Children smaller glasses for some children under 9
4 or more glasses — Teen-agers
2 or more glasses — Adults
Cheese, ice cream and other milk-made foods can supply part of the milk

Meat Group
2 or more servings
Meats, fish, poultry, eggs, or cheese—with dry beans, peas, nuts as alternates

Vegetables and Fruits
4 or more servings
Include dark green or yellow vegetables; citrus fruit or tomatoes

Breads and Cereals
4 or more servings
Enriched or whole grain Added milk improves nutritional values

This is the foundation for a good diet. Use more of these and other foods as needed for growth, for activity, and for desirable weight.

National Dairy Council

The chart on the last page suggests the types of food you should be eating every day. By eating some of each group you get a **_balanced diet_**. A balanced diet helps your body grow and repair itself. It provides you with energy to move and keep warm. A balanced diet helps protect you against disease.

Review the foods you ate in the last 24 hours.

23. **Milk foods contain most things you need in a balanced diet. What milk foods have you eaten?**

24. **The meat group can help you grow. What foods in the meat group have you eaten?**

25. **Vegetables and fruits contain vitamins to keep you healthy. What vegetables and fruits have you eaten?**

26. **Breads and cereals contain energy food. What breads and cereals have you eaten?**

© 1964, Parke, Davis & Co.

Dr. Joseph Goldberger was a pioneer in the study of human diets. He discovered how to cure diseases that were due to meals that lacked vitamins. By using volunteers in controlled experiments, he isolated the special vitamins needed for good health.

These chickens also took part in a controlled

diet experiment. The one on the right was given a balanced diet. The other was deprived of certain kinds of foods.

27. **Describe the differences you observe between the two chickens.**

28. **What might happen to animals that don't take in a balanced diet?**

29. **What four food groups do you need for a balanced diet?**

30. **What kind of food did the yeast plants take in?**

31. **What must yeast, sharks, and people take in to stay alive?**

C. DON'T BE A JUNK FOOD JUNKIE

It's great to be alive. It's exciting to grow up and change. It feels good to respond to the stimulus of music. It's a pleasure to take clean air and water into your body. But are you taking a balanced diet into your body? Are you a junk food junkie?

Food scientists estimate that over half of America's teenagers suffer from poor diet. Here are some bad diet habits common among young people.

Excessive snacking on junk food that has little value to the body.

Substituting soda pop for milk or fruit juice.

Following food fads.

Eating the same foods constantly instead of a variety of foods, causing an unbalanced diet.

Skipping breakfast.

Overuse of sugary, sweet foods.

Johnson/deWys

M. L. Sunde/Univ. of Wisconsin

Controlled experiments with rats proved that many breakfast cereals have little food value. Rats fed certain cereals did not grow or gain weight. On the other hand, some breakfast cereals contain over 50% sugar. Too much sugar can cause overweight and tooth decay.

32. **Review these bad habits. Are you guilty of any of these? Explain.**

33. **Why is a balanced diet especially important for people your age?**

34. **What would happen to living things that did not take in food?**

35. **Besides air and water, what do all living things need?**

CONCEPT

WORDS TO KNOW

The following words have been used in this Idea. Carefully review the Idea and define each of them on your data sheet.

Balanced diet	Protoplasm
Carnivore	Pupil
Classification	Radicle
Cotyledon	Respiratory therapy
Embryo	technician
Epicotyl	Response
Herbivore	Retina
Hypocotyl	Seed coat
Iris	Spiracle
Lens	Stimulus
Metamorphosis	Stomate
Omnivore	Taxonomer
Optic nerve	Tropism
Phototropism	

SUMMARY OF THE IDEA:
THE CHARACTERISTICS OF LIFE

You've come to the end of the second Idea. This Idea has been about the characteristics of life. How can we tell if something is alive? What are the differences between living and non-living things?

Life is not easy to define. All we can be sure of is that living things carry on certain activities and have certain needs. Although people consider themselves unique, they share the same life characteristics with all plants and animals.

No one characteristic can discriminate between living and non-living things. An airplane can show motion. A crystal of salt can grow. A candle can need both air and "food" in the form of wax. A Volkswagen has a definite size and shape. But these are still not alive in the sense that a canary is.

Robert Schuster

Tardigrade

This weird creature is called a Tardigrade. It can exist for over 100 years in what appears to be a non-living state. Yet, when it is moistened, it immediately springs back to life. The Tardigrade demonstrates how difficult it is to completely define life.

To be alive, living things need not show all the characteristics of life. A plant may not respond to a certain stimulus that brings a quick response from an animal. A leaf does not move around in search of food the way a fish does. A yeast plant does not grow and reproduce the way you do. In general, however, any plant or animal will display a majority of the life characteristics.

You will discover other characteristics of life later in this book. In Idea 3 you will use the microscope to discover another important difference between living and non-living things.

In this Idea on life characteristics you have studied six concepts.

1. State these six concepts.

Gymnasts don't doubt that Nadia Comaneci is alive. During the 1976 Olympics she scored a record 10 with her parallel bars routine. This is the highest score possible in the Olympic event. Let's use Nadia to review this Idea.

Does she have a definite shape and size?

Has she grown and changed?

Does she respond to applause from the audience?

Does she need to take in and give off air and water?

Does she need to take in a balanced food diet?

2. How do you know Nadia is alive?

3. How do you know her parallel bars are not alive?

4. Why do you expect a seed to grow and change?

5. Why do you expect a fly to respond when you swat at it?

6. What three things do all living things need?

7. How can you tell if something is alive?

Re-read this section. Summarize the entire Idea.

IDEA SUMMARY

ENRICHMENT

1. Try the yeast experiment with other sugary foods. Use molasses, bits of fruit, or various cereals.

2. Collect cereal box labels. Compare them for the amount of sugar and food value.

3. Check your cafeteria menu. Are all the kinds of food needed for a balanced diet on the menu?

4. Find out about jobs you might like in the food industry. Interview a cook or a dietician. Check the newspaper want ads to see what jobs are available.

5. There are many false ideas about food. Some people believe that fish is brain food. Some think that brown eggs are healthier than white eggs. Make a collection of these false ideas and discuss them with the class.

6. Research the subject of vitamins and report to the class on what you learned.

Investigation 1

Learning To Use The Microscope

Studying small objects can sometimes be a difficult and tiring task. The reason is a simple one. The human eye is not powerful enough to do the job. Like most other parts of the body, the eye also has its limits. It can see only so much. An example of this is right at your fingertips. It's your fingerprints.

Fingerprints are ridges and creases found on the inside surfaces of the fingers and palms. These ridges and creases are also found on the toes and soles of the feet. Scientists are not completely certain about the function of fingerprints. But they do know that monkeys, apes, gorillas, and some birds have them.

Your fingerprint is like your name. It belongs only to you. The chances of any two fingerprints being identical are more than 70 billion to 1. They may look alike, but they are different. The question, then, is, how do we tell fingerprints apart?

FBI

| PLAIN ARCH | TENTED ARCH | LOOP | LOOP |

| PLAIN WHORL | CENTRAL POCKET LOOP | DOUBLE LOOP | ACCIDENTAL |

A. LOOKING AT FINGERPRINTS

Fingerprints are most often thought of in police work. But there are many important uses for fingerprints, all having to do with identification. Strange as it may seem, hospitals record the footprints of newborn babies to avoid mixing them up. Many companies fingerprint their employees. Accident victims are often identified by their fingerprints. For all of these reasons, it is often necessary to make permanent fingerprint records.

1. **Look at the tips of several of your fingers. Can you identify a fingerprint pattern?**

2. **Look at your fingertips again. This time use a magnifying glass.**

Even with a magnifying glass, identification and matching of fingerprints are not that easy. But there is another way.

3. **Put a clean glass slide on top of a piece of black paper.**

4. **Firmly press your index finger down on the center of the slide.**

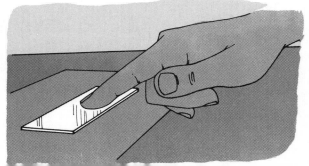

73

5. Sprinkle some powder on the glass where you pressed your finger.

6. Gently brush away the powder.

7. Look carefully at your fingerprint. Compare your print with those shown on page 73.

8. **How does your print compare?**

If you had difficulty comparing your fingerprint, remember what you learned earlier. The eye has its limits. Let's try Step 7 again, this time using a magnifying glass. A magnifying glass is a curved piece of glass. Scientists call this kind of curved glass a _lens_. Some lenses can make things look smaller than they really are. Other lenses can make things look larger.

9. **Use the lens to look at your fingerprint. How does your fingerprint compare with those on page 73?**

10. **How did the lens help you in making your comparison?**

11. **Based upon your experiment, what effect did the lens have on the size of the object you were studying?**

12. **Why do you think lenses are important instruments for scientists?**

B. TYPES OF MICROSCOPES

Many things that scientists study are so small that lenses are needed to see them.

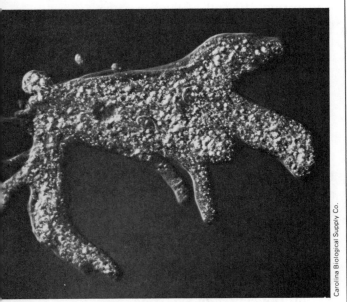

Carolina Biological Supply Co.

Microscopes use lenses to _magnify_ or make objects look larger. A simple microscope uses only a single lens. Thus, a simple microscope can magnify objects 5 or 10 times.

Sometimes, this low magnification is not very helpful. A more powerful microscope is needed.

Magnifying glass

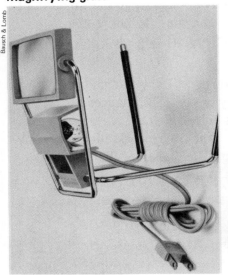

Bausch & Lomb

Compound microscope

This is a _compound microscope_. It uses a combination of lenses to magnify objects. Some compound microscopes can magnify almost 2,000 times.

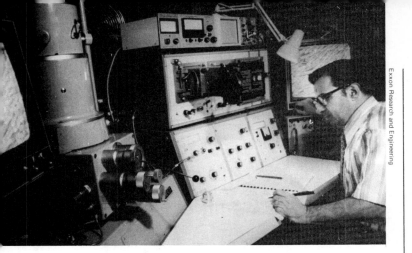

Electron microscope

The *electron microscope* is the newest and most powerful of all microscopes. It uses magnets for lenses and can magnify objects up to 200,000 times. Specially equipped electron microscopes can magnify up to 2 million times.

13. **What is a simple microscope?**

14. **What is a compound microscope?**

15. **What is an electron microscope?**

16. **In what way are each of these microscopes the same?**

17. **In what way are each of these microscopes different?**

18. **Why do scientists use microscopes?**

C. PARTS OF THE MICROSCOPE

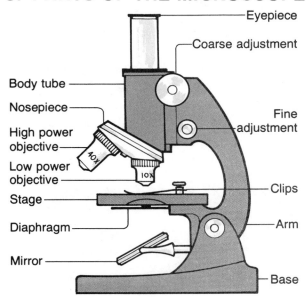

- Eyepiece
- Coarse adjustment
- Body tube
- Nosepiece
- Fine adjustment
- High power objective
- Low power objective
- Stage
- Diaphragm
- Clips
- Arm
- Mirror
- Base

19. **Study the picture of the compound microscope. Find the parts on your microscope.**

20. **Find the eyepiece. The magnification is printed on it.**

21. **What is the magnification of the eyepiece?**

22. **Find the low power objective. The magnification is printed on this, too.**

23. **What is the magnification of the low power objective?**

24. **What is the magnification of the high power objective?**

25. **How can you tell the two objectives apart?**

26. **Use lens paper to clean the eyepiece, objectives, and mirror.**

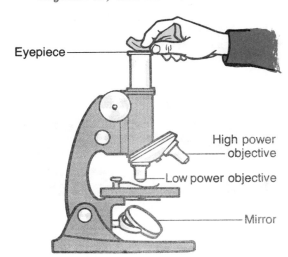

- Eyepiece
- High power objective
- Low power objective
- Mirror

27. **Carefully turn the nosepiece until the low power objective is in place. Listen for the click.**

28. **While looking from the side, turn the coarse adjustment knob. Carefully lower the body tube as far as it can go.**

29. **Check to see that the diaphragm is wide open.**

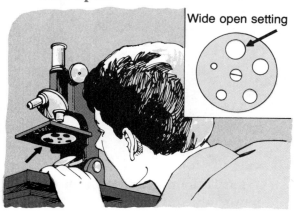

30. **What do you think is the job of the diaphragm?**

31. **Look into the eyepiece. Tilt the mirror until you see a bright circle of light.**

32. **What does the mirror do?**

Learning how to use the microscope is an important part of this Idea. And thus far you have done very well. But the interesting part comes when you prepare things to look at. This is where the excitement really begins.

D. FIND THE MISSING LETTER

33. **Clean a microscope slide and cover slip with lens paper.**

34. **Use your dropper. Place a drop of water on the center of your slide.**

35. **Cut the letter "k" from a newspaper.**

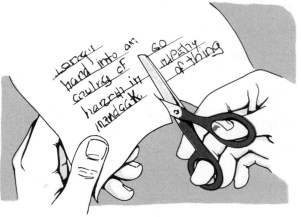

36. With your forceps, put the letter "k" on the drop of water.

37. Touch the cover slip to the edge of the drop of water.

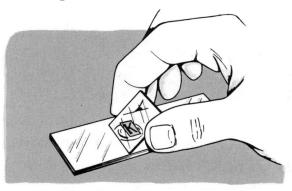

38. Gently lower the cover slip onto the drop of water.

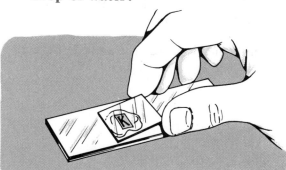

39. Why is it important to clean the slide and cover slip?

40. Repeat Step 31.

41. Place your slide on the stage. Be sure the letter "k" is directly over the opening in the stage.

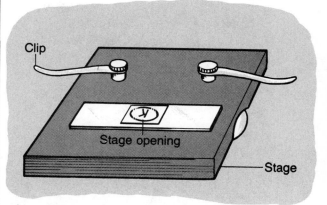

Clip

Stage opening

Stage

42. Place the clips on the slide.

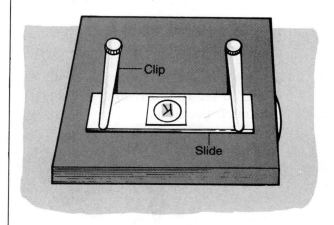

Clip

Slide

43. What are the clips used for?

44. Look through the eyepiece. Slowly turn the coarse adjustment knob toward you. Stop when the object is clear.

45. Use the fine adjustment knob to get a clearer picture.

46. In Space A, draw what you see.

47. Carefully click the high power objective in place. From the side, watch to see that the objective does not touch the slide.

48. Why is it important to watch as the objectives are changed?

49. Use the fine adjustment to get a clear picture.

50. Explain why *only* the fine adjustment is used with the high power objective.

51. In Space B, draw what you see.

52. What does the compound microscope help you do?

53. Why do you think scientists need such an instrument?

Re-read Questions 12, 18, and 52. State the concept.

CONCEPT

ENRICHMENT

1. Prepare and examine slides of hair, fur, insect wings, and lines drawn with a pencil or pen. Make drawings of your observations and discuss your results with the class.

2. Look at a metric ruler. Note the length of 1 mm. Look up and define the term micrometer. What is the symbol for this word? What is the size of 1 micrometer?

3. When you look at letters in a newspaper, the edges of these letters appear smooth. Describe the edges of the letter you viewed in this Investigation. How can you explain what you saw?

Investigation 2

Early Microscopes

Spanish National Tourist Office

Interest in plants and animals dates back to prehistoric times. Early cave dwellers had to know which plants could be used as foods. They thought that some plants had a mysterious power and could heal wounds. They had to know which animals could be hunted for food. They had to know which animals could be used for clothing. What were the habits of these animals? Where could they be found?

Thousands of years later, scientists were still asking these same questions, and more. Every answer led to new ideas, and each idea raised more questions. What were living things made of? How did they function as they did, and why?

Answers to these and many other questions were slow in coming and were often incorrect. It was not until the late sixteenth and early seventeenth centuries that things began to happen. And they happened because of the development of the compound microscope. The microscope has been used to study living things for almost 400 years. Many things have been learned about plants and animals. Many questions have been answered. One of the most important things learned was an answer to the question, "What are living things made of?"

Monroe/dpi

A. ANTONY VAN LEEUWENHOEK

One of the first people to study living things under the microscope was a Dutchman, Antony van Leeuwenhoek. Do you have a hobby? Leeuwenhoek's hobby was grinding glass into small lenses. Leeuwenhoek made more than 200 lenses. Some of these lenses were able to magnify objects as much as 270 times. Using these homemade lenses, Leeuwenhoek built a simple microscope.

This is what Leeuwenhoek's microscope looked like.

Bausch & Lomb

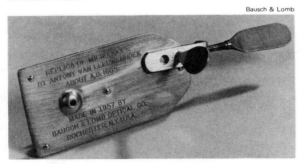

Leeuwenhoek observed many things. He collected and examined rainwater from a large, wooden barrel. He also looked at pond water. Leeuwenhoek took careful notes and made accurate drawings of what he observed. He called the microscopic animals that he observed ''Beasties.''

You can study them too.

1. Using lens paper, clean the eyepiece, objectives, and mirror of your microscope.

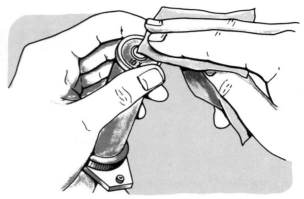

2. Clean a microscope slide and cover slip.

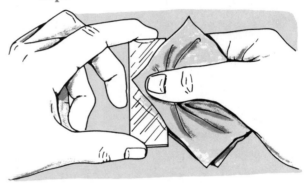

3. Use your dropper. Add a drop of pond water to the center of your slide.

4. Touch the cover slip to the edge of the drop of water.

5. Gently lower the cover slip onto the drop of water.

6. Gently blot away any water that seeps out from under the cover slip. Use a paper towel.

7. **Which objective will you use?**

8. **How will you know it is in place?**

9. **What has to be done to the diaphragm?**

10. **What has to be done to the mirror?**

11. Place your slide on the stage of the microscope.

12. Make sure that the drop of water is over the opening in the stage.

13. While looking from the side, turn the coarse adjustment knob. Carefully lower the body tube as far as it will go.

14. Focus on the slide.

If you don't see anything, ask your teacher for help. You may also want to make another slide. Don't give up; Leeuwenhoek didn't.

15. In Space A, draw what you see.

16. **Describe what you saw.**

17. **How could you tell if anything was alive?**

18. **How many living things did you see?**

19. **How were they different?**

Here are some microscopic animals that Leeuwenhoek observed and drew. Did you see any of these?

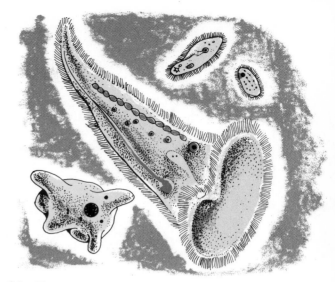

20. **Remove your slide and clean up.**

B. ROBERT HOOKE

Historical Pictures Service, Chicago

Leeuwenhoek was not alone in using the microscope to study living things. While he was studying microscopic animals, Robert

Hooke, an Englishman, was studying plants. Hooke designed and developed his own compound microscope. It looked very different from the one you are using.

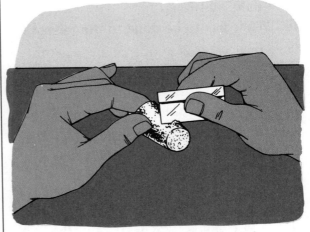

Rare Book Room, New York Public Library

Hooke examined very thin shavings of dry cork. He noticed that the cork was made up of many little boxes. Hooke made careful drawings and wrote about the tiny boxes. They reminded him of the honeycomb of a bee. Hooke called these tiny boxes "cells." Robert Hooke was the first to describe and draw them, and to use the word cell.

Here is one of Hooke's drawings.

Rare Book Room, New York Public Library

Let's see if you can get similar results.

21. Use a razor to scrape the edge of a piece of cork.

22. Carefully place the cork scraping on a slide. Use your forceps.

23. Add a drop of water to the cork.

24. Add a cover slip.

25. Examine under low power.

26. Examine under high power.

27. In Space B, draw what you see.

28. What does the cork look like?

29. How does your drawing compare with the drawing made by Hooke?

30. What did Hooke call the tiny boxes in cork?

31. Who was the first to use the word cells?

32. What did Leeuwenhoek call the microscopic animals he studied?

33. Why was the work of Leeuwenhoek important?

34. Why was the work of Robert Hooke important?

C. STUDYING CELLS

The work of Leeuwenhoek and Robert Hooke was the true beginning of microscopic study. Since then, scientists have studied many living things under the microscope. Scientists today still use the word first introduced by Robert Hooke. They now know that all living things share at least one property. All living things are made of cells.

35. Who was one of the first people to look at animal cells?

36. Who was one of the first people to look at plant cells?

37. What instrument did these people use to study cells?

Re-read your answer to Question 37. State the concept.

CONCEPT

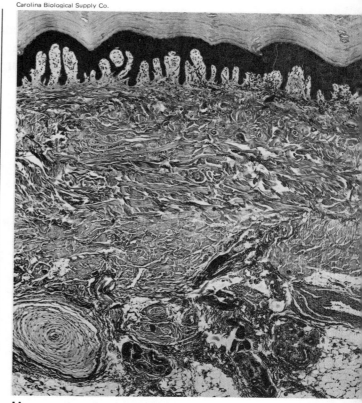

Human skin, cross section

ENRICHMENT

1. Leeuwenhoek and Robert Hooke pioneered the way for the formulation of the Cell Theory. Research and report on the Cell Theory and its importance in biology.

2. Prepare a collection of various sized lenses similar to the ones used by Leeuwenhoek. These can be made by heating a piece of glass rod over a Bunsen burner. As the rod softens, pull it apart to form a fine glass wire. Separate the two sections of rod and slowly feed each into the burner flame until it begins to build on itself. Report your results to the class.

3. Research and report on the structure and function of cilia, pseudopods, and flagella as means of locomotion in protozoa.

4. Devise a system for measuring the size of organisms under the microscope. Explain how you arrived at this system and describe its accuracy.

5. Describe and report on the basic similarities and differences between the simple and compound microscope.

6. Objects studied with an electron microscope were formerly measured in angstroms. Define the word. How is an angstrom related to a micrometer? What is an angstrom now called?

7. Research and report on the discovery and use of the electron microscope.

8. Observe threads of wool, cotton, and nylon under the microscope. Draw and label what you see. How is the structure of these threads related to their use in clothing?

Investigation 3

Cells Come in Many Shapes and Sizes

The idea that all living things are made of cells did not develop quickly. ***Biology***, the study of living things, developed early in the history of Greek civilization. The foundations of biology were laid by the Greeks and Romans. Then, suddenly, everything seemed to stop. For nearly 1,000 years, investigation in biology came to a standstill. This was the period of the Middle Ages, the Dark Ages. It was a period when people believed that all questions in biology were already answered. It was a period when people believed that there was nothing else to be discovered.

Then, just as suddenly as it ended, scientific curiosity awakened. It first opened its eyes in 1590 with the invention of the compound microscope. But it yawned and stretched with the work of Leeuwenhoek and Hooke during the late seventeenth century. The microscopes used at this time remained almost unchanged for nearly 200 years. But after 1830, new, improved microscopes were developed. More and more living things were studied. Soon afterwards, it was generally agreed that all living things are made of cells.

1. **Define biology.**
2. **What did the Greeks and Romans contribute to biology?**

3. **During what period in history did investigation in biology come to a standstill?**
4. **Explain why this was so.**
5. **What marked the awakening of scientific curiosity?**
6. **What idea came about as a result of this awakening?**

DO YOU KNOW...
SCIENTISTS LEARNED THAT SOME LIVING THINGS ARE MADE OF ONLY ONE CELL.
SOME ARE MADE OF MILLIONS OF CELLS.

ALL LIVING THINGS ARE MADE OF CELLS.

The "Beasties" studied by Leeuwenhoek were one-celled animals. You studied some of these animals in the last Investigation. Do you remember what they looked like?

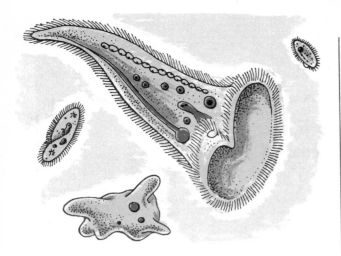

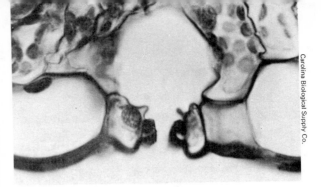

Guard cells

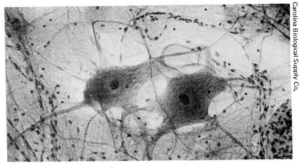

Nerve cells

7. How are these animals different? List some of the differences you can see.

8. How are the animals in the picture different in size?

9. How are their shapes different?

A. CELL SHAPE AND SIZE

In Idea 2, you learned that living things have a certain size and shape. Do cells have a certain size and shape?

Here are some pictures of different plant and animal cells.

Look at each group of cells carefully.

10. How do the white blood cells compare in size with one another?

11. How do the white blood cells compare in shape with one another?

12. How do the skin cells compare in size and shape with one another?

13. How do the guard cells compare in size and shape with one another?

14. How do cells within each group compare in size and shape with one another?

15. How does a cell in one group compare to the cells in the other groups in terms of size and shape?

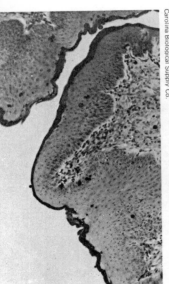

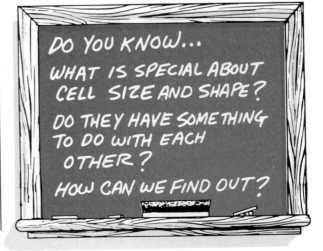

DO YOU KNOW...

WHAT IS SPECIAL ABOUT CELL SIZE AND SHAPE?

DO THEY HAVE SOMETHING TO DO WITH EACH OTHER?

HOW CAN WE FIND OUT?

Skin cells   **White blood cells**

B. LOOKING AT CELLS

Hundreds of years ago, knights wore suits of metal armor to protect them. Because these suits had a special job, they were specially designed. Plants and animals also need protection. Their "suits" also have a special job and design. But the armor of plants and animals is not metal. Their special armor is made of covering cells. Let's look at some of these cells.

16. Carefully scrape the inside of your cheek with the flat end of a toothpick.

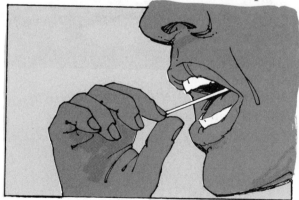

17. Carefully spread the scrapings on the center of a clean slide.

18. Add a drop of iodine solution to the scrapings.

19. Carefully place a cover slip on the slide.

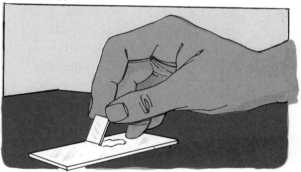

20. Examine the slide under low power with your microscope.

Objects to be studied with the microscope are usually thin and transparent. This means that you can often see right through them without even knowing it. *Cytologists* are people who study cells.

They want to know about the structure of cells. To do this, they must be able to see the many cell parts. Stains are used to help them do this. Iodine is only one of the many stains used in cytology.

21. Examine the cells under high power.

22. In Space A, draw what you see.

23. Describe the shape of these cells.

24. Why might the shape of these cells be good for protection?

25. What does the shape of a cell have to do with its job?

C. CELL FUNCTION

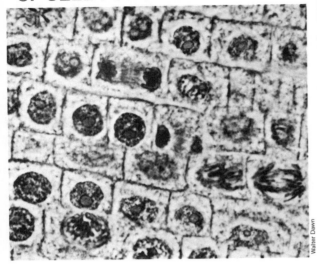

Walter Dawn

You're doing great. Let's continue your work in cytology by looking at some onion cells. Let's see how these compare with the protecting cells from inside your cheek.

26. Can you predict how these cells might look?

27. Explain your prediction.

28. Cut a small slice from an onion.

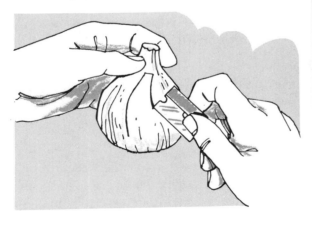

29. Gently pull the slice apart.

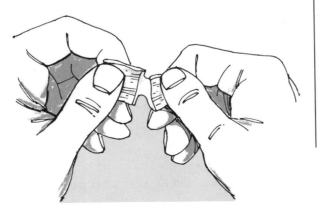

30. Place a drop of iodine solution on the center of a clean slide.

31. Using your forceps, pull off a very thin piece of onion skin.

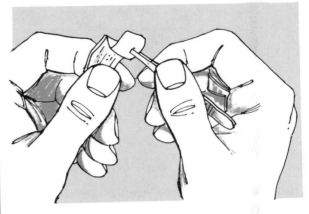

32. Carefully place this skin on the drop of iodine. Try to keep if from folding.

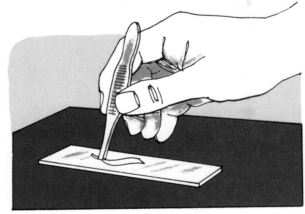

33. Add a cover slip.

34. Examine under low power.

35. **Find the cells under high power.**

36. **In Space B, draw what you see.**

37. **Why did you add iodine to the onion skin?**

38. **What is the shape of the cells?**

39. **How are these cells similar to your cheek cells?**

40. **How are they different?**

41. **What job do you think these onion cells have?**

42. **Why do you think this is so?**

43. **What does the shape of a cell have to do with its job?**

D. DO YOU GET THE MESSAGE?

You have seen that plant and animal cells have different shapes. Why is this so? To find the answer, let's put together what you've learned.

Look at the picture of guard cells on page 86. These cells look like tiny lips. By opening and closing, they control the amount of gases that move into and out of the leaf.

44. **What shape do guard cells have?**

45. **Why do you think this is a good shape?**

Telephone wires carry messages. These messages can travel from your home to your friends' homes. Telephone wires can carry messages from city to city or state to state.

46. **What is the shape of a telephone wire?**

47. **Why do you think the wires are made this way?**

This is a picture of two nerve cells. Nerve cells are like telephone wires. They carry messages from one part of the body to another.

48. **What shape does a nerve cell have?**

49. **Why do you think this is a good shape?**

50. **Your skin is made of the same kind of cells as the inside of your cheek. Why is this important?**

51. **What does the shape of a cell have to do with its job?**

Re-read your answers to Questions 25, 43, and 51. Write the concept.

CONCEPT

ENRICHMENT

1. Research and report on the contributions of Theodor Schwann in the field of cell study.

2. Research and report on the contributions of Matthias Schleiden in the field of cell study.

3. Examine a blood smear. Identify the cells present. How many different types of white blood cells did you observe? How are their shape and function related?

4. Examine a slide or picture of sickle cells. Research and report on sickle cell anemia. What relationship is there between the shape of sickle cells and the function of red blood cells? Why are cell shape and function important in sickle cell anemia?

5. Prepare slides of cheek and onion skin cells using methylene blue or other stains. Report on your results.

6. Cytologists are people who study cells. What are the requirements for a career in cytology? Why is cytology an important subject in the field of medicine?

7. What is a goblet cell? In what part of your body are goblet cells found? How are the shape and function of goblet cells related?

Investigation 4

The Cell Does It All

The discovery of **_cells_** as the building blocks of living things led to many new ideas. One of the most important was the Cell Theory. The Cell Theory stated that all parts of plants and animals are made of cells. With this concept in mind, scientists were now eager to focus their attention on the cell. Leeuwenhoek and Hooke made accurate drawings of cells. But they did not fully understand what they were looking at. They had no way of knowing what these cells contained or how important they really were. This was to be learned more than 150 years later.

Newer and better microscopes allowed scientists to study the inner structures of the cell. Now, for the first time, scientists could examine how a cell functions. They could study the microscopic machinery necessary for life. You can too.

A. PARTS OF THE CELL

1. **Make a slide of onion cells. You did this in the last Investigation.**

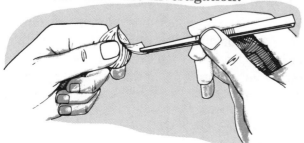

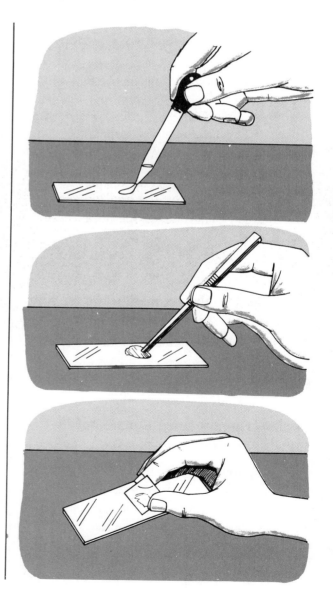

2. **Examine the cells carefully.**

3. **In Space A, draw one of the cells.**

4. **Look at your cell drawing. It has several parts.**

The outside covering of the cell is called the **cell wall**. The cell wall is made of **cellulose**, a nonliving material manufactured by the cell. A cell wall is always present in plant cells. Its function is to protect the cells and help them keep their shape.

5. **Label the cell wall on your drawing.**

6. **Where is the cell wall found?**

7. **Of what is the cell wall composed?**

8. **What is cellulose?**

9. **What type of cells always contain a cell wall?**

10. **Describe the function of the cell wall.**

Just inside the cell wall is a thin covering called the **cell membrane** or **plasma membrane**. The plasma membrane is a thin, strong, elastic membrane made of living material. The main function of the plasma membrane is to allow food and oxygen to enter the cell. The plasma membrane also allows waste material to leave the cell. In this way, the plasma membrane controls what enters and leaves the cell.

11. **Label the plasma membrane on your drawing.**

12. **Describe the location of the plasma membrane.**

13. **Of what is the plasma membrane composed?**

14. **Describe the main function of the plasma membrane.**

The dark, rounded structure located inside the cell is called the **nucleus**. Most cells contain only one nucleus, but there are cells which contain two or more nuclei. Very few cells contain no nucleus. An example of a cell which does not have a nucleus is the red blood cell of humans. The nucleus controls cell growth, reproduction, and, in general, everything that goes on inside the cell.

Scientists have learned that if the cell nucleus is removed, the cell soon dies.

15. **Label the nucleus.**

The material between the nucleus and the plasma membrane is called the **cytoplasm**.

16. **Label the cytoplasm.**

Under the control of the nucleus, the cytoplasm performs most of the life functions of the cell. Using the electron microscope, scientists have found that the cytoplasm consists of a system of membranes. These membranes are connected to form a network. Within this network everything that keeps the cell alive happens.

17. **Describe the location of the cytoplasm.**

18. **Of what does the cytoplasm consist?**

19. **Of what importance is the network of membranes?**

20. **List the parts of the cell just studied. List their functions also.**

B. WHAT'S IN THE FISH TANK?

Chuck Druss/Crystal Aquarium

Do you have an aquarium at home? If you do, you probably have water plants growing in it. Elodea is a common water plant. Let's take a very close look at this interesting and important plant.

21. Add a drop of water to a clean slide.
22. Pull off a small leaf from near the top of the plant.

23. With your forceps, place the leaf on the drop of water.
24. Add a cover slip.
25. Examine the cells under low power.
26. Examine the cells under high power.
27. In Space B, draw one of the cells.
28. Label the nucleus and cytoplasm. Also label the cell wall and plasma membrane.

The small green structures scattered throughout the cytoplasm are called **chloroplasts**. Chloroplasts are small storage sacs that contain **chlorophyll**.

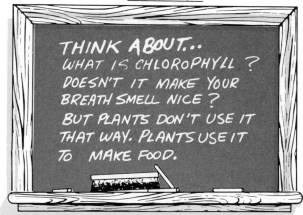

THINK ABOUT...
WHAT IS CHLOROPHYLL?
DOESN'T IT MAKE YOUR
BREATH SMELL NICE?
BUT PLANTS DON'T USE IT
THAT WAY. PLANTS USE IT
TO MAKE FOOD.

29. Label the chloroplasts on your drawing.
30. Try to find a _vacuole_. These are small, clear spaces in the cytoplasm. They are used for storage.

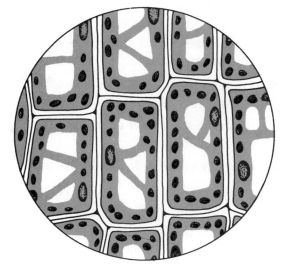

31. What are chloroplasts?
32. What is chlorophyll?

C. PLANT CELL WALLS

33. Make a fresh slide of Elodea.
34. Examine under low power.
35. Add a drop of salt water to one edge of the cover slip.

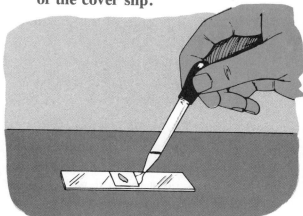

36. Touch the opposite edge of the cover slip with a piece of paper towel.

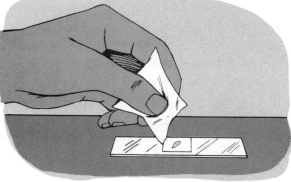

37. **Look carefully at the cell wall and plasma membrane.**

38. **Turn to page 92 and read about the plasma membrane.**

39. **Describe the effect of adding salt water to the cell.**

40. **How do you think this happened?**

Plant cell walls are very porous. This means that many different sized particles can pass through them in order to enter or leave the cell. However, this is not the case with the plasma membrane. The plasma membrane is highly selective. It contains tiny openings or *pores* which normally allow only certain sized particles to pass through them. One of the basic functions of the plasma membrane is to keep the cell in balance with its surroundings. When Elodea is placed in salt water, the number of water particles inside the cell is greater than outside. To keep the balance, water particles move from the cell out into the surroundings. The result is that the cell contents shrink.

41. **Describe the difference between the cell wall and plasma membrane.**

D. IT ALL HAPPENS HERE

You have examined and drawn cheek cells, onion skin cells, and Elodea cells.

42. **What parts do all these cells have in common?**

43. **What is the function of the nucleus?**

44. **What is the function of the plasma membrane?**

45. **What happens in the cytoplasm?**

46. **Where do the life functions of a cell take place?**

Re-read your answers to Questions 19, 45, and 46. State the concept.

CONCEPT

ENRICHMENT

1. Why could it be said that the cork cells studied by Robert Hooke were lifeless boxes?

2. Research and report on the composition of the cell wall. How does the cell wall originate? Are all cell walls composed of cellulose? Explain.

3. Define the term semipermeable. Why is the plasma membrane semipermeable? What do scientists suspect is the structure of the plasma membrane?

4. The cytoplasm contains both living and nonliving materials. Define the terms inclusions and organelles. How do these differ? How are they related to the cytoplasm? Cite examples of each.

5. Spread tomato pulp out in a drop of water on a clean slide. Add a cover slip and observe the tomato cells under low power. Locate the cell wall, vacuole, and nucleus. Locate the pigment granules which give the tomato its color. Draw and label what you see.

Investigation 5

The Wonderful World of the Cell

The microscope is a window through which scientists can look at the world of cells. Because of this, the microscope is thought of as the single most important instrument in cell biology. Careful microscopic observations led to the discovery of many cell structures. But with every question answered through the use of the microscope, new questions arose. It soon became clear that the microscope could not supply all the answers. The microscope could identify structures, but it could not explain function.

Following the statement of the Cell Theory, many things began to happen in cell biology. There was a period of scientific exploration marked by enormous activity. Information was collected, new experimental techniques were developed, and theories were suggested to explain new findings. Scientists wanted to know what types of cells and cell structures are found in plants and animals. They wanted to know how the cell behaves under different conditions. To do this, they had to know what substances enter and leave the cell, and how the movement happens.

A. PASS THE SALT

Your teacher will show you two labeled jars. Jar A contains Elodea and pond water. Jar B contains Elodea and salt water.

Pond water   Salt water

1. Use your dropper. Place a drop of water from Jar A onto a clean slide.

2. Use forceps to remove the Elodea from Jar A.

3. Pull off a small leaf from near the top of the plant.

4. With the forceps, place the leaf on the drop of water.

5. Add a cover slip.

6. Examine under low power.

7. Examine the cells under high power.

8. In Space A, draw one of the cells.

9. Label the nucleus and plasma membrane.

10. Label the vacuole.

11. Study your drawing carefully.

12. **Describe the shape of the cell.**

13. **Describe the location of the chloroplasts.**

14. **Describe the shape of the vacuoles.**

15. **Remove the slide from the microscope.**

16. **Use a clean dropper. Place a drop of water from Jar B onto a clean slide.**

17. **Remove the Elodea from Jar B.**

18. **Pull off a small leaf from near the top of the plant.**

19. **Place the leaf on the drop of water.**

20. **Add a cover slip.**

21. **Examine under low power.**

22. **Examine the cells under high power.**

23. **In Space B, draw one of the cells.**

24. **Describe the shape of the cell.**

25. **Describe the location of the chloroplasts.**

26. **Describe the shape of the vacuoles.**

27. **How do these cells compare with those from Jar A?**

28. **What do you think caused this change?**

29. **What evidence is there that particles moved through the plasma membrane?**

30. **Why is it important for materials to be able to move through the plasma membrane?**

Pure water is more concentrated than salt water. This means that there are more water particles in pure water than in the same volume of salt water. The movement of water out of a cell takes place in response to concentration. Thus water leaves the cell. The result is that the cell contents shrink. This process is known as *plasmolysis*. In plant cells, the cell wall is rigid. Thus, the cell keeps its original shape while the cytoplasm shrinks. In animal cells, where no cell wall exists, the plasma membrane shrinks with the cytoplasm. If plasmolysis continues, the cell soon dies from lack of water.

31. **Define plasmolysis.**

32. **What may happen if plasmolysis continues?**

33. **What do you think must take place for plasmolysis to be reversed?**

34. **What does the life of a cell seem to depend upon?**

B. GOING INTO A CELL

When salt dissolves in water, the salt breaks apart into very tiny particles. These particles are called *molecules*. You can taste the salt molecules, but you cannot see them. Many substances dissolve in water. When this occurs, they too become molecular in size. Many dissolved substances can move into and out of cells. In this way, cells are able to take in what they need. These materials are changed and used by the cell. The waste materials that form are also molecular in size. Thus, these molecules can move out of the cell.

35. **What are molecules?**

36. **Why are molecules important to cells?**

37. **Remove your slide from the microscope.**

38. **Add 2 drops of pond water from Jar A to the edge of the cover slip.**

39. **With paper towel, touch the liquid on the opposite side of the cover slip.**

40. **Examine the leaf cells under the microscope.**

41. **Describe the shape of the cells.**

42. **Remove the slide. Add 2 more drops of pond water to the edge of the cover slip.**

43. **Repeat Steps 39 and 40.**

44. **What has happened to the cell?**

45. **What do you think caused this change?**

Sometimes too much water entering a cell can be just as harmful as too much water leaving. If the amount of water entering a cell is not controlled, the cell may stretch, burst, and die. In plant cells, the rigid cell wall usually prevents this from happening. It maintains pressure and thus prevents too much water from entering the cell.

In some one-celled animals, such as Ameba,

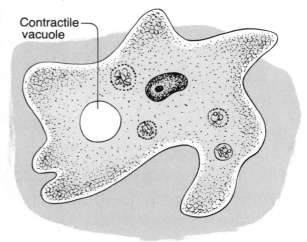

Contractile vacuole

and Paramecium,

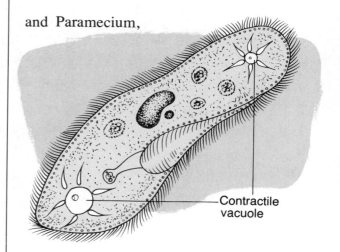

Contractile vacuole

special vacuoles are present. These are called *contractile vacuoles*. Contractile vacuoles collect excess water and collapse, thus giving off the water to the surroundings. Contractile vacuoles are a defense against cell rupture.

C. THE KEY TO IT ALL

46. How do materials enter and leave the cell?

47. Why must materials dissolve before they can enter the cell?

48. Why must materials be able to pass into and out of the cell?

49. Why is this important?

50. What does the life of a cell depend upon?

Re-read your answers to Questions 34, 49, and 50. Write the concept.

CONCEPT

ENRICHMENT

1. Experiment with red blood cells from a frog. A 0.7% salt solution is the normal surrounding for frog red blood cells. Test and report on your results when using stronger and weaker salt solutions.

2. With respect to what you have learned in this Investigation, report on the use of salt and sugar in preserving foods. What effect might concentrations of these solutions have on bacteria?

3. Define and give examples of the terms *osmosis* and *diffusion*. How are they different?

4. Research and report on active transport.

5. What is the sodium pump? How is it related to the movement of materials out of a cell?

Investigation 6

Cell Organization

The Cell Theory is considered a cornerstone of biology. It is as important today as it was when first stated in 1839. Two German biologists, Matthias Schleiden,

Culver Pictures, Inc.

and Theodor Schwann,

Culver Pictures, Inc.

are generally credited with the discovery of the Cell Theory. Actually, the bits and pieces were supplied by many scientists. Leeuwenhoek and Robert Hooke were pioneers in cell biology. The French biologist, Rene Dutrochet, realized the importance of cells in 1824. He claimed that all living things are made of cells, which are arranged in different ways.

French Cultural Services

99

The presence of a cell nucleus was first described in 1831 by a British biologist, Robert Brown.

It was Schleiden and Schwann who fit together the puzzle pieces supplied by these and many other scientists. Using the information supplied by others, they combined this with their own research and results. The final product was the Cell Theory.

1. **Who are generally credited with the discovery of the Cell Theory?**

2. **How did the discovery come about?**

The modern Cell Theory is not very much different from the original. The basic difference is that new information has been added as a result of new research findings. An important part of this new information deals with the organization of cells in living things. Let's take a microscopic look and see if you can arrive at any conclusions based upon your own observations.

A. TISSUES ARE MADE OF CELLS

Roots, stems, and leaves are often used to study the structure and organization of plant cells. The microscope reveals this structure and organization. One of the many leaves often used is that of the lilac.

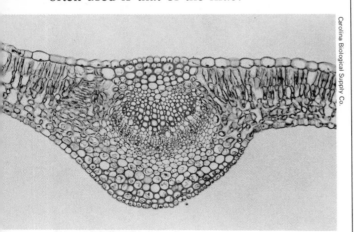

Lilac leaf, cross section
The general structure and organization of cells in the lilac leaf is very similar to that of many plant leaves.

You will be given a slide showing a cross section of a lilac leaf. A cross section shows a leaf cut as illustrated.

Objects viewed under the microscope appear upside down. You will be comparing your slide to a drawing of a lilac leaf. To make things easier, it will be helpful to study the slide in the same position as the leaf drawing.

3. Hold your slide up to the light. Notice that the leaf has a shape similar to that of an almost flattened V.

4. Place the slide on the microscope stage so that the bottom of the V is facing away from you.

5. Examine your slide under low power.

6. Compare your slide with the drawing of a lilac leaf on your data sheet.

7. Study the slide carefully. Notice the single layer of cells at the top and bottom of the leaf.

8. Follow each of these layers of cells by slowly moving the slide sideways. Examine both sides.

9. **Where do the top and bottom layers of cells meet?**

10. **Are these layers continuous or broken?**

The outer layer of leaf cells is known as the *epidermis*. The term *layer* is important. It indicates that these cells fit closely together to perform a definite function. And indeed they do. The function of these cells is to cover and protect the leaf.

11. **Are these epidermis cells different or similar to one another?**

12. **What is the basic function of each of these cells?**

Groups of similar cells that are organized to perform a specific function are very important in cell biology. Groups of similar cells that perform a specific function are known as *tissues*.

The word tissue was first used by the French biologist, M. Bichat, at the beginning of the 19th century. Dutrochet later described tissues as cells which appear to be united. Today, the study of tissues is an important part of hospital work. *Histology* is the study of tissues.

Forsyth/Monkmeyer

Forsyth/Monkmeyer

An *histologist* prepares tissues to be examined by a doctor. The results of this tissue examination may be used to help diagnose and treat tissue diseases.

13. **What is a tissue?**

14. **How are cells organized?**

15. **Identify and label the upper and lower epidermis tissue on the drawing on your data sheet.**

16. **Examine the *palisade cells* on your slide. These are located directly beneath the upper epidermis.**

17. **Are the palisade cells different or similar to one another?**

18. **What are the many structures scattered throughout the cytoplasm of these cells?**

19. **What do these structures contain?**

20. **Explain the function of chlorophyll in plants.**

21. **What do you think is the function of these cells?**

22. **What is a tissue?**

23. **Explain why these cells make up a tissue.**

24. **Identify and label the palisade tissue on the drawing on your data sheet.**

25. **Examine the *spongy cells*. These are the loosely arranged cells located beneath the palisade tissue.**

The spongy cells are storage cells. These cells also allow for the movement of gases throughout the leaf.

26. **Are the spongy cells different or similar to one another?**

27. **Explain why these cells make up a tissue.**

28. **Identify and label the spongy tissue on the drawing on your data sheet.**

Just as cells are common to both plants and animals, so are tissues. Histologists generally recognize four basic types of tissues in animals, including people. These four basic types are:

epithelial (covering, protective),

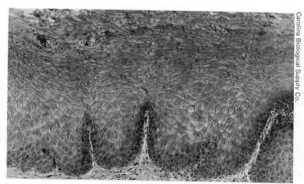

Carolina Biological Supply Co.

Epithelial tissue

muscle (movement),

Muscle tissue

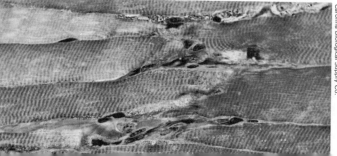

Carolina Biological Supply Co.

connective (including blood and bone),

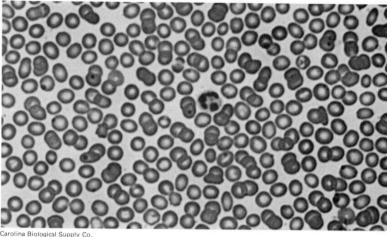

Carolina Biological Supply Co.

Blood tissue

Carolina Biological Supply Co.

Bone tissue

and nerve tissue.

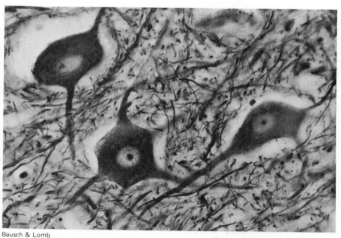

Bausch & Lomb

Nerve tissue

Each of these animal tissues performs a specific function. Each is composed of similar cells.

102

B. ORGANS ARE MADE OF TISSUES

Just as cells function cooperatively to form specialized tissues, tissues also work together. However, there is one basic difference. Groups of *similar* cells are organized to form tissues, but groups of *different* tissues are organized to form **organs.** Like tissues, organs perform specific functions. Examples of organs in plants are roots, stems, and leaves.

29. **Which tissues did you identify in the leaf?**

30. **What is an organ?**

31. **What is a leaf?**

Wings, fins, hearts, and stomachs are examples of animal organs. The organs of your body have special functions. For example, the arms and legs are organs used for movement, protection, and getting food.

32. **Can you predict which tissues you might find in the arm?**

33. **Remove page 000 from your book.**

34. **Cut each of the pieces from the page along the dotted lines. Piece A represents the forearm. Piece B represents the upper arm.**

35. **Paste the data sheet pieces onto a piece of cardboard.**

36. **Carefully cut along the solid outlines.**

37. **Assemble the arm model as shown.**

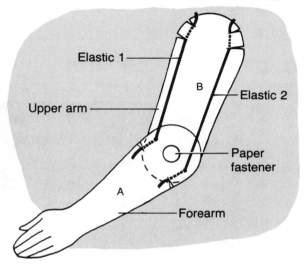

Congratulations! You've made a working model of the arm.

38. **Hold your model arm as shown. Pull the elastic upward.**

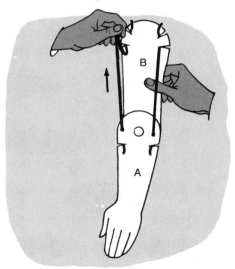

39. **Describe what happens when you pull the elastic upward.**

40. Which body tissue causes movement?

41. Which body tissue does the elastic represent?

42. To which body tissue is the elastic attached?

43. Which two tissues does your model represent?

44. Look at the tissues on page 102. Which of these tissues are also found in the arm?

45. Compare your answers to Questions 43 and 44 with the prediction you made in Question 32. How do your answers compare?

46. How do the tissues of your arm work together?

47. What do we call groups of different tissues that are organized to do a job?

48. What is an organ?

C. GROUPS OF ORGANS

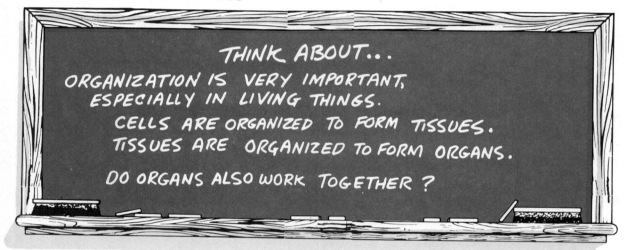

THINK ABOUT...

ORGANIZATION IS VERY IMPORTANT, ESPECIALLY IN LIVING THINGS.

CELLS ARE ORGANIZED TO FORM TISSUES.

TISSUES ARE ORGANIZED TO FORM ORGANS.

DO ORGANS ALSO WORK TOGETHER?

That's not a difficult question to answer. Groups of organs do work together. Working together, groups of organs form *organ systems*. Like tissues and organs, each organ system has a special job. Working together, the organ systems of living things keep them alive.

We can illustrate the organization in living things with a pyramid.

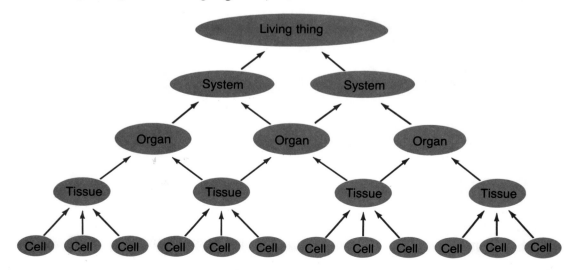

49. **Study the pyramid carefully.**

50. **What are tissues made of?**

51. **What do we call groups of cells that are organized to do a job?**

52. **What are organs made of?**

53. **What do we call groups of tissues that are organized to do a job?**

54. **What are systems made of?**

55. **What do we call groups of organs that are organized to do a job?**

Re-read your answers to Questions 50-55. Look at the pyramid again. State the concept.

CONCEPT

WORDS TO KNOW

The following words have been used in this Idea. Carefully review the Idea and define each of them on your data sheet.

Biology	Histologist
Cell	Histology
Cell membrane	Lens
Cell wall	Magnify
Cellulose	Molecule
Chloroplast	Nucleus
Chlorophyll	Organ
Compound	Organ system
microscope	Palisade cell
Contractile vacuole	Plasma membrane
Cytologist	Plasmolysis
Cytoplasm	Pore
Electron	Spongy cell
microscope	Tissue
Epidermis	Vacuole

SUMMARY OF THE IDEA: THE ORGANIZATION OF CELLS

Congratulations! You've travelled through almost 2000 years of history, and explored the fields of cytology and histology. But equally important, you've completed another Idea. This Idea has been about cells. And from what you've learned, it should not be difficult to understand why cells are considered the building blocks of living things. Scientists think of cells in many ways. Some living things, like the Paramecium and Ameba, are made of only one cell. Other living things are composed of billions of cells.

Scientists do not think of the organization of cells in living things as accidental. Each cell does not only function to stay alive, but specializes in some complex way. Thus, cells are organized into tissues. The major breakthrough in cell study emerged as the Cell Theory. Beginning with the work of Leeuwenhoek on animals and Robert Hooke on plants, ideas about cells began to expand. But it is difficult to imagine learning about cells without the microscope. The research of Robert Brown, Rene Dutrochet, Schleiden, and Schwann are proof of this. All of these people have contributed to the Cell Theory, which you have studied in detail in this Idea.

In your study of cells, you have learned six concepts.

1. State these six concepts.

Robert Hooke was one of the first people to study plants under the microscope. You studied cork under the microscope, just as he did.

2. What did Robert Hooke call the tiny boxes in cork?

We still use this name today. For nearly 400 years, scientists have used the microscope to study cells.

3. What have scientists learned that plants are made of?

Leeuwenhoek was one of the first people to study tiny animals under the microscope.

4. What are animals made of?

5. What is the basic statement of the Cell Theory?

6. What are all living things made of?

Summarize the Idea.

IDEA SUMMARY

ENRICHMENT

1. Visit a butcher or local fish market. Obtain several animal organs. Identify these organs and the tissues of which they are composed.

2. Examine prepared microscope slides of various plant roots and stems. Define the terms xylem and phloem. What are they? Where are they found? What tissues are present in roots and stems? Why are these plant parts considered organs?

3. Examine a prepared microscope slide showing a cross section of a corn leaf (Zea mays). Compare this slide with the lilac leaf just studied. Report on your findings.

4. Define the terms cross section, oblique, and longitudinal as these are related to microscope slides. Use a piece of rubber tubing. Cut and draw a representative section of each.

5. Research histology as a career. What are the requirements for becoming an histologist in a hospital or private laboratory?

6. Prepare a report on epidermal tissue in plants and animals. Is the outer layer of epidermal cells in people alive? How are these cells replaced? What is scar tissue and how does it form?

Investigation 1

Roots and Conduction Tissues

You are familiar with cells, tissues, organs, and systems in plants and animals.

Onion skin is composed of cells.

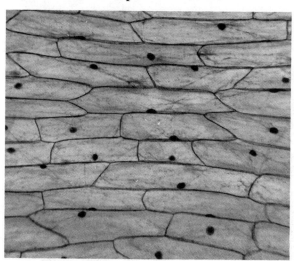

Grant Heilman

Muscle is a tissue.

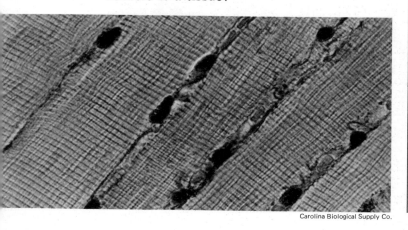

Carolina Biological Supply Co.

The circulatory system is a system.

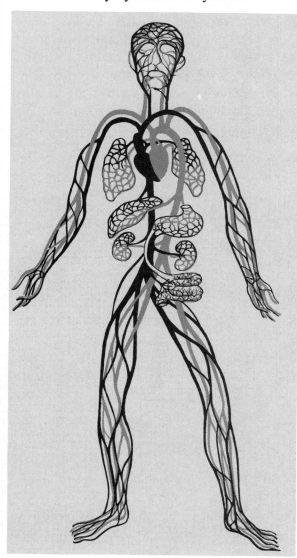

The leaf is an organ.

The major organs in most plants are the roots, stems, and leaves. Some plants also have flowers and fruits. In plants, several organs work together to form systems. The most important systems are the food-making system, the conduction system, and the reproductive system.

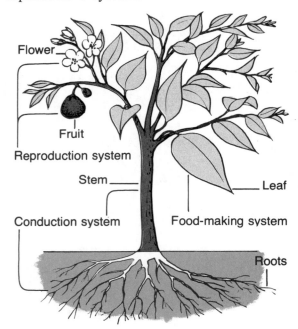

Flower

Fruit

Reproduction system

Stem

Conduction system

Leaf

Food-making system

Roots

We will study the conduction system in this Investigation. This is the system that transports water and dissolved materials throughout the plant.

A. FUNCTION OF ROOTS

There are two basic types of roots: taproots and fibrous roots. A **_taproot_** has one long, tapering root, with a few small branches. A carrot has a taproot. **_Fibrous roots_** are a network of many roots, all about the same size. Grass has fibrous roots. Both kinds of roots have the same functions. One function is to absorb water and dissolved minerals from the soil. But how do the water and minerals reach the other parts of the plant?

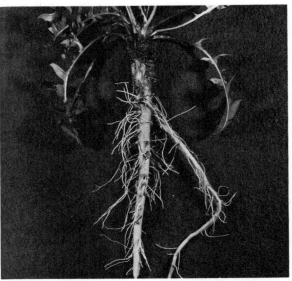

A taproot   Grant Heilman

Fibrous roots   Grant Heilman

Your teacher will give you two roots. One root has been placed in water and the other in water containing a red dye. Your teacher will also give you something to help you make very thin slices. We'll call it our thin slicer. You'll use it to cut roots and stems, not baloney.

1. **Cut off one of the roots just below the seed.**

2. **Cut a piece of carrot to fit easily inside the thin slicer.**

3. **Cut the piece of carrot in half lengthwise.**

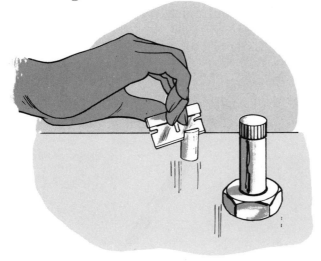

4. **Place the root upside down between the two pieces of carrot.**

5. **Place the root and the pieces of carrot inside the thin slicer.**

6. **With a razor, cut the root.**

7. Turn the knob at the bottom of the thin slicer very slightly.

8. Cut the root again making a thin slice. Discard the carrot.

9. Repeat Steps 7 and 8 several times. You need a slice thin enough to examine under the microscope.

10. Use your forceps. Carefully place the thinnest root slice on a clean microscope slide.

11. Add a drop of water to the root slice.

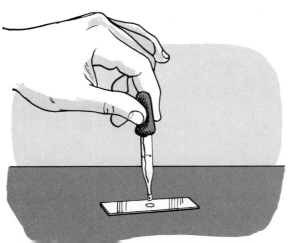

12. Repeat Steps 1 to 11 with the other root.

13. Add a cover slip.

14. Examine both root slices under low power.

15. In Space A on your data sheet, draw what you see.

16. Which root is the control?

17. Describe how the two roots differ.

18. Name one function of roots. How do you know?

Your slices have cut across some cells of the root. Remember that groups of cells that have the same job are called tissues.

19. Are all the cells stained red? Which part of the root tissue is stained red?

20. What is the shape of this tissue?

21. What is the job of the tissues that are stained red?

22. Plants have different kinds of tissues. What is the job of one kind of tissue?

B. SPECIAL TISSUES

You don't have to be doctor to know that celery can't get measles. But how can you explain red spots on celery?

23. Stand a celery stem in a beaker of water containing red dye.

24. **After several minutes, remove the celery from the beaker.**

25. **Cut the celery about 1 cm from the bottom.**

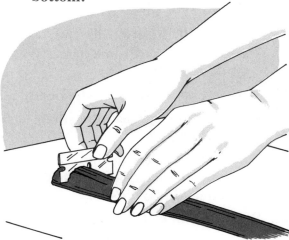

26. **Examine the parts of the stem which are colored red.**

27. **In Space B on your data sheet, draw what you see.**

28. **Carefully cut through one of the red colored parts.**

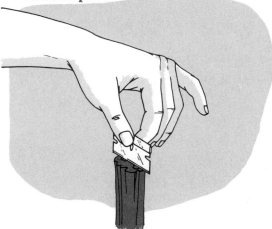

29. **In Space C on your data sheet, draw what you see.**

30. **What does the stained part look like?**

31. **In which direction do you think the water is moving? Explain.**

32. **What do you think is the job of these stem tubes?**

33. **How are these tubes like those you found in the root?**

A cut across a stem shows different kinds of tissues. Different tissues have special jobs. The tissues for conducting water are arranged in bundles. In some plants the bundles of conduction tissue are in the form of a ring. In other plants the bundles of conduction tissue are scattered.

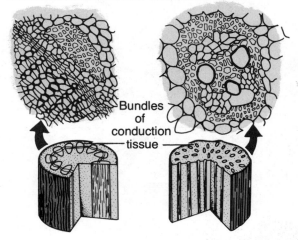

Bundles of conduction tissue

There are several different kinds of cells that conduct water. One of these cells is pictured below. Columns of these cells with holes at the ends form the main pipeline in the plant. Together, they form the **_conduction tissue._**

Conduction tube cell

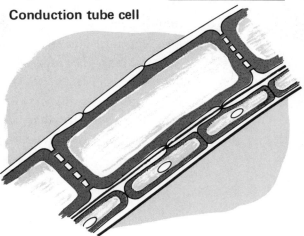

34. **How are conduction tissues arranged?**

35. **Where are the conduction tissues located in the stem?**

36. **How does water move from one cell to the next?**

37. **What is the job of one kind of tissue?**

38. **What do you call this kind of tissue?**

C. STILL GOING STRONG

39. Put the celery stem back into the beaker of red colored water.

40. Label the beaker with your name and section.

41. Store your experiment for 1 day.

42. After 1 day, carefully examine the leaves of your plant.

43. What happened to the leaves?

44. Where did the red come from? What does this show?

45. Where does water enter the plant?

46. How does water reach the stems and leaves of plants?

47. Plants have different kinds of tissue. Re-read Questions 44-46. What is the job of one kind of tissue?

48. What do you call this kind of tissue?

Re-read Questions 47 and 48 before writing the concept.

CONCEPT

ENRICHMENT

1. Use your thin slicer to make a slice of the celery stem. Make a drawing of your observations.

2. Use your thin slicer to make cuts of different kinds of roots and stems. Make drawings of your observations and tell how they compare.

3. Look up the words *vascular bundle, phloem,* and *xylem.* Tell how they relate to what you have learned.

4. Write a report on how water gets to the top of tall trees.

5. Obtain some white daisies or carnations. Stain the petals different colors using what you have learned. How did it happen?

Stomates and Gas Exchange

Where there is no water, there are no plants. No plant can live without water, and many can live only in water. Plants that live on land need a source of water. Rain is the major source. As rain goes, so goes the amount of plant life.

Ellena/dpi

Ahrens/Bruce Coleman, Inc.

0 cm   The Mohave Desert

Arizona Desert   10 cm

25 cm   Great Basin, Nevada/Utah

Grant Heilman

60 cm   **Mid-West Grasslands, Great Plains**

100 cm   **Forest, Appalachian Mountains**

250 cm   **Olympic National Park, Washington**

Water and dissolved minerals enter a plant through the roots. The root systems of some plants grow very deep and spread very wide. Alfalfa roots may be found 10 meters down in a two-year-old field. Their roots have been found 40 meters deep in mine shafts. A single rye plant may have 14 million roots with a total length of over 600 km.

The roots branch and grow out, seeking new water daily. Near the end of every root there are thousands of tiny *root hairs*. Each is part of a single cell which is able to take in water. If you add up the millions of root hairs, the total length of the root system is very long indeed.

Root hairs on a radish seedling

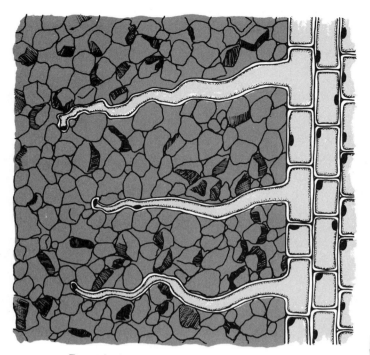

Root hairs pushing through soil

Water that enters the roots is carried upwards by conduction tissue. This conduction tissue continues up through the stem or stems. Conduction tissue can be dead cells that have lost their contents and end walls. These cells, stacked end to end, now form a continuous tube through which water moves.

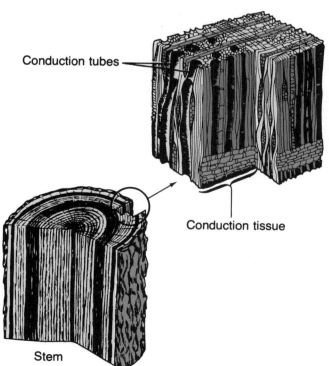

Conduction tubes

Conduction tissue

Stem

Finally, the conduction tissue branches out into every leaf.

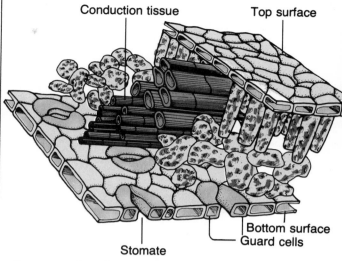

Conduction tissue — Top surface

Bottom surface
Guard cells
Stomate

Cut-away drawing of a leaf

The tubes that carry the water start in the roots and end in the leaves. What happens to the water in the leaves? After answering some questions, you will make a prediction.

1. **Name one substance needed by a plant.**
2. **Name one function of the root.**
3. **Explain why roots grow very deep and spread out.**
4. **What are root hairs?**
5. **What is the function of root hairs?**
6. **How can a root system be many kilometers long, yet be only a few meters deep?**
7. **Through which tissue is water carried upward in a plant?**
8. **How is conduction tissue constructed?**
9. **Where does conduction tissue start and end?**
10. **What do you think happens to water when it reaches the leaves? Make a prediction.**

Scientists constantly make predictions. Predictions, or educated guesses, are possible answers to questions. Let's see if your prediction is the answer to the question.

A. THE CONTROL SYSTEM

Your teacher will give you a plant leaf.

11. **Place a drop of water on a microscope slide.**

12. **Fold the leaf in half so that the top is outside.**

13. **Gently tear the leaf with a twisting motion.**

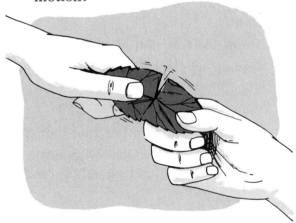

14. **Using forceps, pull off a piece of the thin, transparent bottom skin.**

15. **Place the skin in the drop of water.**

16. **Add a cover slip.**

17. **Examine under low power with your microscope.**

18. **Look for tiny football-shaped openings.**

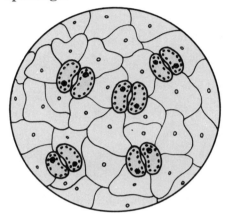

19. **In Space A, draw what you see.**

Scientists call these tiny openings **_stomates_**. Stomate means "little mouth" in Greek. The two cells around each stomate are called **_guard cells_**. A single sunflower leaf may have as many as 2 million stomates. Most of these are on the bottom side of the leaf.

20. **How many stomates can you count?**

21. **Are the stomates bunched up or spread out over the leaf?**

22. **Are the stomates open or closed?**

To help you answer Question 22, look at the two pictures below.

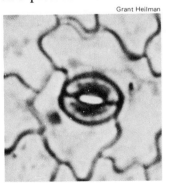

Grant Heilman

Open stomate

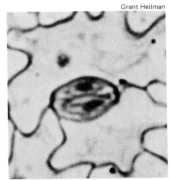

Grant Heilman

Closed stomate

116

The stomates are the control system of a plant's transportation system. A plant's transportation system is like your home plumbing system. Water enters the pipes of a house underground. The pipes branch and carry water to all the faucets, toilets, and showers. From them the water passes out of the pipes.

Plants have a similar system. Water enters the tubes in the roots. These tubes branch and carry water to all the leaves. From there the water passes into the air. Water returns to the air through the stomates in the form of a gas, *water vapor*.

What if the amount of water entering a plant is reduced? What slows down or stops the water vapor from leaving the plant?

23. What controls the loss of water vapor from the leaves?

24. Name one gas that leaves by way of the stomates.

25. What is the function of the stomates?

B. COLOR IT YELLOW

You learned about one gas, water vapor, in Part A. You will learn about another gas, *carbon dioxide*, in this part.

Bromthymol blue is used to test for carbon dioxide. If the gas is present in water, the bromthymol changes from blue to green or yellow. The new liquid is called *bromthymol yellow*. Bromthymol yellow changes back to blue when carbon dioxide is removed from the water.

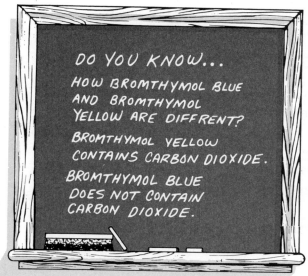

DO YOU KNOW...

HOW BROMTHYMOL BLUE AND BROMTHYMOL YELLOW ARE DIFFRENT?

BROMTHYMOL YELLOW CONTAINS CARBON DIOXIDE.

BROMTHYMOL BLUE DOES NOT CONTAIN CARBON DIOXIDE.

26. Get two test tubes. Label them with your name and section.

27. Label one test tube A. Label the other test tube B.

28. Fill both test tubes ¾-full with bromthymol yellow.

29. Place some Elodea in Tube A.

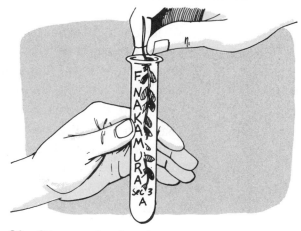

30. Stopper both tubes.

31. Place both tubes under a lamp. Do not disturb for 1 day.

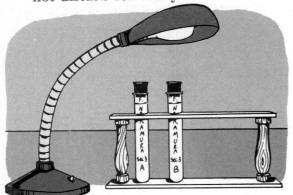

32. After 1 day, examine both tubes.

33. What color change took place in Tube A?

34. What does this show?

35. What do you think caused this change?

36. What happened in Tube B?

37. What does this show?

38. How can you explain this?

39. What does bromthymol yellow contain? (Hint: Look at the last chalkboard.)

40. What did the plant remove from Tube A?

41. Where do you think the gas entered the plant?

42. What enters and leaves the stomate?

C. PUTTING IT TOGETHER

43. What gas did you learn about in Part A?

44. Where does this gas leave the leaf?

45. What gas did you learn about in Part B?

46. Where does this gas enter the leaf?

47. Explain what happens at the stomates.

CONCEPT

ENRICHMENT

1. Root hairs increase the surface area of the root. Fold a strip of paper like an accordian. Use this model to explain the concept of increased surface area. Construct a control.

2. Water is able to rise many meters up conduction tissue because of many factors. Explain these factors.

3. Repeat Steps 11-16. Place a drop of 10% salt solution at the edge of the cover slip. Observe a stomate under high power. Explain your observations.

4. Water enters the root hairs by *osmosis*. Water also enters and leaves the guard cells by osmosis. What is osmosis?

5. Repeat Steps 11-17 with different kinds of leaves. How do the number of stomates differ?

6. Where are the stomates on a water lily?

7. Use your thin slicer to make a slice of a leaf. Find the cells pictured in the drawing on page 111.

8. Write a paper on transpiration.

9. Investigate how desert plants protect themselves from drying.

10. Guard cells have a thin-walled side and a thick-walled side. Explain how these work to open and close the stomates.

Investigation 3

Green Power

One of the most obvious things about most plants you see is that they are green. True, not all plants are green; but it's the green plants that dominate the plant world. It is also true that not all parts of green plants are green. It's mainly the leaves that are green. But a plant has so many leaves that green overshadows everything else. So, green is just about all you see, and green plants are truly what they are commonly called.

A. THE PIGMENT IS GREEN

Green is the basic _**pigment**_ of plants. A pigment is a coloring agent. There are thousands of pigments in the plant world. Yellow pigments give the daffodil its color.

Red apples get their color from red pigments.

Even parts of plants growing underground have pigments, like the carrot.

Suva/dpi

And when fall comes, the leaves turn a rainbow of pigmented colors.

But green is the basic color, and the green pigment is called **chlorophyll**.

Chlorophyll can be extracted, pulled apart, and studied.

1. **Make a pencil mark in the center of a filter paper circle.**

2. **Place a leaf, top side down, over the pencil mark.**

3. **With a nail, push down on the leaf over the pencil mark.**

4. **Repeat Step 3 30-40 times, moving the leaf occasionally, until you get a dark green spot on the paper.**

5. **Cut the filter paper as shown.**

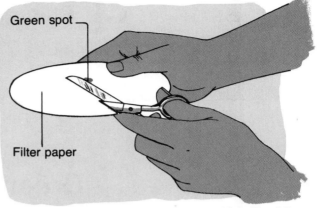

Green spot

Filter paper

6. **Fill a petri dish bottom half-full with the liquid provided.**

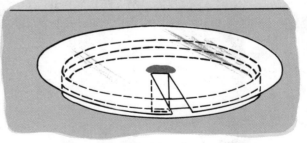

7. **Place the cut filter paper over the petri dish.**

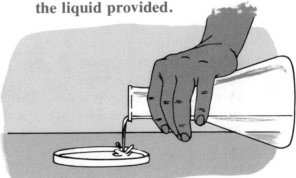

8. **Observe for 10-20 minutes. Then draw the results in Space A.**

Many different chemicals compose living things. These can be separated and studied in different ways. You have just used one way. It is called **paper chromatography**. The word chromatography means "to write with color." The materials in the spot are dissolved and carried along by the liquid in

120

the petri dish. The different pigments in the spot move at different rates and are separated along the filter paper. These are shown as rings on the paper. The one or two green rings are chlorophyll.

9. **What is a pigment?**

10. **What is chlorophyll?**

11. **Where is chlorophyll found?**

12. **How did you remove the chlorophyll from the leaves?**

13. **What technique did you use to study chlorophyll?**

14. **How did the chlorophyll appear in your drawing in Space A? Go back and label the rings that are chlorophyll.**

15. **Make a prediction. Why do you think chlorophyll is important to a plant?**

16. **Again, what is chlorophyll?**

B. THE LOCATION OF CHLOROPHYLL

That was no ring around the collar you got on the filter paper. Those were rings of chlorophyll, the green pigment in plants. You released the chlorophyll when you crushed a part of the leaf with the nail. There's a reason why you were asked to turn the leaf top side down too. Let's see why.

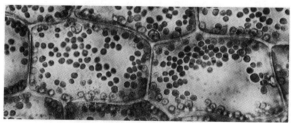

Elodea showing chloroplasts

Grant Heilman

In Idea 3, Investigation 4, you looked at the cells of Elodea under a microscope. The round, green structures are *chloroplasts*. The green color, of course, is our friend chlorophyll. Chlorophyll is found only in the chloroplasts. The rest of the cell is colorless.

In fact, most of a cell is colorless; yet you see green.

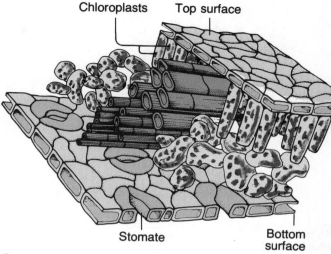

Cut-away drawing of a leaf

You may remember this cut-away drawing of a leaf. You might have even made a thin section with your thin slicer. In the last Investigation you learned about the stomates. These are found mostly on the bottom surface of a leaf. The bottom surface is less likely to get covered with dirt and dust. Most of the chloroplasts, however, are found near the top surface of a leaf. Why is this important?

17. **What are chloroplasts?**

18. **In what structure is chlorophyll found in a leaf?**

C. IT'S MORE THAN FOOD COLORING

You can't keep a plant alive with green food coloring. The plant makes its own chlorophyll, and the chlorophyll is necessary for life.

19. **Place wet towels in the bottom halves of two petri dishes.**

20. Your teacher will give you some seeds. Place half of them in each dish.

21. Cover both dishes; label each with your name and section.
22. Place one dish in the light. Place the other in the dark.
23. Check the dishes daily for water. Observe what happens after about 5 days.
24. What color were the seedlings grown in the light?
25. What gave the seedlings this color?
26. What do you predict will happen to these seedlings if planted in the light?
27. What color were the seedlings grown in the dark?
28. What were these seedlings unable to make?
29. What do you predict will happen to these seedlings if kept in the dark?
30. What pigment does a plant need for life?

D. ALBINO CORN

Grant Heilman

This is a photograph of corn seedlings. The dark leaves have chlorophyll. The light colored leaves do not have chlorophyll. They are on plants called *albino* corn and, because of a defect, will not make chlorophyll. When the reserve food stored in the seed is used up, the albino plant dies.

31. What pigment is in the dark-colored leaves?
32. What will happen to these corn plants if planted in the light?
33. What pigment is lacking in the light-colored leaves?
34. What will happen to these corn plants if planted in the light?
35. What pigment does a plant need for life?

Re-read Questions 30 and 35 before stating the concept.

CONCEPT

ENRICHMENT

1. Research the names and colors of some other pigments.
2. Use the paper chromatography technique on different kinds of leaves. Compare your results.
3. In what way is chlorophyll similar to hemoglobin? Explain.
4. Obtain some green and albino corn seeds. Plant them and see what happens.
5. Explain what causes some leaves to change color in autumn.

Investigation 4

Some Light on the Subject

Eat, drink, and breathe. We take these for granted; yet we know we must eat, drink, and breathe to live.

Richard Knapp/© TWA Ambassador Magazine

Plants are no different. Plants are living things, too. All living things must eat, drink, and breathe in their own way. The key words

are "in their own way." In the last three Investigations you have studied how plants drink and breathe in their own way.

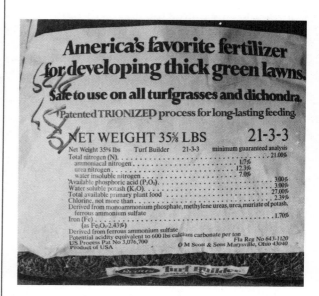

Plants obtain water by absorbing it through their roots. Dissolved in the water are many different kinds of minerals. **_Minerals_** are chemicals that occur in the soil. Examples are phosphates, nitrates, and sulfates. These are the major minerals found in fertilizers. Just as sugar enters your body cells when dissolved in water, minerals enter a plant when dissolved in water.

123

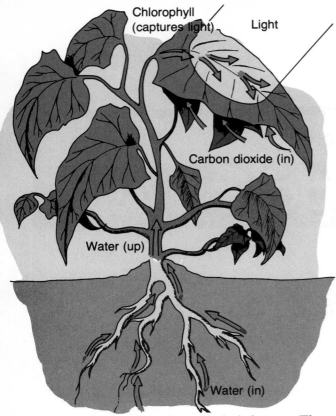

Chlorophyll (captures light)

Light

Carbon dioxide (in)

Water (up)

Water (in)

Plants obtain gases through their leaves. The main gas that is needed is carbon dioxide. Carbon dioxide enters the leaves through the stomates.

So now we know how plants drink and breathe in their own way. What about eating? Do they eat in their own way too? How do plants obtain energy? Light is energy for a plant. To see how plants obtain energy, we need to look at chlorophyll again. Chlorophyll is the green pigment you learned about in the last Investigation. Plants get their energy with the help of chlorophyll.

1. **How do plants absorb water?**

2. **What else is obtained with the water?**

3. **Name some common minerals.**

4. **Where are minerals naturally found?**

5. **How can minerals be added to plants by people?**

6. **What gas is needed by plants?**

7. **How does this gas enter a plant?**

8. **What is energy for a plant?**

9. **What substance do you predict helps a plant get this energy?**

A. IS CHLOROPHYLL RED?

Your cooperation and contribution will be necessary for this class activity.

10. **Your teacher will have a beaker of alcohol boiling gently.**

CAUTION

ALCOHOL BURNS AND MUST NEVER BE USED NEAR AN OPEN FLAME!

11. **Place a few crushed leaves in the alcohol. Boil gently for 5 minutes.**

12. **Continue to add leaves until the alcohol is a dark color.**

13. **Allow the alcohol to cool.**

14. Pour some into a small bottle until it is almost full.

15. Add alcohol to another small bottle until it is almost full.

16. Add green food coloring until it is the same dark color as the alcohol in the other bottle.

17. What color is the alcohol that had the leaves in it?

18. What do you predict is causing this color?

19. What color is the alcohol with green food coloring in it?

20. Hold the liquid with the green food coloring in a strong light beam.

21. Look down from above through the neck of the bottle at the upper surface of the liquid.

22. What color do you see?

23. Hold the liquid with the chlorophyll in it in a strong light beam.

24. Look down from above through the neck of the bottle at the upper surface of the liquid.

25. What color do you see?

Surprise! Chlorophyll reflects red. Something must have happened when the sunlight struck the chlorophyll.

To understand what happened, you must realize that light is a form of energy. Energy is what drives the world. Energy causes things to happen. *Energy* is the ability to do work. Life runs on energy. You get your energy from food. A plant gets its energy from sunlight. The sunlight is absorbed by the chlorophyll to reflect red. Without chlorophyll a plant could not capture the energy in the sunlight.

26. **What is light a form of?**

27. **What substance in a plant absorbs light energy?**

28. **What happens to chlorophyll when it absorbs light energy? What does this indicate?**

29. **What can chlorophyll absorb from light?**

B. CHLOROPHYLL AND LIGHT ENERGY

Ultimately, the source of all energy for living things is the sun. Most organisms cannot see light energy directly. Green plants, however, can directly use the sun's energy. This is because green plants have chlorophyll. Chlorophyll can absorb energy from light. The change in the color of the chlorophyll indicates the light has been absorbed.

Below is a series of photographs of two pots of corn seedlings. Both pots have been in the light.

Pot A was in the light. Pot B was kept in the dark.

30. **What happened to the seedlings in Pot A?**

31. **What happened to the seedlings in Pot B after one week? Explain why.**

32. **What happened to the seedlings in Pot B after two weeks? Explain why.**

33. **What is the relationship between chlorophyll and light energy?**

34. **What does chlorophyll have the ability to do?**

Re-read Questions 29 and 34. State the concept.

CONCEPT

After one week

After two weeks

ENRICHMENT

1. Duplicate the experiment described in Part B to see if you get the same results.
2. Write a paper about white light and the color spectrum.
3. Not all green plants have green leaves. Give some examples and explain how they obtain energy.
4. How does a plant live after it has lost its leaves in the fall?

Investigation 5

A Plant Feeds Itself

Let's get one thing straight. You don't feed a plant. A plant feeds itself. Fertilizer is not food. Light is not food. Carbon dioxide is not food. Neither is water food. A plant makes its own food. Then it lives off this food.

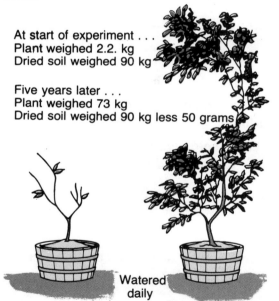

At start of experiment . . .
Plant weighed 2.2. kg
Dried soil weighed 90 kg

Five years later . . .
Plant weighed 73 kg
Dried soil weighed 90 kg less 50 grams

Watered daily

This can be shown by an experiment that was done nearly 400 years ago. Jan Baptista van Helmont lived from 1577 to 1644 in Belgium. In one experiment he placed 90 kg of dried soil in a pot. A willow branch weighing 2.2 kg was planted in the soil and watered daily with rain water. After 5 years the willow had grown large and strong and had increased in weight by 73 kg. After drying the soil, van Helmont could find a loss of only about 50 grams. He concluded that a plant's growth came entirely from water.

Van Helmont did not realize that plants take up carbon dioxide from the air. This is easy to understand. Air is only 0.03 percent of this gas. The importance of carbon dioxide was not discovered until about 200 years ago.

Water and carbon dioxide are ***raw materials***. They are taken in and used by plants. Plants use these raw materials to make their own food. Yes, you don't feed a plant. A plant feeds itself. This process of food-making in green plants is called ***photosynthesis***.

THINK ABOUT...
PHOTOSYNTHESIS IS A BIG WORD, BUT THE CONCEPT IS NOT DIFFICULT.
"PHOTO" MEANS "LIGHT."
"SYNTHESIS" MEANS "PUTTING TOGETHER."
SO "PHOTOSYNTHESIS" MEANS "PUTTING TOGETHER USING LIGHT."

A. IODINE ISN'T ONLY FOR CUTS

Sugar and *starch* are the foods that green plants make. These foods are made of carbon, hydrogen, and oxygen. They are called *carbohydrates*.

During photosynthesis, plants make sugar. Some of the sugar is changed to starch. The plant then uses some of the carbohydrate as its own source of food energy. The unused carbohydrate is stored by the plant.

National Dairy Council

1. Place a few drops of water in a petri dish.

2. Add enough starch to the water to make a paste.

3. Mix the starch paste.

4. Add 1 drop of iodine solution to the starch paste.

5. What color is the starch paste alone?

6. What color is the iodine solution alone?

7. What color change takes place when the iodine is added to starch?

Iodine is used to test for starch. If iodine is mixed with starch, a blue-black color always results.

8. Add 1 drop of iodine solution to a sugar cube.

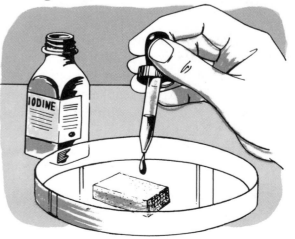

9. **Describe what happens.**

10. **What does this show?**

11. **Add 1 drop of iodine solution to a slice of potato.**

12. **Describe what happens.**

13. **What does this show?**

14. **What two raw materials are needed by green plants?**

15. **What do plants make from the raw materials?**

16. **What is the process of food making in plants called?**

17. **Explain the statement: "You do not feed a plant; a plant feeds itself."**

18. **What does a plant make during photosynthesis?**

B. BOILED LEAVES

You boiled some leaves in alcohol in the last Investigation. You then looked at the dark green chlorophyll solution. Your teacher may have saved the leaves.

19. **If there are no leaves, repeat Investigation 4, Steps 10-12.**

20. **Spread a leaf out in a petri dish.**

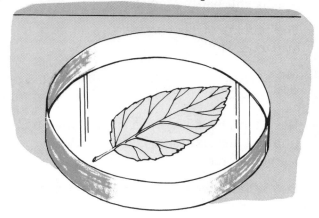

Notice that the leaves are light colored. The chlorophyll has been removed from the leaves. This makes it easier to see the results of a starch test. With the chlorophyll taken out, your results will be easier to see.

21. **Add enough iodine to cover the leaf.**

22. **What color change takes place?**

23. **What does this show?**

24. **What do we call food-making in green plants?**

25. **What does a plant make during photosynthesis?**

C. PLANTS MAKE THEIR OWN FOOD

Scientists are still trying to learn how green plants make food. We know what raw materials enter the process of photosynthesis. We know what product results. We also know that photosynthesis takes place in the leaves of green plants. How this whole process happens is still partly a mystery.

The process of photosynthesis can be summarized as follows:

$$\text{Carbon dioxide} + \text{Water} \xrightarrow[\text{Chlorophyll}]{\text{Light energy}} \text{Carbohydrate} + \text{Oxygen}$$

We'll talk about oxygen in the next Investigation and the next Idea. Let's see what we've learned so far.

26. **What raw materials does a green plant need?**

27. **What is the process of food making in plants called?**

28. **Where does photosynthesis take place?**

29. **What substance in the leaves is necessary for photosynthesis?**

30. **What kind of energy is necessary for photosynthesis?**

31. **What does a plant make during photosynthesis?**

Re-read your answers to Questions 18, 25, and 31.

CONCEPT

ENRICHMENT

1. Would a plant make starch if deprived of carbon dioxide, water, or light? Design an experiment to test one of these. Then test a leaf for starch.
2. Melvin Calvin won a Nobel Prize in 1961 for his work on photosynthesis. What did he discover?
3. Light energy and chlorophyll are not raw materials. This is why they are shown above and below the arrow in the equation. Explain why this is so.
4. Write a paper on the chemistry of sugar, starch, and carbohydrates.

The Biggest Recipe of All

Can you imagine a recipe that makes 300 billion tons of sugar a year from free materials?

General American Transportation Corp.

Each of these hopper cars holds 100 tons of sugar. You would need 3 billion hopper cars, end to end, to hold 300 billion tons of sugar. They would require a railroad track that circles the earth 1000 times.

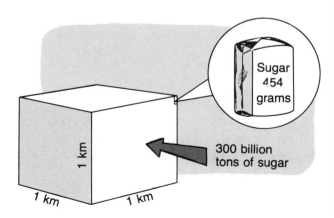

Sugar 454 grams

1 km

1 km x 1 km

300 billion tons of sugar

If all of this sugar were packed in 454-gram boxes and then stacked, the stack would be 1 km x 1 km x 1 km.

No sugar refinery could keep up with this output, yet green plants make this much sugar every year. The process by which green plants take raw materials and make sugar is called photosynthesis. It is indeed the biggest recipe of all, and the recipe is unknown.

The recipe may be unknown, but not the results. We depend upon green plants to produce the food needed by all of the animals and other plants in the world. Green plants are the source of energy for all living things.

A. UP GOES WATER, DOWN COMES SUGAR

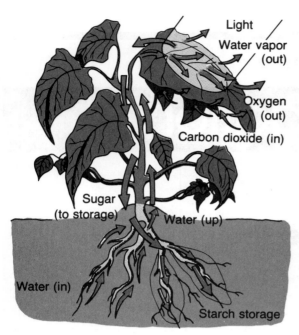

Light
Water vapor (out)
Oxygen (out)
Carbon dioxide (in)
Sugar (to storage)
Water (up)
Water (in)
Starch storage

THINK ABOUT...
DURING PHOTOSYNTHESIS PLANTS CHANGE RAW MATERIALS INTO FOOD. PLANTS USE CHLOROPHYLL AND LIGHT TO DO THIS. PLANTS ARE REALLY FOOD FACTORIES.

The diagram above completes the story of photosynthesis which began in the first Investigation. Water enters the roots and travels up through special conduction tissue to the leaves. At the same time, carbon dioxide enters the leaves. Chlorophyll, in the leaves, captures the light energy and changes it into chemical energy. The chemical energy is used to hold the carbon dioxide and water molecules together. The new molecule is called sugar. Some of the sugar is changed to starch. Sugar and starch, also called carbohydrates, are transported to all the cells of the plant by special conduction tissue again. Plants are the source of energy for all living things, even the plant itself.

1. What is the biggest recipe of all?
2. What does this recipe make?
3. How much does this recipe make a year?
4. Where does this process take place?
5. What do plants make with carbon dioxide and water?
6. How do plants hold together the larger molecules that they make?
7. What do plants supply for all living things?
8. How are the products of photosynthesis transported throughout a plant?
9. What do plants supply to all living things?

B. DO BEANS SPROUT?

Peas, carrots, and broccoli. Strawberries, orange juice, and French fries. All of these, and all the other things you eat, are made possible because of people like Walt Sorenson. Walt is a farmer.

Farming is a highly complicated business. You have to be many things and know many things.

You have to be a chemist. You must know how to use the many different kinds of fertilizers, insect killers, and weed killers.

You must be a mechanic. You must know how to buy, operate, and use equipment. A tractor costs over $25,000. A combine costs between $35,000 and $50,000.

You must be an economist. An economist is someone who understands money, like a banker. You must know when to sell your crops because the prices change daily.

You must be an accountant. You must know mathematical skills to keep records of your money. You have to know how to borrow money, use money, and pay money. This is like keeping the check book in balance, only on a much larger scale.

A farm may be worth over one million dollars, including equipment worth over $100,000. When you farm, you manage a small business. You farm with your head, not your back.

Farming is a major source of jobs. One out of 4 jobs in private employment relates to farming. Four million people work on farms. Another 13 million work at jobs related to farming.

USDA

Food processing technician

Farming involves big money. One dollar out of every three dollars spent by the public goes for items that come from farms. These include fabrics for clothes, tobacco, beverages, and food.

Grant Heilman

The chief source of food for most people in the world is seeds. Seeds usually result after

the flower and fruit have formed. Cereal grains, corn, rice, and beans are all seeds. Seeds supply the energy to start a plant growing until it can make its own food. Seeds can supply energy for you too.

Your teacher will have some alfalfa or mung bean seeds.

10. **Soak some seeds in a beaker for 1 day.**

11. **Carefully drain the water.**

12. **Return the moist seeds to the beaker.**

13. **Cover the beaker with a wet paper towel, folded over many times.**

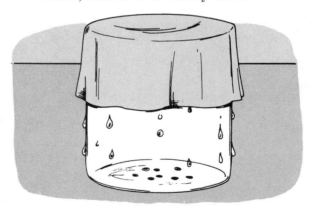

14. **Cover the beaker with a saucer.**

15. Place the set-up in a cool, dark cabinet.

16. Each day, rinse the seeds with fresh water and repeat Steps 11-15.

17. The alfalfa or bean sprouts will be ready to eat in a few days. Bring different fruits and vegetables to class and create a salad.

© copyright Cynara

18. **What do plants supply to all living things?**

Bon appetit.

C. AND FOR DESSERT . . .

We know that we need plants to provide us with food. When we eat carrots, we get the energy that the leaves of the carrot plant captured from sunlight. When a hawk eats a mouse, it is still getting the sun's energy. After all, the mouse ate grass and grain to build its body.

19. **What do plants supply to all living things?**

Re-read Questions 9, 18, and 19. Then state the concept.

CONCEPT

WORDS TO KNOW

The following words have been used in this Idea. Carefully review the Idea and define each of them on your data sheet.

Albino	Mineral
Bromthymol blue	Paper
Bromthymol yellow	chromatography
Carbohydrate	Photosynthesis
Carbon dioxide	Pigment
Chlorophyll	Raw material
Chloroplast	Root hair
Conduction tissue	Starch
Energy	Stomate
Fibrous root	Sugar
Guard cell	Taproot
	Water vapor

SUMMARY OF THE IDEA: THE CHARACTERISTICS OF GREEN PLANTS

This Idea has been about the green plants. A study of early people tells us that people have always known of the importance of plants. Plants have not only meant food, but clothing, weapons, tools, dyes, medicines, shelter and other things. To exist without plants is impossible. Plants are the basis of food for all living things, even other plants.

Plants, like animals, have cells, tissues, organs, and systems. Plants have cells that absorb water. These are root hair cells. Plants have cells that allow carbon dioxide to enter the leaf. These are guard cells surrounding the stomates. Near the top surface of the leaf are cells that contain chloroplasts. The chloroplasts are the only green structures in a plant. This is because they have chlorophyll. Chlorophyll captures energy from the sun and uses this energy to combine water and carbon dioxide. The result is sugar. This process of combining raw materials to make sugar with light energy is called photosynthesis. Because of photosynthesis, plants make food for themselves. When plants die and decay, they become food for other plants. And when plants are eaten, they become food for animals. Plants, in effect, are the basis of all life.

This Idea has been about plants. You have studied six concepts.

1. **State these six concepts.**

2. **What raw materials are needed by plants?**

3. **Explain how plants capture energy.**

4. **What is the product of photosynthesis?**

5. **Explain photosynthesis.**

6. **What does the product of photosynthesis supply to all living things?**

When you ride in a car to a barbecue, you are moving on energy that was trapped and stored by ancient plants. The fire from the charcoal or wood in the barbecue is energy released from plants. The chicken that you eat got its energy from corn. And the milk that you drink came from the grass the cow ate. Directly or indirectly, plants mean energy.

7. **What are plants the source of for all living things?**

Review the six concepts. Then combine your answers to Questions 5-7 to summarize the Idea.

IDEA SUMMARY

ENRICHMENT

1. Eighty percent of the carbohydrates made by green plants is made in the water. The green plants that do this job have no roots, stems, or leaves, but they do have chlorophyll. They are called plankton, the grass of the sea. What are plankton and for what are they the source of food?

2. Plants are the source of food for all living things, not just people. Insects eat much of the plants and farm crops. What else needs plants for food?

3. What part of a plant is an artichoke, asparagus, potato, eggplant, strawberry, peanut, and string bean?

4. Prepare a display showing how a potato grows and is harvested.

5. What are some of the mysteries that remain about photosynthesis?

6. Grow mushrooms. Explain why plants are the source of energy for mushrooms.

7. Make cheese. Explain how plants are the source of energy for cheese.

8. Grind corn meal and make corn bread.

9. What is a botanist?

10. How could you become a landscape gardener, nursery operator, or farmer?

IDEA **5** RESPIRATION
Oxygen Intake
Investigation 1

The Breath of Life

In the last Idea you studied photosynthesis. You found out how green plants capture and store energy.

In this Idea you will discover how living things use that stored energy. It's this stored energy that helps frogs jump, birds fly, and seeds sprout. This same stored energy keeps you warm, moves your muscles, and lets you grow.

UPI

Gerd Bonk

It takes a lot of energy to raise 252.5 kg above your head. This energy must come

from the food you eat. The process by which living things release energy from food is called ***respiration***. Respiration is, in many ways, the opposite of photosynthesis. During photosynthesis, energy is stored. During respiration, energy is released. Photosynthesis stores energy into food packages. Respiration releases that same energy as needed to carry on life activities. Carbon dioxide and oxygen are exchanged in both processes, but in different directions. Also, photosynthesis consumes water, while respiration releases water.

Let's investigate the respiration process that goes on in all plant and animal cells.

A. ALL AIR IS NOT THE SAME

1. **Obtain 2 test tubes and 2 rubber stoppers with rigid tubing inserted. Mark one test tube "Control" and the other "Experiment."**

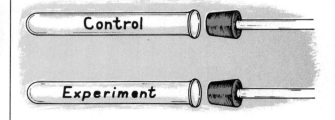

137

2. **Place a wad of moistened steel wool inside the Experiment test tube. Place the stoppers with rigid tubing in *both* test tubes.**

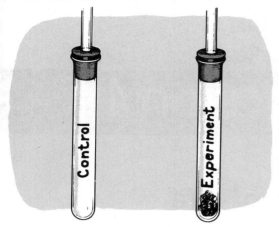

3. **Add about 2 centimeters of water to a tall jar.**

4. **Place both test tubes upside down in the jar. Handle the test tubes as little as possible. Your warm hands can affect the results.**

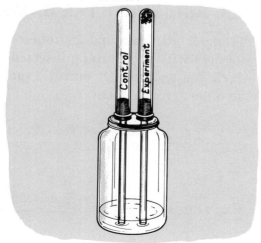

5. **Measure the height in millimeters that water rose in each rigid tubing. Measure from outside the jar as shown.**

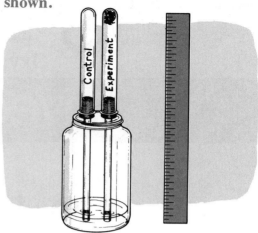

6. **Record your results as "Starting Height" in Table 1 on your data sheet.**

7. **What time is it now?**

8. **Wait 12 minutes.**

9. **What is the *only* difference between the two test tubes?**

10. **What has been kept the same for both test tubes?**

11. **After 12 minutes, measure the height of the water in each rigid tubing. Measure the same way you did in Step 5.**

12. **Record the results in the Table 1 as "Height after 12 Minutes."**

13. **In which test tube did the water rise higher?**

THINK ABOUT...
WHAT THE EXPERIMENT PROVES.
THE STEEL WOOL MUST BE USING UP SOME OF THE AIR.
THE WATER IS RISING UP TO REPLACE THE USED AIR.
ARE THERE MORE FACTS YOU SHOULD KNOW?

The air you breathe is really a mixture of gases. About 20 percent is oxygen. The rest is mostly nitrogen. A very small amount is the carbon dioxide you tested for in Idea 4.

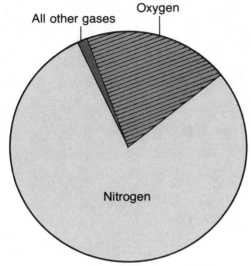

Have you ever seen a rusty nail or a rusty bridge? When iron rusts, it combines with oxygen in the air. Steel wool is made of thin strands of iron. Strange as it may seem, there is also iron in your blood. Red blood cells contain iron as a red pigment called **_hemoglobin_**. Hemoglobin combines with oxygen in your lungs and then carries oxygen to all the cells of your body. The combining of oxygen with iron or any other substance is called **_oxidation_**. The rusting of the steel wool in your test tube is an example of oxidation.

Let's see if you understand what happened with the steel wool.

14. **What metal was being rusted?**

15. **What gas combined with this metal?**

16. **What is this combining process called?**

17. **What gas did the water replace?**

18. **Suppose you wanted to do an experiment with air that was lacking in oxygen. How could you remove the oxygen?**

B. IS THERE LIFE WITHOUT OXYGEN?

Grant Heilman

19. **Obtain 2 test tubes and 2 rubber stoppers with rigid tubing inserted. Mark one tube "Control" and the other "Experiment."**

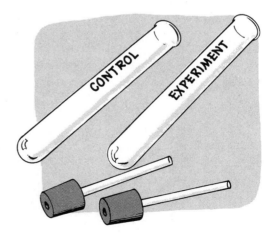

20. Place a wad of moistened steel wool inside the Experiment tube.

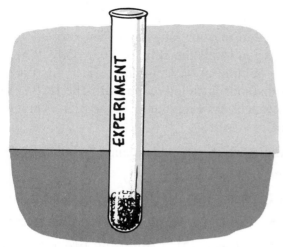

21. Place 10 soaked corn seeds in each tube.

22. Place a wad of moist cotton halfway down each test tube.

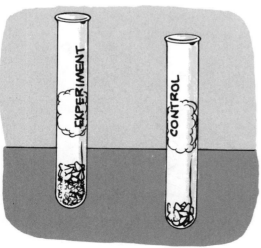

23. Place the stoppers with rigid tubing in *both* test tubes.

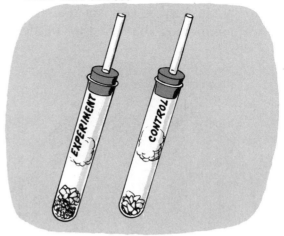

24. Add about 2 centimeters of water to a tall jar. Write your name and section on the jar.

25. Place both test tubes upside down in the jar.

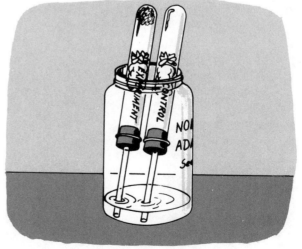

26. Store your experiment for 2 days.

27. **What is the only difference between the two test tubes?**

28. **From what you learned in Part A, what gas will be removed by the steel wool?**

29. **What gas does the Control test tube have more of than the Experiment test tube?**

30. **What do you predict will happen to the seeds in each test tube? Explain the reason for your prediction.**

31. **After 2 days remove the seeds from each test tube and examine them.**

32. **How many Control seeds sprouted?**

33. **How many Experiment seeds sprouted?**

34. **Explain your results.**

35. **What gas in the air is needed if seeds are to sprout?**

36. **Seeds, snails, and seals are all alive. What gas do you think they all need?**

C. THE RESPIRATION STORY

Your seeds didn't grow in the absence of oxygen. Neither would you. Obtaining oxygen is only the first step in the respiration process. But there is much more.

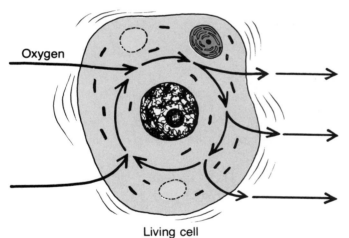

Oxygen

Living cell

Respiration diagram

Look at the respiration diagram. It shows oxygen going into a living cell. Only a few forms of life can exist without oxygen. You'll learn what the other arrows mean in the next Investigations.

Russian scientists forced a rabbit to smoke. Instead of clean air with oxygen, the rabbit took cigarette smoke into its lungs. The tars from cigarette smoke can form a coating

Sovfoto

inside the lungs of both rabbits and people. This prevents cells from obtaining the oxygen they need to carry on respiration.

37. **What is one reason cigarette smoke is harmful?**

38. **What percent of the air you breathe is oxygen?**

39. **Why didn't the seeds sprout in the test tube with steel wool?**

40. **What life process requires oxygen?**

41. **What gas in the air is needed by most living things?**

42. **What do most living things require?**

CONCEPT

ENRICHMENT

1. Attach a candle to a shallow bowl. Half-fill the bowl with water. Light the candle. Place a tall jar or 500 ml graduate over the candle and into the water. Try to interpret what happens on the basis of what you have learned.

2. Make your own oxygen. Mix hydrogen peroxide with a pinch of manganese dioxide. Place a burning candle where the oxygen leaves the test tube.

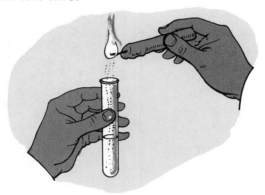

3. Try Enrichment #2 using a mixture of hydrogen peroxide and an active yeast solution.

4. Research some of the rare gases found in the air. These include argon, helium, krypton, xenon, and helium. Report your findings to the class.

5. Some living things don't need atmospheric oxygen. Look up *anaerobic bacteria*. Report to the class.

6. Try growing other kinds of seeds besides corn in an atmosphere with little oxygen. Try large seeds like lima beans and small ones like radish seeds. Be sure to set up a control.

7. Try placing a small insect in an atmosphere with little oxygen. Set up a control.

Investigation 2

Something In, Something Out

You've learned that most living things need oxygen. Animals generally need more oxygen than plants, which are less active. Some animals need much more oxygen than others. Oxygen need depends upon the animal's size and activity.

om Science Year, The World Book Science Annual.
Field Enterprises Educational Corp.

This kangaroo is running on a treadmill. The kangaroo and other animals were tested for oxygen consumption while exercising. The experiments proved that small animals use more oxygen in proportion to their body mass than large animals. An elephant requires less oxygen for its size than a mouse.

Most plants and animals require oxygen to carry on respiration. During respiration, another gas is released. Let's investigate this gas.

A. CARBON DIOXIDE AND EXERCISE

You have tested for carbon dioxide before by using bromthymol blue. Bromthymol blue turns green or yellow in the presence of carbon dioxide. It turns blue again when carbon dioxide is removed.

1. **Pour 10 ml of bromthymol blue into each of two test tubes.**

2. **Blow gently through a straw into *one* of the tubes for one full minute. Do not force the liquid out of the tube.**

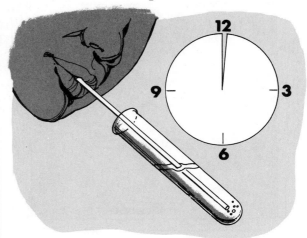

3. **What color change took place?**

4. **What gas must be in the air you are breathing out?**

5. Save the test tube and fluid. You will be needing it as a control.

You've now proved that your breath contains carbon dioxide. Would your breath contain more carbon dioxide if you exercised?

6. **Read Steps 7-9 before beginning the following activity.**

7. **Run in place for 2 minutes.**

8. **Repeat Step 2 with the second test tube.**

9. **Time how many seconds it takes for the bromthymol to become the *same color* as the first control tube.**

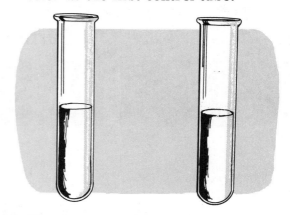

10. **How many seconds did it take to become the same color?**

11. **Which changed the bromthymol blue faster, your normal breath or your breath after exercising?**

12. **What does this prove about the amount of carbon dioxide in your exercise breath?**

13. **When animals are active, what gas do they produce more of?**

14. **What gas do animals give off during respiration?**

B. SEEDS ALSO

THINK ABOUT...
DO PLANTS GIVE OFF CARBON DIOXIDE GAS?

IF THEY DO, THEN BROMTHYMOL BLUE SHOULD DETECT IT.

BUT HOW CAN YOU MAKE THE EXPERIMENT WORK?

15. **Obtain two baby food jars. Place 10 sprouting seeds in one of the jars.**

16. Pour bromthymol blue into the jar until the seedlings are barely covered.

17. Pour the same amount of bromthymol blue into the second jar. This will serve as your control.

18. Place the lids tightly on both jars. You don't want any air to enter.

19. Wait 15 minutes. Then observe the two jars.

20. Describe what happened in the control jar.

21. Describe what happened in the experimental jar.

22. In which jar did a color change take place?

23. What does this prove is being given off by the seedlings?

24. What do plants and animals give off during respiration?

C. ANOTHER ARROW FOR RESPIRATION

In Investigation 1 you discovered that oxygen is needed for the process of respiration. Now you've seen that a different gas leaves living cells during respiration.

25. Fill in the top arrow on the right side of the respiration diagram on your data sheet.

Carbon dioxide is the same gas taken in by green plants during photosynthesis. It's also the gas that makes the bubbles in soft drinks and the fizz in Alka-Seltzer. It's the gas given off by yeast which makes bread dough rise. Don't confuse carbon *dioxide* with carbon *monoxide*. Carbon monoxide is a deadly gas found in polluted air.

In 1790, a French scientist first studied the process of respiration. His name was Antoine Laurent Lavoisier. His wife helped him with his experiments. Lavoisier measured the oxygen intake and carbon dioxide output of various people. He tested them while they rested, exercised, and ate.

26. Both you and Lavoisier tested for carbon dioxide before and after exercising. Based upon your results, what do you think Lavoisier discovered?

27. **Which give off more carbon dioxide, active or inactive animals? Explain your answer.**

28. **What gas do both you and seedlings release during respiration?**

29. **What gas do most living things give off during respiration?**

CONCEPT

ENRICHMENT

1. Does a burning candle produce carbon dioxide? Set up an experiment using bromthymol blue to test this idea. Write a game plan first.

2. Does an insect give off carbon dioxide? Place an insect on a screen above bromthymol blue in a small closed jar.

3. Re-read the Elodea experiment you did in Idea 4, Investigation 2. Try the same experiment using bromthymol blue and *darkness* instead of light. Report to the class on the experiment's results and what they prove.

4. Research carbon monoxide gas. Report to the class on how it is formed and why it is dangerous.

5. Place a branch with many leaves in a big jar. Add a thin layer of bromthymol blue to the bottom of the jar. Seal the jar and place it in the dark overnight. Report to the class on the results and what they prove.

Investigation 3

Fish Respiration

You've learned that living things require oxygen and give off carbon dioxide during respiration. Even fish, in their watery world, carry on respiration.

Fish are dying in this polluted lake. They are dying from a lack of oxygen. People dump sewage into lakes. The sewage provides food for the microorganisms that live in the lake. They grow and reproduce so fast that they use up most of the oxygen in the water. Because of this, the fish and the microorganisms begin to die. The water

Leo deWys, Inc.

in the lake begins to look, taste, and smell bad. Only by proper sewage treatment can the lake be restored to good health.

A. OXYGEN TEST

In the last Investigation you learned that people and seedlings give off carbon dioxide. You did this by testing the air with bromthymol blue.

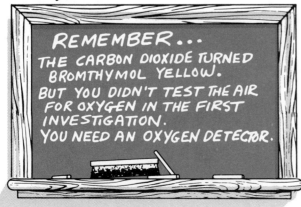

REMEMBER...
THE CARBON DIOXIDE TURNED BROMTHYMOL YELLOW.
BUT YOU DIDN'T TEST THE AIR FOR OXYGEN IN THE FIRST INVESTIGATION.
YOU NEED AN OXYGEN DETECTOR.

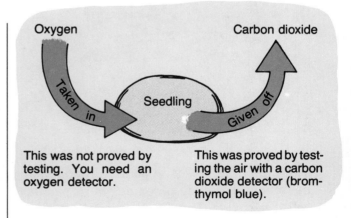

Oxygen — Taken in — Seedling — Given off — Carbon dioxide

This was not proved by testing. You need an oxygen detector.

This was proved by testing the air with a carbon dioxide detector (bromthymol blue).

In this Investigation you will do another chemical test. You will see if living things remove oxygen from air and water.

147

1. Put 3 ml of distilled water into each of 2 small test tubes.

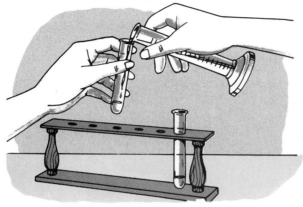

2. Add 1 drop of "oxygen booster" to one of the tubes. Label it E for experiment.

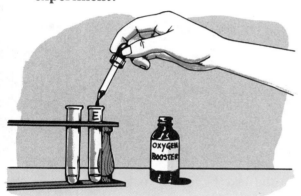

3. Label the other tube C for control.

The "oxygen booster" you used is common household hydrogen peroxide. Most people call it peroxide. It is used to clean wounds and to bleach hair. Peroxide will supply the extra oxygen needed in this experiment. Steps 4-8 are your oxygen test.

4. To each tube, add 1 drop of oxygen detector solution #1.

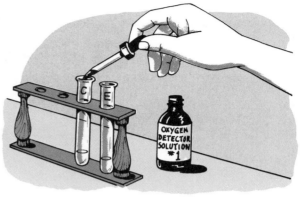

5. To each tube, add 3 drops of oxygen detector solution #2.

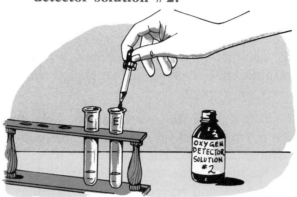

6. Gently shake both tubes.

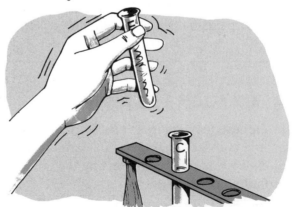

7. Your teacher will add 1 drop of acid to each tube.

8. DO NOT shake the tubes.

Here's how to read your oxygen test. Look for the color of the solid particles that form in the test tubes.

Dark brown solid ———→ Lots of oxygen present
Light brown solid ———→ A little oxygen present
White solid ———→ No oxygen present

9. Describe the color of the solid in each test tube. Tell what these colors mean.

10. Record your data in Table 1 on your data sheet.

Now you have learned how to test for oxygen. You know all that's needed to carry out the rest of the Investigation.

B. TESTING THE FISH

Grant Heilman

11. Read Steps 12-16 and Steps 23-32 first. If you do not understand the directions, ask your teacher.

12. Fill 2 clean jars about ¾-full with water.

13. Add 4 drops of "oxygen booster" to each jar.

14. Gently net a fish. Quickly transfer it to one of your jars. Transfer a second fish to the *same* jar.

15. Add water to the very top of both jars. Try not to leave an air space. Tightly cap each jar.

16. Record the starting time on your data sheet.

17. What will the time be 20 minutes from now?

18. Wait 20 minutes before going on to Step 23.

19. Which jar is the control?

20. Which jar is the experiment?

21. What do you predict will happen to the water in the control jar?

22. What do you predict will happen to the water in the experimental jar?

Now that you have waited 20 minutes, do Steps 23-32.

23. Get 2 small test tubes. Label one C for control. Label the other E for experiment.

24. Remove 10 ml of water from the jar with no fish. Add this to the control tube. Use a dropper to transfer the water.

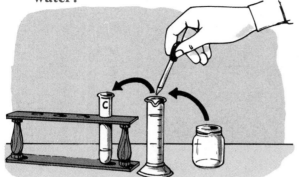

25. Rinse the dropper with water.

26. Remove 10 ml of water from the jar with 2 fish. Add this to the experiment tube. Use the dropper.

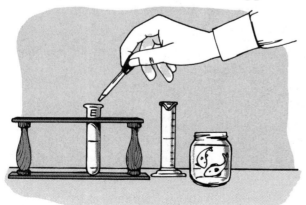

27. Recap both jars and save the water. Leave the fish in the jar.

28. To each tube, add 1 drop of oxygen detector solution #1.

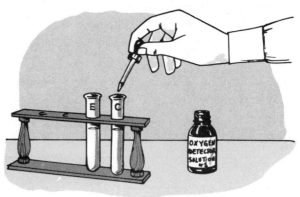

29. To each tube, add 3 drops of oxygen detector solution #2.

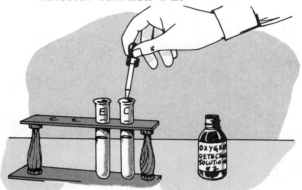

30. Gently shake both tubes.

31. Your teacher will add 1 drop of acid to each tube.

32. DO NOT shake the tubes.

33. In which tube did the darker solid form? Check back to page 149 to read your oxygen test.

34. Which jar has more oxygen?

35. Explain what happened to the oxygen in the jar with the fish.

C. DOES ANYTHING COME OUT?

You have just seen that fish use up some of the oxygen in the water. Even without the oxygen booster, there is enough oxygen in water for fish. Normally there are seven milliliters of oxygen dissolved in every liter of water. Some of this oxygen comes from air that gets mixed with water. Most of the oxygen comes from water plants during photosynthesis.

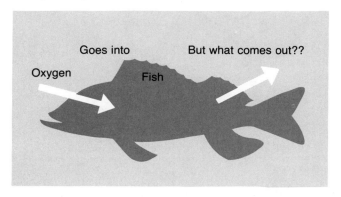

Oxygen Goes into Fish But what comes out??

36. What gas do you predict is produced by the fish?

37. What test can you run to check your answer to Question 36?

38. Get 2 small test tubes. Label one C for control. Label the other E for experiment.

39. Add 10 ml of water from the jar with no fish to the control tube. Use a dropper to transfer the water.

40. Rinse the dropper with water.

41. Add 10 ml of water from the jar with 2 fish to the experiment tube. Use the dropper.

42. Add 3 drops of bromthymol blue to each tube.

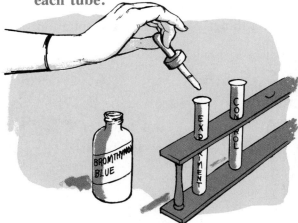

43. Which tube of water changed color?

44. Which jar has more carbon dioxide?

45. Where must this carbon dioxide have come from?

46. What gas do fish, and other living things, give off?

47. Gently pour your fish into a net over a sink.

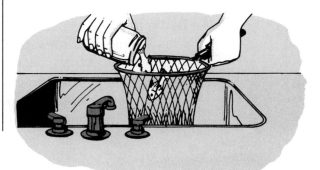

48. Quickly transfer them to the class aquarium.

In Idea 4 you discovered that plants do something else during photosynthesis. During photosynthesis they take in carbon dioxide and give off oxygen. Your fish took in oxygen and gave off carbon dioxide. Most living things do this during respiration.

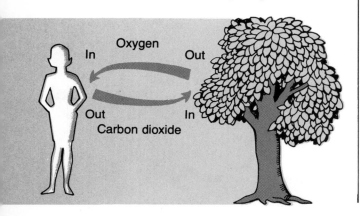

Now you can see why animals and plants need each other. The carbon dioxide animals give off is taken in by plants. The oxygen the plants give off is taken in by animals.

Lorenz © 1970 The New Yorker Magazine, Inc.

"I'll tell you what I'm doing to protest environmental pollution. I'm taking in carbon dioxide, but I'm not giving off oxygen."

49. Explain why plants and animals need each other.

50. During respiration, what gas is taken in by both plants and animals?

51. During respiration, what gas is given off by both plants and animals?

52. What two gases are exchanged by living things?

CONCEPT

ENRICHMENT

1. Repeat the experiment in Part B using ice water. Find out how the results vary.

2. Repeat Part B after adding Alka-Seltzer to the water. Alka-Seltzer increases the amount of carbon dioxide in the water.

3. Research how fish use gills for breathing. Report to the class.

4. Boil some water and allow it to cool. Try the oxygen test to find what boiling does to water. Predict how a fish might react to boiled instead of normal water.

5. Design an experiment to show how insects react to an atmosphere of carbon dioxide. You can pour vinegar on baking soda to produce carbon dioxide gas.

Investigation 4

Sugar and Respiration

So far you've discovered that respiration involves two gases, oxygen and carbon dioxide.

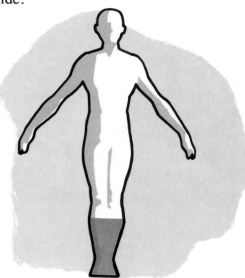

Only 0.03 percent of the air around us is made of carbon dioxide gas. Yet this small percentage of gas provides the carbon that makes up a large part of living things. Your own body consists of almost 20 percent carbon. Materials that contain carbon are called *organic*. Most of the materials in plant and animal cells are organic.

Organic materials make up a large part of what you eat and drink. Starch has a complicated arrangement of carbon atoms combined with atoms of hydrogen and

oxygen. Proteins, fats, and oils are also complicated carbon combinations. Sugar is a much simpler organic material.

There are many organic materials around you besides foods and living organisms. Coal, gasoline, and natural gas were all formed from ancient life and contain carbon. Most of the plastics in your home are organic materials.

You now know that sugar is organic. What role does sugar play in the respiration process?

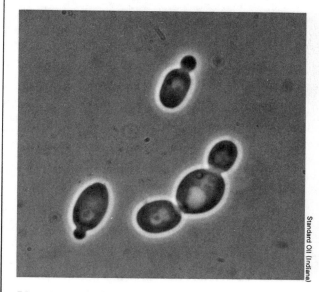

Standard Oil (Indiana)

Yeast can help us find the answer. Yeast is sold in grocery stores and is used for baking.

Bread dough rises as it sits at room temperature. This is due to carbon dioxide gas produced by yeast cells in the dough. You studied yeast cells in Idea 2. Yeast cells are like the seedlings and fish. They are alive and can produce carbon dioxide. This brings up some questions.

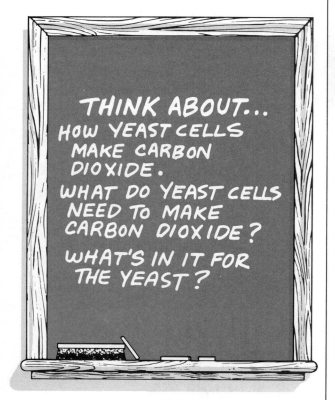

THINK ABOUT...
HOW YEAST CELLS MAKE CARBON DIOXIDE.
WHAT DO YEAST CELLS NEED TO MAKE CARBON DIOXIDE?
WHAT'S IN IT FOR THE YEAST?

You will answer these questions in this Investigation.

A. BRING ON THE YEAST

1. Read Steps 2-8 before starting.

2. Get 2 large test tubes. Label one "Control." Label the other "Experiment."

3. Half-fill both test tubes with warm yeast mixture.

4. Measure out 1 gram of sugar.

5. Add the sugar to the Experiment tube.

6. Attach rubber tubing and stoppers to both test tubes as shown.

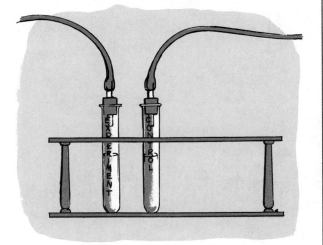

7. Add 2 ml of warm water to each of 2 small test tubes. Add 1 drop of bromthymol blue to each tube.

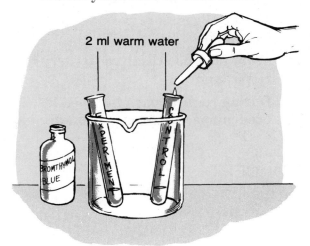

2 ml warm water

BROMTHYMOL BLUE

8. Set up the equipment as shown.

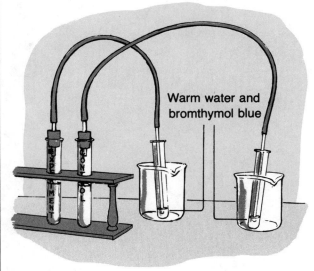

Warm water and bromthymol blue

9. Observe all 4 test tubes for 10-15 minutes.

10. What is the only difference between your experiment and your control?

11. Which of the larger tubes is giving off more bubbles?

12. What is bromthymol blue being used to test for?

13. Which small tube turned green or yellow?

14. What does this color change tell you?

15. What food must yeast cells have before they can produce carbon dioxide?

B. LIVING THINGS HAVE A SWEET TOOTH

Yeast and other living cells produce carbon dioxide from sugar. During respiration, sugar is broken apart to form carbon dioxide. Without sugar or a similar food, cells cannot carry on respiration.

Now you are ready to fill in another respiration arrow.

16. Fill in the lower left arrow of the respiration diagram in your data book.

This is the Viking Lander. It carried out experiments to try to detect life on Mars. Soil from the Martian surface was scooped into a container. A "soup" containing sugar was mixed with the soil. If the soil contained living cells like those on Earth, carbon dioxide gas would be produced. Sugar being changed to carbon dioxide is an indication of respiration and life.

17. **Suppose the Viking experiment showed no carbon dioxide gas. What might that prove about life on Mars?**

18. **Why did the "soup" in the experiment contain sugar?**

19. **What two gases are exchanged during respiration?**

20. **What food do cells need to carry on respiration?**

21. **During respiration, what food is broken apart to form carbon dioxide gas?**

CONCEPT

ENRICHMENT

1. Will yeast cells give off carbon dioxide when they are cold? Try the experiment using ice cold water.
2. Research carbon dioxide. Report to the class on the various uses of carbon dioxide. Be sure to consider carbon dioxide in the atmosphere.
3. Test for life on Earth. Try the experiment using *rich* garden soil, instead of yeast.
4. Build and demonstrate a model of one of the Viking's experiments to detect life.
5. Place a warm yeast sugar solution in a flask. Attach a balloon to the mouth of the flask. Explain what happens.

You Need Energy

Oxygen, carbon dioxide, and sugar are all involved in the respiration process. But, where does respiration actually take place in living things?

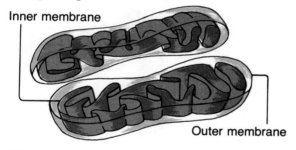

Inner membrane

Outer membrane

These sausage shaped structures are called _mitochondria_. Mitochondria are found inside plant and animal cells. They can be seen only with powerful electron microscopes. There can be as few as 10 or as many as 1000 mitochondria inside a single cell. The more active the cell, the more mitochondria it has. For example, liver cells are very active and have many mitochondria.

Respiration takes place mainly inside these mitochondria. In a complex series of chemical reactions, the mitochondria store energy obtained from sugar. As the cell carries on respiration, energy is released as needed. Because of their ability to store and release energy, mitochondria are called the powerhouses of cells.

Marshmallows are not mitochondria. Yet

marshmallows can help us investigate another part of the respiration process carried on by mitochondria.

A. THE BURNING MARSHMALLOW

1. **Eat a marshmallow.**

2. **Describe the taste. What must be in marshmallows that makes them taste this way?**

You eat many foods that contain sugar. By burning a marshmallow you can find out what sugar does for your body.

3. **Use forceps to hold a small marshmallow. Hold the marshmallow over a plate or pan. Carefully light it with a match.**

Observe the light and heat coming from the marshmallow. Light and heat are forms of *energy*. Things that have energy can do work. Work can mean moving a train or moving your muscles.

Sugar really does burn inside of you. That's part of respiration. The sugar you eat burns very slowly in your cells. It burns so slowly that heat, but not light, is produced.

The marshmallows still have something to teach us about respiration.

4. **Use forceps to hold another small marshmallow. Hold the marshmallow over a jar. Carefully light it and drop it into the jar.**

5. Place a lid on the jar.

6. **Describe what happened to the marshmallow.**

7. **How can you explain this?**

8. **What gas in the air did the marshmallow need to keep burning? Hint: It's the same gas needed for respiration.**

You've learned that living things break down sugar to carbon dioxide during respiration. Did this also happen to the burning marshmallow?

9. **Remove the lid. Add about 1 centimeter of bromthymol blue to the jar.**

10. **Replace the lid tightly. Swirl the jar around to mix the air in the jar with the liquid.**

11. **What color did the liquid turn?**

12. **What gas must have been produced by the burning of the sugar?**

13. **When sugar is burned in air, what two forms of energy are given off?**

14. **What form of energy is given off when sugar is burned slowly in your body?**

B. HEATING UP YOUR MUSCLES

15. **Sit down. Place the bulb end of a thermometer in your clenched fist for 1 minute.**

CAUTION! BE SURE TO STAY SEATED WHILE TAKING THE TEMPERATURE. BE CAREFUL HANDLING GLASS THERMOMETERS.

16. **Read the temperature while the thermometer is still in your fist.**

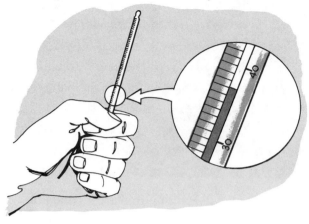

17. **What is your fist temperature?**
18. **Place the thermometer CAREFULLY on the table.**
19. **Rub your hands together vigorously for 1 minute.**
20. **Repeat Steps 15 and 16.**
21. **What is your fist temperature after rubbing?**
22. **How much did your fist temperature rise after rubbing?**
23. **What food do you think gave you the energy to rub your hands together?**

The energy in the sugar you eat doesn't change only into heat. This rock climber needs two kinds of energy. Some of the energy in sugar helps keep her warm. Some of the energy in sugar helps power her muscles while she climbs. Rock climbers and athletes often suffer from fatigue. Their muscles need more sugar and oxygen to carry on respiration and give them more energy.

24. **Long distance runners often sip fruit juice or eat candy bars. Explain why they do this.**
25. **What tissues in an athlete's body need more energy during exercise?**
26. **What food provides heat and muscle energy for your body?**
27. **Based upon this experiment, what else is released during respiration besides carbon dioxide?**

C. YOUR CELLS AND RESPIRATION

Review time. Your cells must take in oxygen and sugar to carry on respiration. During respiration they give off carbon dioxide. And something else. Back to our respiration diagram.

28. **Fill in the middle arrow on the right side of the respiration diagram on your data sheet.**

Jen & Des Bartlett/Bruce Coleman, Inc.

California kangaroo rat

Two gases are formed as a result of respiration. One is the carbon dioxide you have tested for. The other is water vapor. Some desert animals, like this California kangaroo rat, drink very little water. They get most of the water they need from the respiration process.

29. **Fill in the last arrow on the respiration diagram on your data sheet.**

Ruggles/Courtesy Appalachian Mountain Club

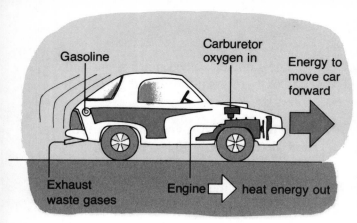

Gasoline

Carburetor oxygen in

Energy to move car forward

Exhaust waste gases

Engine ⟹ heat energy out

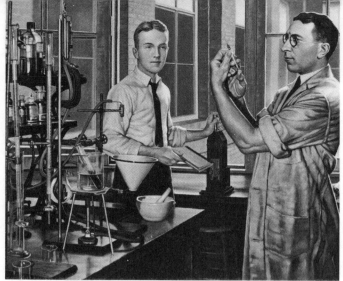

© 1964, Parke, Davis & Co.

Your cell is somewhat like an automobile. Cells need organic sugar and automobiles need organic gasoline. Both carry on oxidation by combining oxygen with fuel. Both burn their fuel to provide heat and motion. Both give off carbon dioxide and water vapor.

There is a vast difference between cell respiration and auto combustion, though. Cell respiration releases energy much more slowly than automobile combustion. Cells waste much less energy than automobiles. Auto combustion is a relatively simple burning process. Cell respiration is much more complicated and goes through many steps.

The various steps in cell respiration depend on *enzymes*. Enzymes are special proteins produced by living things. Enzymes control the chemical reactions inside the cell. Many enzymes must do their work before cell respiration can release energy.

Drs. Banting and Best discovered *insulin*. Insulin is an enzyme the body needs. It converts sugar to a form that can be used by the cell. Insulin is normally made by your body. If your body doesn't make enough insulin, sugar builds up in your blood. This causes a disease called *diabetes*.

Thanks to Drs. Banting and Best, diabetic people can lead normal lives. They can be given the insulin their bodies do not produce. This allows their cells to carry on respiration.

30. **Explain what enzymes do.**

31. **What can happen to your body if it doesn't produce enough insulin?**

32. **In what ways is automobile combustion like cell respiration?**

33. **What two gases are released during respiration?**

34. **Besides gases, what does a cell release during respiration?**

35. **What two things must go into a cell before it can carry on respiration?**

36. **What food provides the fuel for respiration?**

37. **What food must be broken apart before the cell gives off energy?**

Re-read Questions 36 and 37. Then write the concept.

CONCEPT

ENRICHMENT

1. Do growing yeast cells produce heat energy? Set up a controlled experiment to find out.

2. Ask a doctor or nurse for the special test paper used to test for sugar in urine. Demonstrate the paper's use to the class by substituting various sugar-water solutions for urine.

Investigation 6

Foods For Energy

This Idea has been about respiration. Living cells release energy through respiration. All they need is a supply of oxygen and the right kind of food. In this Investigation, you will learn more about the kind of food needed.

A. CALORIES AND CARBOHYDRATES

USDA

These foods are called ***carbohydrates***. Carbohydrates are foods that contain sugars and starches. They all have stored energy. Carbohydrates make up about half the food you consume each day.

TABLE 1 CALORIE CONTENT OF FOODS

Food	Amount	Calories
apple	medium size	70
bacon	2 slices	100
banana	1	90
bread	1 slice	60
cake, choco- late (w/icing)	1 slice	445
candy bar (chocolate)	28 grams	200
cereal, cold	28 grams	100
cheese, American	1 slice	105
cola drink	1 glass	96
doughnut, plain	1	125
egg	1 medium	80
fruit juice	100 ml	65
hamburger (ground beef)	85 grams	245
hot dog	1	150
ice cream (vanilla)	½ cup	200
milk	200 ml	160
pizza, cheese	1 slice	185
potato chips	10 medium size	115
spaghetti with tomato sauce	1 cup	260
sugar, white	1 tablespoon	46

The table shows the ***calorie*** content of some common foods. Calories measure the energy in food. A bowl of cold cereal without the milk has about 100 calories. A chocolate bar

161

has about 200 calories. That's enough energy for you to take a 40 minute walk. You'll notice bacon on the calorie list. Bacon is rich in fat rather than carbohydrates. Your body can use both carbohydrates and fats to release energy during respiration.

You need about 3000 calories of energy for a normal day. Most girls need fewer calories than boys. Old people need fewer calories than teenagers. Office secretaries need fewer than active workers.

1. **Which item on the list has the most calories?**

2. **How many more calories are there in a hamburger than in a hot dog?**

3. **How many calories would you take in if you ate a cheese sandwich? (Don't forget the two pieces of bread.)**

4. **How many calories are there in a meal of two slices of pizza, one cup of spaghetti with tomato sauce, and a cola drink?**

5. **What two kinds of foods make up carbohydrates?**

6. **What do carbohydrate foods provide that the body needs?**

B. WHERE DOES THE STARCH GO?

Cells use only sugar during respiration. What happens to all the starches you eat? How can starch foods give energy to the cell?

7. **Put a cracker in your mouth.**

8. **Chew on the cracker for 2-3 minutes. Do not swallow the cracker.**

9. **What change do you notice in the taste of the chewed cracker?**

Here's what happened. A cracker contains starch. Saliva contains enzymes. These enzymes begin to convert starch to sugar. Enzymes in the intestines also help. Starches must be changed into sugar before they can get into the blood.

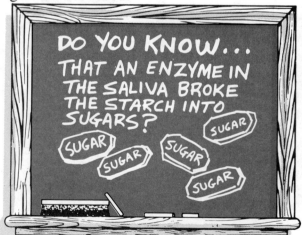

DO YOU KNOW... THAT AN ENZYME IN THE SALIVA BROKE THE STARCH INTO SUGARS?

SUGAR SUGAR SUGAR SUGAR SUGAR

You've learned that sugar and starch are carbohydrates. Both are made of carbon, hydrogen, and oxygen. Starch is nothing more than many sugars joined together.

10. **What does the enzyme in saliva turn starch into?**

11. **What do sugars provide the cell with during respiration?**

C. SEARCHING FOR SUGARS

You are about to test various foods for sugar. The "sugar detector" is called Benedict's solution. It turns greenish yellow for a little sugar. It turns orange or red if there is lots of sugar.

12. **Place 15 ml of prepared sugar solution into a test tube.**

13. **Rinse the graduated cylinder with water.**

14. **Add 15 ml of Benedict's solution to the test tube. Notice that the solution is blue.**

15. **Heat gently over a flame. Use your test tube holder.**

CAUTION!
DO NOT POINT THE MOUTH OF THE TEST TUBE AT YOURSELF OR ANYONE ELSE!

16. **Look for a color change from blue to greenish or orange. This tells you that sugar is present.**

You are now on your own. Your teacher will give you different foods. Write the names of the foods in the first column of Table 2 on your data sheet. After you test each food for sugar, write "yes" or "no" in the second column.

Some common foods have different kinds of sugar. Your Benedict's solution cannot detect these kinds. For example, common table sugar cannot be tested using Benedict's solution. Other tests must be used.

17. Add a *small* amount of food to be tested to a test tube. If the food is solid, add 5 ml of water. Then gently break up the food with a stirring rod.

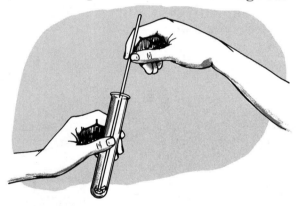

18. Repeat Steps 14-16.
19. Clean the test tube after each test.

20. Which foods had sugar?
21. Which foods showed little or no sugar?

22. What two kinds of foods make up carbohydrates?
23. What must your body do to starchy foods before it can use them?
24. What do carbohydrates store that your cells need for respiration?

D. DEMONSTRATING RESPIRATION

You've learned that the main activity of respiration takes place inside cells. It is not possible for you to observe respiration directly. Therefore, your teacher will demonstrate a chemical reaction that has some features similar to respiration. This is not the way respiration is really carried out. Respiration is much more complex and proceeds much more slowly.

25. Half-fill a beaker with sugar.

26. Add acid to cover the sugar. Wait a few seconds.

27. **Describe what happened.**

28. **The acid speeds up the breaking apart of sugar. What does this inside your body? (Hint: Think of saliva and insulin.)**

The acid broke sugar into the same two gases given off during respiration. One you observed as steam coming out of the beaker. The other is an invisible gas.

29. **What two gases are given off during respiration?**

30. **Your teacher will have a student carefully touch the side of the beaker. Is it hot or cool?**

31. **When sugar is broken apart, what form of energy is released?**

32. **Besides sugar foods, what other group of foods is considered carbohydrates?**

33. **What do carbohydrate foods store that cells need during respiration?**

Re-read Questions 31-33. State the concept.

CONCEPT

WORDS TO KNOW

The following words have been used in this Idea. Carefully review the Idea and define each of them on your data sheet.

Calorie	Insulin
Carbohydrate	Mitochondria
Diabetes	Organic
Energy	Oxidation
Enzyme	Respiration
Hemoglobin	

SUMMARY OF THE IDEA: RESPIRATION

In Idea 4 you studied how energy is stored in food during photosynthesis. This Idea has been about how organisms release this energy during respiration.

Respiration begins with the oxidation of food. This results in a slow, steady release of energy to the cell. This energy can be used for growth, movement, or warmth. There is a constant flow of energy into and out of living organisms.

The breakdown of sugar during respiration takes many steps. Each step is controlled by an enzyme. Each enzyme does a specific job. The final result is a chemical that can provide energy to the cell on demand.

Carbohydrates are the main source of energy for respiration. Fats and proteins can also be used. Starches, and even many sugars, must first be converted to a certain sugar. This certain sugar is called *glucose*. Glucose is first broken down and then oxidized to release energy.

Two products are formed as a result of respiration. One is carbon dioxide, which you have tested for. The other is water. In some cases, half the food oxidized to release energy is converted to water.

In this Idea on respiration you have studied six concepts.

1. **State these six concepts.**

John H. Girard/National Audubon Society

2. **What does food provide this tortoise?**

3. What does air provide the tortoise?

4. What two gases does the tortoise give back to the air during respiration?

5. Name two things that cells must take in for respiration to occur.

6. Name three things given off during respiration.

7. Why are carbohydrates an important food?

8. During what process do living things release energy?

Re-read this section. Then summarize the entire Idea.

IDEA SUMMARY

ENRICHMENT

1. How many calories do you take in one day? Keep a record of the kind and amount of food you eat in one day. Add up the calories using a calorie chart or the one on page 161.

2. How do scientists measure calories? Look up how to build a simple *calorimeter*. Run tests on some easily burned foods like marshmallows and peanuts.

3. Research and report to the class on low-calorie diet foods. Perhaps you can make a display of labels or ads.

4. Prove to yourself that your saliva changes starch to sugar. Crush ¼ of a cracker into a powder. Place it in a test tube and add saliva. Stir a few minutes. Then use Benedict's solution to test for sugar.

Investigation 1

What Happens When You Eat?

Welcome to a new Idea. Before proceeding, let's tie together the last three Ideas. Then this new Idea will make more sense.

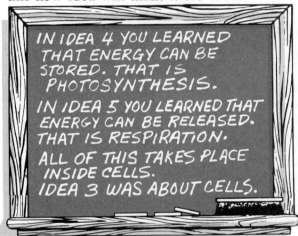

IN IDEA 4 YOU LEARNED THAT ENERGY CAN BE STORED. THAT IS PHOTOSYNTHESIS.

IN IDEA 5 YOU LEARNED THAT ENERGY CAN BE RELEASED. THAT IS RESPIRATION.

ALL OF THIS TAKES PLACE INSIDE CELLS.

IDEA 3 WAS ABOUT CELLS.

Lizabeth Corlett/dpi

Food is like a battery. It is stored energy. This energy is captured by plants and stored in the food they make. You learned that this process is called photosynthesis. The food can be broken apart, releasing the energy. This process is called respiration. Both photosynthesis and respiration take place inside cells.

You're alive because your cells are alive. This means that the cells in your body need energy. For green plants, this is easy. They make their own food, then transport it to all their cells. But what about you? How do your cells get energy?

A. INSIDE, YET OUTSIDE

How can something be inside, yet outside? This is the case with the food in your body. Foods that you eat or drink enter a tube which is open at both ends. Even though food is inside the tube, it is outside of all the cells in your body. How foods get to the cells is part of a process called *digestion*. During digestion food is broken down into smaller molecules. When the molecules are small enough, the body can absorb the food and transport it to all the cells.

167

Digestion takes place in the food tube. This food tube is part of a group of organs which make up the **_digestive system._**

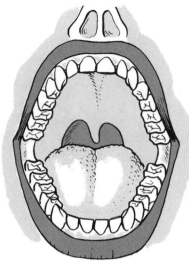

The *mouth* prepares the food for digestion. It moistens the food with *saliva*. The saliva also starts to break down certain types of food.

The *teeth* chew and grind the food into smaller pieces. There are 32 teeth in an adult mouth.

The *tongue* helps move food around and pushes it to the back of the mouth where it can be swallowed. The tongue is also an organ of taste.

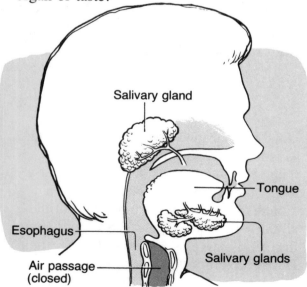

When food is swallowed, the air passage closes. The food goes down the *esophagus*.

The esophagus is lined with muscles which move the food along.

The walls of the *stomach* are lined with strong muscles and millions of cells which make *gastric juice*. The muscles grind, push, and squeeze the food, mixing it with the gastric juice. This goes on for four hours until the food is soft and almost liquid.

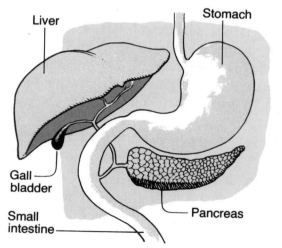

The **_small intestine_** is only 2 to 3 cm in diameter, but 7 meters in length. It is tightly coiled to fit into your body. The small intestine makes digestive juices which chemically break the food down.

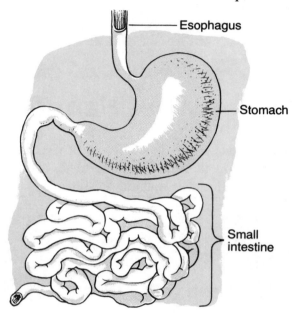

Three other organs, the *gall bladder, liver,* and *pancreas,* also make digestive juices.

These juices are carried into the small intestine by tubes.

When the remaining food reaches the *large intestine,* it is very liquid. Your body cannot afford to lose that much water. So the large intestine re-absorbs most of the water. Then the remaining solid waste is discharged through the *anus.*

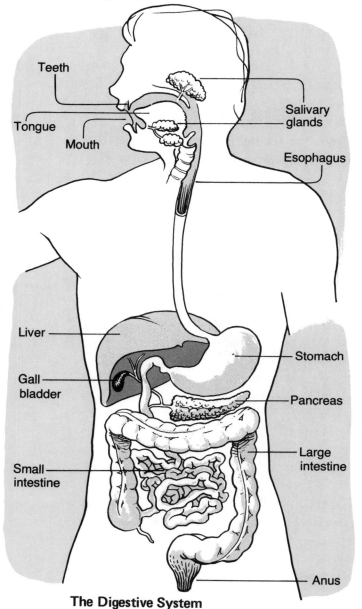

The Digestive System

From beginning to end, the food takes about twenty-four hours to travel through the food tube. The muscles in the stomach and intestines work very hard. No wonder you feel sleepy after a meal.

1. **Name the organs, in order, through which food passes.**
2. **Explain the function of saliva.**
3. **How many teeth are in the adult mouth and what is their function?**
4. **Name two functions of the tongue.**
5. **Where is the esophagus and what does it do?**
6. **What are the walls of the stomach lined with?**
7. **What do the small intestine, liver, gall bladder, and pancreas have in common?**
8. **How long is the small intestine and how does it fit into your body?**
9. **Explain the function of the large intestine.**
10. **What is digestion?**
11. **What is the digestive system?**
12. **What is the function of the digestive system?**

B. CHEMICAL DIGESTION

We eat to stay alive. After food is eaten, it must be changed before it can be used by cells. You can't squeeze a hamburger into a cell. But you can get the parts of a hamburger into a cell. You do this by **chemical digestion.** Chemicals break food down into substances small enough to be absorbed by the cell.

In Idea 5, you learned of the three types of food: carbohydrates, proteins, and fats. A hamburger is all three. The bun is carbohydrate, the meat protein, and the butter fat. The body makes chemicals that digest food. Different ones do different jobs. Some break down carbohydrates, some proteins, and some fats.

STARCH
STARCH IS JUST A LOT
OF SUGARS
JOINED TOGETHER.

In Idea 5, Investigation 6, you saw saliva break down a carbohydrate. When you chew on a cracker, it breaks down from large starch molecules to small sugar molecules.

Here are two more experiments that will help you to see how digestion works. Your teacher will give you two lengths of rigid tubing. There is cooked egg white in each tubing. Egg white is a protein. Your teacher will also give you some artificial gastric juice. This is like the digestive juice found in the stomach. It is made of pepsin and hydrochloric acid.

13. Place one piece of tubing in a beaker and cover with gastric juice.

14. Place the other piece of tubing in another beaker and cover with water.

15. Label the beakers.

16. After 2-3 days, observe and measure the egg in both tubes.

17. **Which beaker is the control?**

18. **How much protein was digested in each tube?**

19. **What caused the protein to be digested?**

20. **What is gastric juice?**

21. **What do digestive juices do to food?**

22. **What must happen to food before it can be used by cells?**

23. **What is digestion?**

24. **What is the function of the digestive system?**

C. DIGESTIVE JUICES

Here is the second experiment. It uses a different digestive juice.

25. **Get 2 test tubes. Label one "Experiment" and the other "Control."**

26. **Put 1 drop of oil into each tube.**

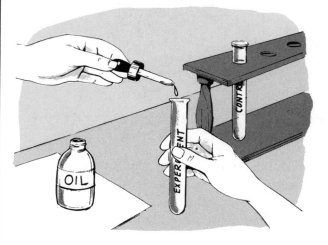

27. Add ¼-test tube of water to each tube.

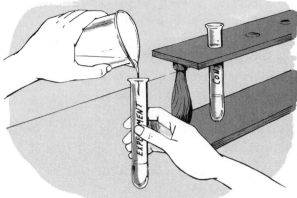

28. Add 5 drops of digestive juice to the Experiment tube.

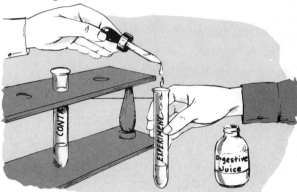

29. Shake both tubes.

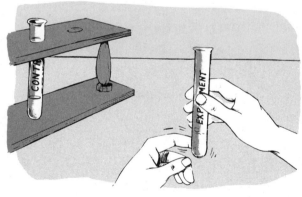

30. Use a clean dropper. Put a drop from the Experiment tube on a clean microscope slide.

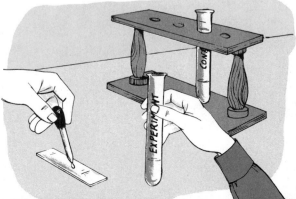

31. Add a cover slip.

32. Examine under your microscope.

33. Repeat Steps 30-32 with a drop from the Control tube.

34. **What difference do you see in the size of the oil particles?**

35. **What caused the difference?**

36. **What do digestive juices do to food?**

37. **What is the function of the digestive system?**

THINK ABOUT...
THE FOOD TUBE IS LIKE AN ASSEMBLY LINE, ONLY THE OPPOSITE TAKES PLACE.

IN AN ASSEMBLY LINE, PARTS ARE PUT TOGETHER ALONG THE WAY.

IN DIGESTION, PARTS ARE BROKEN UP ALONG THE WAY.

What you saw in Parts B and C takes place in the stomach and small intestine. Most all of the digestion takes place here. Many different kinds of digestive juices pour into these two organs.

38. **What do digestive juices do to food as it moves through the digestive system?**

39. **What is digestion?**

40. **What is the function of the digestive system?**

CONCEPT

ENRICHMENT

1. Repeat the experiment in Part B, except use either pepsin or hydrochloric acid alone. Try different temperatures and different mixtures.
2. Chew on a clean rubber band to cause saliva to flow. Fill a test tube ¼-full with saliva. Add a small piece of cracker. The next day test the cracker and a fresh cracker for sugar with Benedict's solution.
3. Write a paper on William Beaumont's "window in the stomach" experiment.
4. Explain why digestive juices do not break down the wall of the intestine.
5. What are ulcers?
6. Prepare a graph showing the level of protein eaten by various peoples in the world.
7. Prepare a chart listing the major digestive juices, their sources, and the foods digested.
8. What are some differences between children's teeth and adult's teeth?

Investigation 2

Breathing and Smoking

Martin/dpi

Monroe/dpi

Poets write about it.

Scientists warn against polluting it.

Van Campen/dpi

And underground workers pipe it in.

We're talking about air, of course. Long, long ago, before people knew anything at all about the human body, they knew that breathing was connected to life. ''The breath of life'' is a saying that is found in many ancient languages we know. But how is breathing connected with life?

In the last Investigation you studied one human system, the digestive system. It is responsible for a life activity that keeps the body alive, digestion. You may feel hungry, but you cannot feel digestion going on. It's even difficult to feel your heart beating. But there is no question that you breathe. You can feel it. You can see it. You can even hear it.

This Investigation is about another human system, the respiratory system. Let's quickly get one thing straight. Breathing and respiration are two different things, but they are related to each other. Breathing is a part of respiration in higher animals. **_Breathing_** is the process of pumping air into and out of the body. **_Respiration_** is the taking in of oxygen and the release of carbon dioxide with the production of energy.

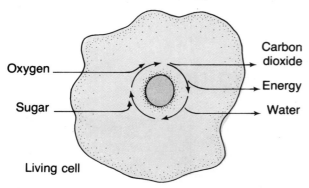

Oxygen

Sugar

Carbon dioxide

Energy

Water

Living cell

Respiration

All the organs that have to do with breathing are part of the **_respiratory system_**. If all of this has come at you too fast, let's take a breather. We'll slowly discuss each of these terms in this Investigation.

A. TAKE A DEEP BREATH

Breathing takes place in the respiratory system. This is a system of organs that begins at the nose and ends at the lungs.

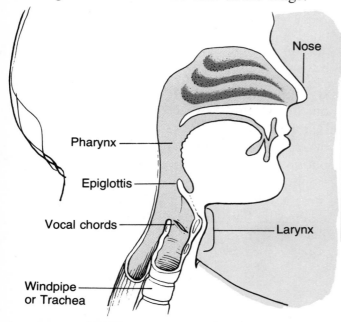

Nose

Pharynx

Epiglottis

Vocal chords

Larynx

Windpipe or Trachea

Air enters the body through the _nose_ and mouth. As air passes through the nose, it is warmed and moistened. The air is also filtered by hairs, which trap particles of dust and dirt.

From the nose, air enters the _pharynx_. This is the throat area at the back of the mouth through which both air and food pass. At the back of the pharynx are two passageways. One tube, the esophagus, carries the food. The other tube, the _trachea_, carries the air.

The entrance to the trachea, or windpipe, is guarded by a flap called the _epiglottis_. During swallowing, the epiglottis covers the trachea. During breathing or speaking, the trachea remains open.

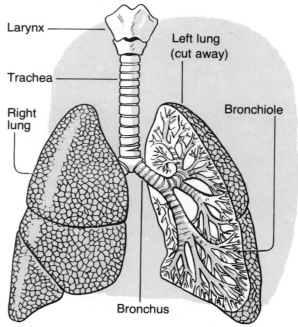

Larynx

Trachea

Right lung

Left lung (cut away)

Bronchiole

Bronchus

The _larynx_, or voicebox, is at the top of the trachea. Within the larynx are the _vocal cords_. These are two thin membranes arranged in a V-shape. Air passing between them causes them to vibrate and create different sounds.

The trachea divides at the bottom into two branches, the _bronchi_. One bronchus enters each of the two lungs. Inside a lung, the bronchus divides again and again, becoming smaller and smaller like the branches of a tree. These tiny tubes are called _bronchioles_.

174

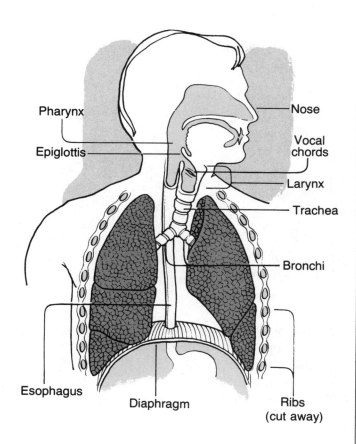

Pharynx

Epiglottis

Nose

Vocal chords

Larynx

Trachea

Bronchi

Esophagus

Diaphragm

Ribs (cut away)

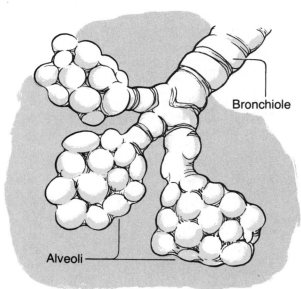

Bronchiole

Alveoli

Each bronchiole ends in a tiny air sac called an *alveolus*. The alveoli look like clusters of grapes. Some scientists say that there are nearly one billion alveoli in the lungs.

Surrounding the lungs are 12 pairs of *ribs*. These are joined at the back and curve around to form a protective cage. The lungs

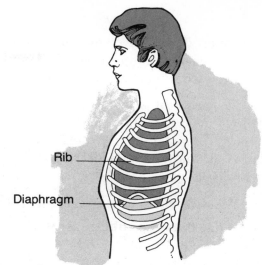

Rib

Diaphragm

fill the chest cavity from the neck to the *diaphragm*. The diaphragm is a muscle that divides the body into two parts.

1. **Name the organs, in order, through which air passes.**
2. **What are some functions of the nose?**
3. **What happens at the pharynx?**
4. **What prevents food from entering the trachea?**
5. **How do you speak and make sounds?**
6. **Describe the inside of the lungs.**
7. **What are the alveoli?**
8. **Where are the lungs located?**
9. **What protects your lungs?**
10. **What is the diaphragm?**

B. HOW DO YOU BREATHE?

175

Your lungs do not have any muscles. They cannot expand or contract on their own. Then how does breathing take place?

Your teacher will pass a model of the chest cavity around the room. Scientists use models to explain the real thing. Refer to Part A as you use the model and answer these questions.

11. **What do the balloons represent?**

12. **What does the rubber sheet represent?**

13. **What does the tube at the top represent?**

14. **What do the branches represent?**

15. **What does the container represent?**

16. **Label the drawing in the data book on page D108.**

17. **Gently pull down slightly on the rubber sheet.**

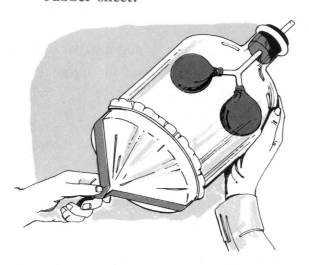

18. **Gently release or push up on the rubber sheet.**

19. **Repeat Steps 17 and 18 several times.**

20. **What is trapped inside the container?**

21. **When you pull down on the rubber sheet, what does this do to the area inside the container?**

22. **When you release or push up on the rubber sheet, what does this do to the area inside the container?**

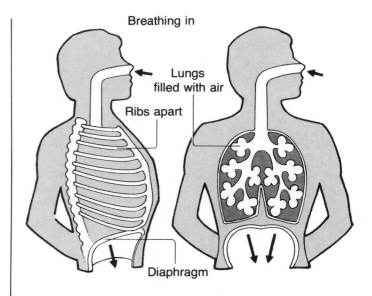

Breathing in

Lungs filled with air

Ribs apart

Diaphragm

When you breathe in, or *inhale*, several things happen. First, the diaphragm moves downward. Then rib muscles pull outward. The space inside your chest becomes bigger. Air flows in through your nose to fill the extra space. Your lungs expand.

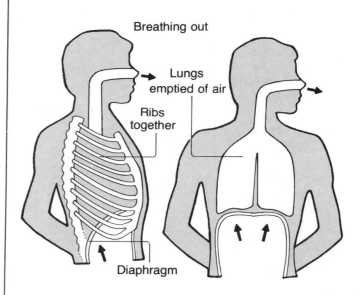

Breathing out

Lungs emptied of air

Ribs together

Diaphragm

When you breathe out, or *exhale*, exactly the opposite happens. The muscles of the diaphragm relax, and so do the muscles connecting the ribs. The space inside your chest becomes smaller. This forces the air out of your lungs.

23. **What causes the balloon to fill up?**

24. **What causes the balloon to flatten?**

25. **Explain how and when the balloon changes.**

26. **Explain how breathing takes place.**

27. **What flows into and out of the lungs during breathing?**

28. **What is the function of the respiratory system?**

C. SMOKERS VS. NON-SMOKERS

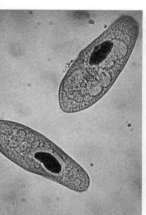

Grant Hellman

All animals do not breathe, but all animals use a process called respiration. Paramecium, worms, and jellyfish do not breathe. They exchange certain gases in the air or water between their cells and the environment directly. Whether it's paramecium, porpoises, or people, all living things need to exchange gases. The gases that are exchanged are *oxygen* and *carbon dioxide*.

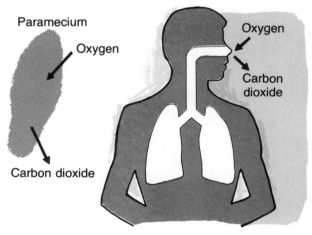

29. **What gas enters your body when you inhale?**

30. **What gas leaves your body when you exhale?**

During respiration, your body is only interested in two gases. The respiratory system makes every effort to prevent all other materials from entering your body. There are hairs in your nose, and there is moisture in your respiratory system. They are there to filter out the unwanted materials in the air. But your respiratory system can only take so much.

Your lung is a big bag of millions of tiny tubes and air sacs. The walls of the tubes are usually very thin and soft. Cigarette smoke, coal dust, or air pollution can cause changes in these tubes. The tube walls become thicker and harder. Examination of the lungs of smokers after death shows this. Look at the differences in these pictures.

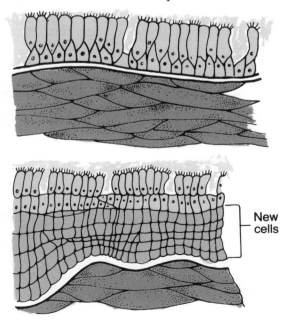

New cells

Materials begin to pile up in the tubes. The smoker tries to get rid of these materials by coughing them out. This is sometimes called "smoker's cough." A summary of five studies shows:

TABLE **1** COMPARISON OF SMOKERS AND NON-SMOKERS

Percent with	Smokers	Non-Smokers
Cough	24	7
Other Respiratory Problems	26	15

As smoking continues, the insides of the tubes become smaller. The smoker coughs, but the air can't come out. Some of the air sacs break. Then more and more air sacs break.

31. **What happens to the amount of air a person can breathe now?**
32. **How does smoking affect respiration?**
33. **What is respiration?**
34. **What is the function of the respiratory system?**

Re-read Questions 28 and 34 before writing the concept.

CONCEPT

ENRICHMENT

1. Explain the statement, "The diaphragm is the chief organ of breathing."
2. The average adult breathing rate is about 16 to 18 times per minute. What is your breathing rate? How do the male and female breathing rates in your class compare? What happens to the breathing rate after exercise? How long after exercise does it take the breathing rate to return to normal?
3. Research and write a paper on the capacity of the lungs. Turn a jug full of water upside down in a pan of water. Insert one end of a rubber tube into the jug and blow into the other end. How much air can you exhale?
4. Draw cigarette smoke into a syringe. Slowly bubble the smoke through the water. Germinate seeds in this water and compare with a control.
5. Explain why you cannot hold your breath for very long.

Investigation 3

The Circulation of Blood

New York Public Library

Over 350 years ago, an English doctor named William Harvey published a book. In it he described how the blood is driven through tubes around the body by the heart. Blood travels through tubes called blood vessels. And the heart supplies the pumping action to keep the blood moving. Dr. Harvey said the blood traveled, "AS IT WERE, IN A CIRCLE." He had the words printed in capital letters, because the idea was so new. Until then his fellow doctors believed that the blood flowed back and forth in the tubes, like the tides.

William Harvey's discovery was most remarkable. You have to realize that oxygen was not discovered until 150 years later. And cells were discovered 200 years later.

In this Investigation you will learn about another life activity, circulation. *Circulation* is the method by which food and gases are transported throughout the body. The heart and the blood vessels make up the *circulatory system*.

A. THE HEART

The heart is the most important organ in the circulatory system. It is about the size of a

179

fist and is one of the toughest muscles in the human body. In a lifetime of 70 years, a heart will pump enough blood to fill a good-sized lake.

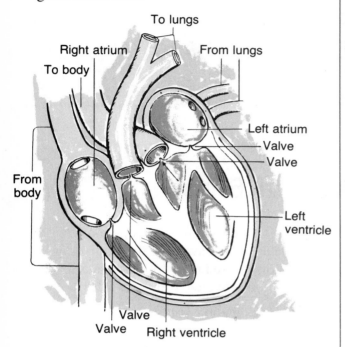

The human heart has four *chambers*. The top chambers are the *atria* (singular *atrium*). The bottom chambers are the *ventricles;* these have strong muscles. The ventricles do most of the work. When they squeeze, the blood is forced out to the lungs or to the body. When they relax, the blood flows into the heart.

1. **Trace the flow of blood through the drawing of the heart on page D111. Begin at "Start" and trace a line to "Finish."**

2. **Where does blood come from when it first enters the heart?**

3. **How many chambers are in the heart?**

4. **What other organ must blood pass through before finally leaving the heart?**

5. **What do you think the blood picks up there?**

6. **Where does blood go when it leaves the heart?**

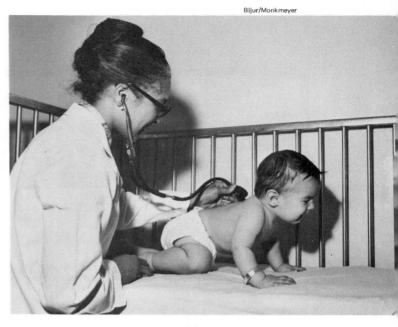

What keeps the blood flowing in the right direction? What does this doctor hear when he or she listens with a *stethoscope?*

7. **Have your partner rest his or her head on the table.**

8. **Place the stethoscope on your partner's back. Move it around until you hear a "lub-dub" sound.**

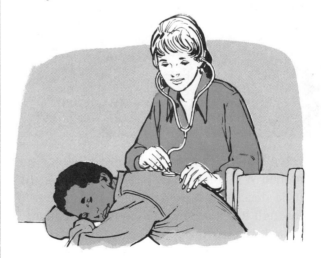

What you hear are the opening and closing of the valves inside the heart. The valves are like one-way trap doors. The valves allow the blood to flow in only one direction. You hear "lub" when the heart squeezes and "dub" when it relaxes. Therefore, count each "lub-dub" as one beat.

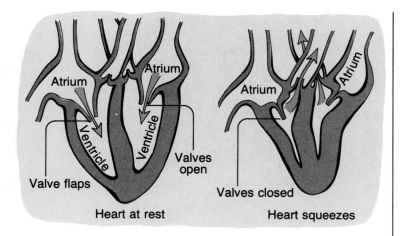

Atrium
Atrium
Ventricle
Ventricle
Valve flaps
Valves open

Heart at rest

Atrium
Atrium
Valves closed

Heart squeezes

9. Count the number of heartbeats you hear in 1 minute. Record the data in Table 1 on your data sheet.

10. Have your partner repeat this count on you. Record the data in Table 1.

11. Run in place for 1 minute. Then count your heartbeats for 1 minute. Record the data in Table 1.

12. Compare your data with your classmates' data.

13. How do the heartbeat rates compare?

14. How does exercising affect the heartbeat rate? Why do you think this happens?

15. What are the names of the heart chambers?

16. Which chambers squeeze and do most of the work?

17. What keeps blood flowing in the right direction? Explain how this is done.

18. What is a stethoscope?

19. What sound do you hear through a stethoscope? What does this sound indicate?

20. State the function of the heart.

21. State the function of the circulatory system.

B. BLOOD VESSELS

TABLE 2 HEARTBEAT RATES OF VARIOUS ANIMALS

Animal	Heartbeats per Minute
Fish	20
Turtle	20
Elephant	25
Horse	35
Lion	45
Cow	70
Human, newborn	140
Human, 3-year-old	100
Human, adult	72
Large dog	80
Small dog	120
Rabbit	135
Pigeon	225
Canary	1000

Each time the muscles of the adult human heart squeeze or contract, about 60 ml of blood are sent out from the ventricles. The heart beats about 72 times a minute. In an hour, it pumps about 450 liters of blood.

Since there are only about six liters of blood in an adult, the blood has to circulate through the body at a fairly fast rate. This is where the blood vessels come into the scene.

Blood is transported to all parts of the body and back again through a system of tubelike vessels. These vessels are of three basic types: arteries, veins, and capillaries.

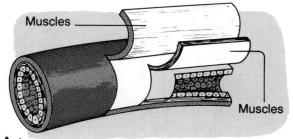

Muscles

Muscles

Artery

The *arteries* are the vessels that carry oxygen-containing blood from the heart to all parts of the body. They have thick, elastic, muscular walls that allow them to expand and contract. Each time the heart beats, the arteries expand. Then they contract, helping to push the blood along.

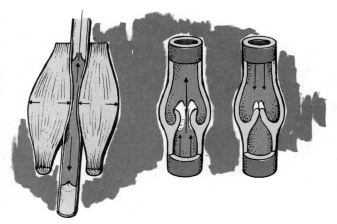

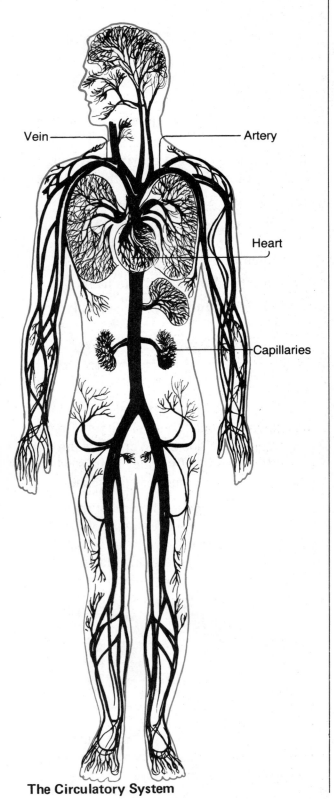

The Circulatory System

The *veins* carry waste-containing blood from the cells back to the heart. Since much of the blood in the veins moves uphill, the veins have valves that prevent the backflow of blood. The blood in the veins is not moved by the force of the heartbeat. Veins frequently pass through muscles. When the body moves and the muscle contract, the veins are squeezed. This forces the blood to move.

Runk/Schoenberger from Grant Heilman

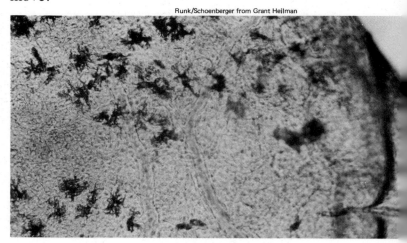

Capillaries

The arteries from the heart branch out, growing smaller and smaller. They finally divide into branches so small that you need a microscope to see them. These tubes are called *capillaries*. The capillaries are longer than all the arteries and veins put together. It is only from the capillaries that food and oxygen can reach the cells of the body. In turn capillaries pick up waste products from the cells.

The capillaries join to form tiny veins. These join, forming larger and larger veins. Finally, two great veins empty blood back into the heart. There, the circle of the blood starts again.

The movement of the blood in the arteries can be felt at certain points on the body. This is where the arteries are close to the skin. One of these places is the inside of the wrist. When you press down on the artery, you can feel the blood pulsating. This is your *pulse*.

22. Place your first two fingers on the inside wrist of your partner. Find the pulse.

23. Count the pulse rate for 1 minute. Record the data in Table 3.
24. Have your partner repeat this count on you. Record the data in Table 2.
25. Run in place for 1 minute. Then take the pulse rate for 1 minute. Record this in Table 2.
26. Compare your data with your classmates' data.
27. **How do the pulse rates compare?**
28. **How does exercising affect the pulse rate?**
29. **Compare the data in Tables 1 and 2. How is the heartbeat rate related to the pulse rate?**
30. **What are the names of three types of blood vessels?**
31. **Explain how the arteries move blood.**
32. **Explain how the veins move blood.**
33. **What is the size of capillaries?**
34. **What is the function of the capillaries?**
35. **What is the function of the circulatory system?**

C. COMPOSITION OF BLOOD

Food, gases, and waste products are carried by the blood in the circulatory system. Blood is called a tissue because it contains special cells that do special jobs. The liquid portion is called *plasma*. It is a clear, yellow fluid.

The solid materials are composed mostly of two kinds of cells. *Red blood cells* carry gases. They carry oxygen from the lungs to the cells and carbon dioxide from the cells back to the lungs. Some carbon dioxide is also carried by the plasma. Red blood cells are able to carry oxygen because they contain a pigment called *hemoglobin*. Hemoglobin gives blood its red color.

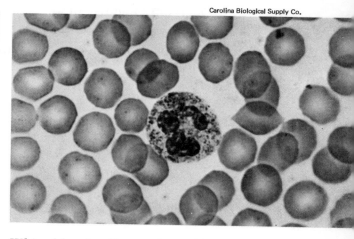
Carolina Biological Supply Co.

White blood cells are the soldiers of the body. They prevent infection by destroying bacteria and other disease-causing organisms. They are outnumbered by the red blood cells by 600 to 1. The large cells with dark nuclei are white blood cells. The smaller ones with light centers are red blood cells. The centers appear light because the cells are thinner in the middle than they are around the edges.

Your teacher will give you a slide of blood.

36. Draw what you see in Space A. Label the plasma, red blood cells, and white blood cells.

37. **What is the liquid part of blood called?**

38. **What is the solid part of blood called?**

39. **Why is blood called a tissue?**

40. **Explain the function of white blood cells.**

41. **Explain the function of red blood cells.**

42. **What gives blood its red color?**

43. **What is the function of the circulatory system?**

44. **Who first described the circulatory system?**

45. **What organs are part of the circulatory system?**

46. **What is the function of the circulatory system?**

CONCEPT

ENRICHMENT

1. Obtain a beef or sheep's heart from the butcher. Carefully dissect it to find the chambers and valves.
2. Research and write a paper on how simpler animals like earthworms and insects transport materials around their bodies.
3. Obtain materials to blood-type yourself. Write a report on blood types and blood transfusion.
4. What is a heart attack? How can heart attacks be prevented? What happens during the healing process?
5. Wrap a goldfish in wet cotton, except for the tail. Focus the tail under the low power of a microscope. Look for capillaries.
6. Explain how blood clots to stop the bleeding when you get a cut.

Investigation 4

Getting It Through to You

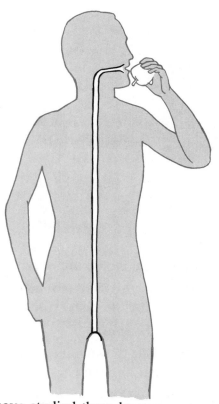

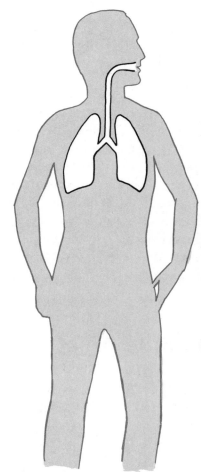

You have studied three human systems so far. The first was the digestive system, which is responsible for digestion. In digestion, food moves through a tube. In the tube it is broken down from large pieces to molecules. Even though the food is inside a tube, it is outside of all the cells in the body. How does food get to the cells?

The second human system you studied was the respiratory system. The respiratory system is responsible for respiration. In respiration, gases are exchanged. Oxygen is inhaled and carbon dioxide is exhaled. Again, the gases are inside a tube and a bag, but outside of all the cells in the body. How do gases enter and leave the cells?

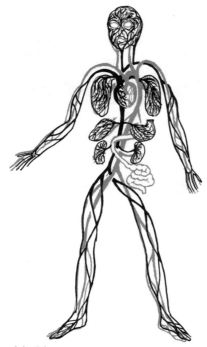

The third human system you studied was the circulatory system. The circulatory system is responsible for circulation. In circulation, blood is pumped around and around in a set of tubes. The role of the blood is to transport food and gases to the cells. The blood must also take the waste products away. How do food and oxygen get into the blood vessels and then into the cells? How are waste materials taken away?

A. RANDOM MOTION

1. **Drop one drop of food coloring into a beaker of water.**

2. **Do not move the beaker. Observe what happens for 1-2 minutes.**

Molecules do not stand still. They quiver; they move; they bump; they get around. They also move at random, which means that each molecule goes every which way. Where there are lots of molecules bunched up together, we say that their *concentration* is high. And where the molecules are spread apart, we say that their concentration is low. Molecules tend to move from where their concentration is high to where the concentration is low. This movement continues until the molecules are all evenly distributed. Then they just go on bumping, quivering, and moving. The random movement of molecules is called **_diffusion_**.

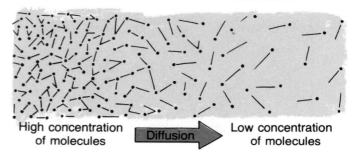

High concentration of molecules → Diffusion → Low concentration of molecules

3. **Describe what happened to the drop of food coloring.**

4. **Molecules move at random. What does this mean?**

5. **In what direction do molecules move?**

6. **Explain why the drop of food coloring spread out in the beaker of water.**

7. **What is diffusion?**

8. **Gently touch the surface of a cup of water. Taste the water.**

9. Drop a sugar cube in the water.

10. Taste the water every 15 seconds.

11. **What happened to the taste of the water?**

12. **What caused the taste of the water to change?**

13. **In Step 9, where was there a high concentration of sugar molecules?**

14. **What happened to the sugar molecules?**

15. **What were the sugar molecules doing?**

16. **What do you call the random movement of molecules?**

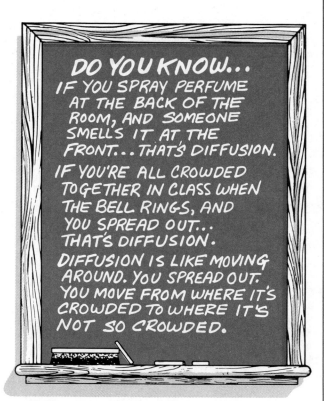

DO YOU KNOW...

IF YOU SPRAY PERFUME AT THE BACK OF THE ROOM, AND SOMEONE SMELLS IT AT THE FRONT... THAT'S DIFFUSION.

IF YOU'RE ALL CROWDED TOGETHER IN CLASS WHEN THE BELL RINGS, AND YOU SPREAD OUT... THAT'S DIFFUSION.

DIFFUSION IS LIKE MOVING AROUND. YOU SPREAD OUT. YOU MOVE FROM WHERE IT'S CROWDED TO WHERE IT'S NOT SO CROWDED.

B. CROSSING THE BORDER

In this next activity you will use a chemical *indicator*. An indicator tells you if something is present. You have used indicators in past Investigations. Bromthymol is an indicator. Do you remember what it indicates? The indicator you will use next is phenolphthalein.

17. Fill a test tube ½-full with water.

18. Add 2-3 drops of phenolphthalein to the water.

19. Wrap a piece of cellophane over the mouth of the test tube. Secure it with a rubber band.

20. **Your teacher will have a bottle of household ammonia in class. Turn your test tube over the open bottle of ammonia.**

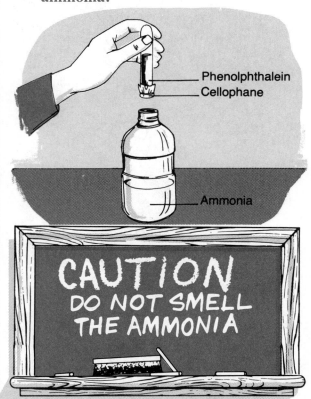

Phenolphthalein
Cellophane
Ammonia

CAUTION
DO NOT SMELL THE AMMONIA

21. **What happened to the liquid in your test tube?**

22. **Where was there a high concentration of ammonia?**

23. **Where was there a low concentration of ammonia?**

24. **Which way did the ammonia move? (Use "concentration" in your answer.)**

25. **What do you call this process?**

The diffusion you just saw differs from the diffusion you saw in Part A. In Part A you dropped food coloring or sugar directly into the water. In Step 16 the ammonia gas passed through a piece of cellophane. Diffusion has taken place through a **_membrane_**. A membrane is like a very thin skin. Gases are able to diffuse through a membrane.

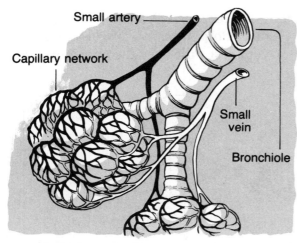

Small artery

Capillary network

Small vein

Bronchiole

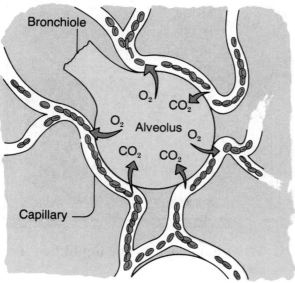

Bronchiole

O_2 CO_2

O_2 Alveolus O_2

CO_2 CO_2

Capillary

Your lungs have millions of air sacs or alveoli. Surrounding each air sac are capillaries. Oxygen diffuses from the air sacs into the capillaries. Carbon dioxide diffuses from the capillaries to the air sacs. Diffusion takes place because the gases are in different concentrations. The diffusion takes place through a membrane.

26. **Explain how gases are exchanged between the respiratory system and the circulatory system.**

27. **Name the process by which materials enter and leave the cells.**

C. DIFFUSION AND DIGESTION

In Part B you saw how gases diffused through a membrane. That explains how gases are exchanged between the respiratory and the circulatory systems. How are materials exchanged between the digestive system and the circulatory system?

Your teacher will show you two jars of raisins. There is water in one jar. The raisins in this jar have been soaking overnight. Your group will be given one raisin from each jar.

28. **Carefully blot the raisins dry. Do not break the skin.**

29. **How do the soaked and unsoaked raisins differ?**

30. **Why do you think they differ?**

31. Use a toothpick to poke a hole in one end of each raisin.

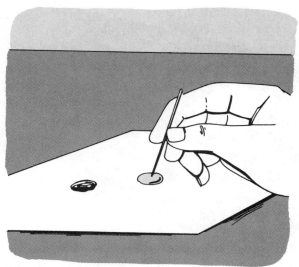

32. Gently squeeze both raisins.

33. What happened?

34. What do you think is coming out of one raisin?

35. How do you think this liquid got into the raisin?

36. What does the skin of the raisin represent?

37. Explain the process of diffusion.

Would you believe that you have thousands of kilometers of intestine inside of you? Yes, you do. The inside surface of the intestine is not smooth. There are finger-like projections, the *villi,* inside the intestine. These villi give the intestine a lot more surface area to absorb food.

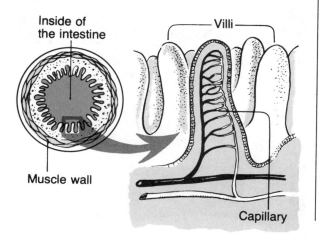

Inside of the intestine

Villi

Muscle wall

Capillary

Imagine that you are a bug walking across a smooth rug. One day you find that the rug has been changed. It is now a shag rug. To walk across the rug, you have to walk up and down every shag. There is now a lot more surface area to walk over to get to the same place.

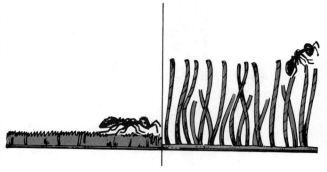

The inside of the intestine is like a shag rug. It is not smooth. It is rough because there are many, many tiny projections. It is these projections that give the intestine so much more area to absorb food.

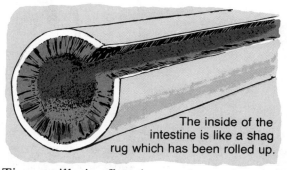

The inside of the intestine is like a shag rug which has been rolled up.

Tiny capillaries flow into and out of each of the millions of villi. The villi pick up the digested food particles by diffusion. The food particles then pass into veins, back to the heart, and are circulated out to all the cells.

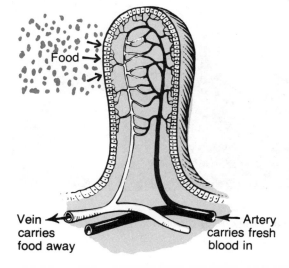

Food

Vein carries food away

Artery carries fresh blood in

38. You will be given a piece of tubing. Tie a knot at one end; then fill it ¼-full with water.

39. Does the tubing leak?

40. Empty the water out of the tubing.

41. Add 3 teaspoons of starch to the tubing.

42. Squeeze the air out of the tubing. Tie a knot at the open end.

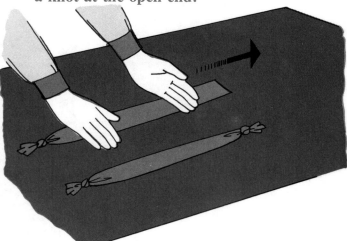

43. Wash the tube off.

44. Feel the tube of starch. How is it like a dried raisin?

45. What do you predict will happen if the tube is soaked in water?

You have used iodine before. It is an indicator for starch. If starch is mixed with iodine, the mixture turns blue-black.

46. Label a beaker.

47. Fill the beaker ¾-full with water. Add 10 to 15 drops of iodine and stir.

48. Tie a paper clip around each knot in the tube. Hang the tube in the beaker of water as shown.

Answer the next four questions before stopping for the day.

49. If the starch turns blue what happened?

50. If the iodine and water turn blue, what happened?

51. If both the iodine and starch turn blue, what happened?

52. What do you predict will happen?

NEXT DAY...

53. What happened in your experiment?

54. How would you explain what happened?

55. Explain how foods are exchanged between the digestive system and the circulatory system.

56. How do materials enter and leave cells?

D. THE LAST BARRIER

You remember learning about the cell membrane in Idea 3. The cell membrane is the outside of the cell. A membrane is like a border. Materials can enter and leave this membrane. No cell is more than a few cells away from a blood capillary. By diffusion, materials are exchanged between the capillaries and the cells.

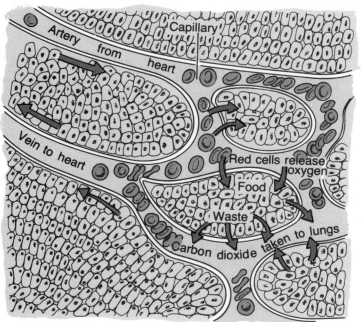

57. Review Part C. What part of the raisin is like a membrane?

58. How is the tubling like a membrane?

59. How does digested food pass out of the intestine into the capillaries?

60. How do gases pass out of the lungs into the capillaries?

61. How do materials enter and leave cells?

Re-read Questions 56 and 61. Then state the concept.

CONCEPT

ENRICHMENT

1. Explain how an open bottle of perfume can be detected across a room.

2. Research and write a paper on osmosis.

3. Draw pictures and explain how materials enter and leave animals like an amoeba, paramecium, or sponge.

4. Slice off the top of a carrot. Remove half of the center core and fill it with corn syrup. Insert a one-hole stopper with a long rigid tube into the core. Stand all of this upright in a beaker of water. Keep the top of the carrot above the surface of the water. Observe what happens and write a paper based on the game plan you learned in Idea 1, Investigation 6.

Investigation 5

How Tall Will You Be?

Les Mahon/Monkmeyer

This man is 249 cm tall.

Wide World Photos

Do you feel sorry for the short boys at the front of the line? Are you embarrassed because you're the tallest girl in class? What about all those freckles on your face? And that changing voice that makes you sound like a frog? Are you self-conscious about all of these things?

Studies made of thousands of children over the past thirty-five years have revealed that girls usually stop growing before boys; that tall children usually stop growing before short children; and that many a short young person becomes a towering adult. For in the race to adulthood, each person runs at his or her own pace. What is the cause of this?

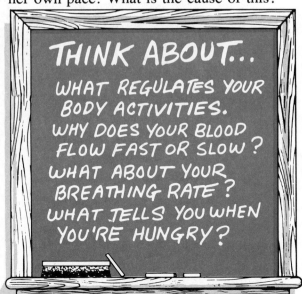

THINK ABOUT...

WHAT REGULATES YOUR BODY ACTIVITIES.

WHY DOES YOUR BLOOD FLOW FAST OR SLOW?

WHAT ABOUT YOUR BREATHING RATE?

WHAT TELLS YOU WHEN YOU'RE HUNGRY?

Living things perform many life activities such as digestion, respiration, and circulation. These activities are run by different systems. They are the digestive system, respiratory system, and circulatory system. The systems do not operate in the same way at all times. They respond to changes. For instance, the heartbeat rate and the breathing rate change. Furthermore, these systems do not act separately. They work with one another. How do these systems work together in such a way that the entire organism functions smoothly?

There are two different ways that the life activities are controlled. These are *chemical control* and *nervous control*. Each is carried out by a system: the *endocrine system* and the *nervous system*. Although they work together, it will be easier to study these systems separately. Let's study the endocrine system first.

A. REGULATION

The ***endocrine system*** consists of a set of glands. They are located at different places in the body.

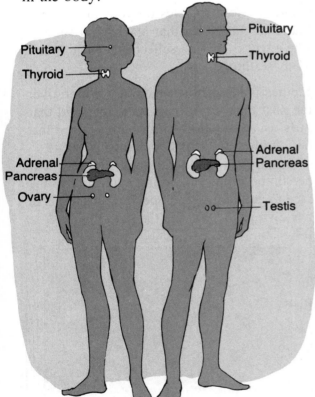

The Endocrine System

The endocrine glands are organs that make one or more substances called ***hormones***. Hormones are chemicals that stimulate cells, tissues, and organs to do different things.

In this way they have a controlling effect on your body.

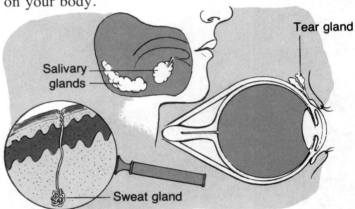

The endocrine glands differ from other glands like the salivary glands. The salivary glands pour their fluids into the body through tiny tubes. Other glands that do this are the sweat glands, digestive glands, and tear glands. The endocrine glands do not have tubes leading from them. They supply their hormones directly into the bloodstream. The blood then carries the hormones to all parts of the body.

Endocrine gland cells

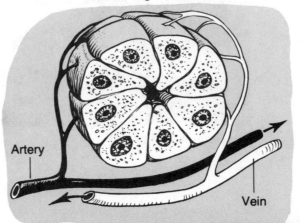

In general, hormones keep the different life activities at a constant level. That is, they keep all the things that go on inside your body in balance. For instance, your body temperature is 37° C. That temperature must be kept constant. If it goes up or down slightly, you become sick. Scientists have a word for keeping things constant or in balance. The word is **_regulate_**.

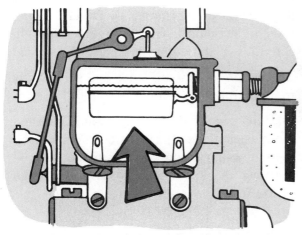

If you look inside the carburetor, you will see a float. This float regulates the amount of gasoline going into the engine. This means it doesn't let too much or too little gasoline into the engine. Either condition would cause the car to stop.

The thermostat on the wall regulates the amount of heat in a room. It turns off the furnace when it gets too hot and it turns on the furnace when it gets too cold. It keeps the temperature in a room constant.

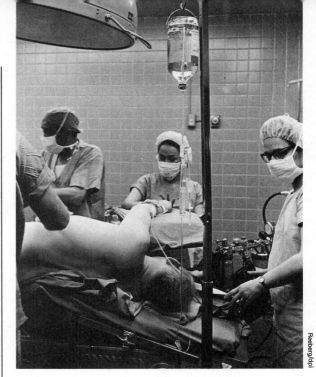

Here's one more example of regulation. Sometimes hospital patients cannot feed themselves. When this happens, they are fed liquid sugar through a tube injected into a vein. The doctor or nurse must regulate the flow of sugar — not too much nor too little.

This activity will illustrate the concept of regulation. You will be given a plastic bottle and a dropper. Your problem will be to keep the dropper floating in the middle of the bottle.

1. **Fill the bottle almost full with water.**

2. **Draw some water into the dropper. Place the dropper in the bottle of water.**

3. **Cap the bottle.**

4. Squeeze the bottle and make the dropper stay floating in the middle of the bottle.

5. After several practices, challenge another student to a contest. See who can keep the dropper floating without any movement in the middle of the bottle.

6. What happens if you squeeze to hard?

7. What happens if you squeeze too little?

8. To keep the dropper in the middle, what must you regulate?

9. Define regulation.

10. What system in your body regulates?

11. What organs make up this system?

12. What substances do these organs make?

13. What do hormones do to life activities?

B. ENDOCRINE GLANDS

Hormones are chemical messengers. They get around the body to all the cells by hitching a ride in the bloodstream. How fast we grow and how strong we are depend on hormones. When we get angry, surprised, or frightened, our bodies tense up due to hormones.

How cells change food into energy also depends on the hormones of the endocrine system. The hormones truly regulate the life activities of the body.

The major endocrine glands and some of the more common hormones are as follows:

Pituitary gland. The pituitary gland is called the master gland. It makes hormones that regulate other glands. It also makes a hormone that regulates growth. The results of too much or too little of the *growth hormone* are pictured below.

Wide World Photos

Thyroid gland. The thyroid gland makes a hormone called *thyroxin*. Thyroxin regulates the rate of cellular respiration. This has to do with how fast a cell burns sugar to release energy. If too much thyroxin is produced, a person becomes nervous. Maybe you've heard of people called *hyper*. If too little thyroxin is produced, an overweight condition called *obesity* will result.

Wide World Photos

The combined mass of these twins is 591 kg.

Adrenal gland. The adrenal gland makes a hormone called *adrenalin*. This is the emergency hormone. The hormone causes the liver to release sugar, the heart to beat faster, and the muscles to tense. Adrenalin is released when a person is angry, afraid, or excited. Sometimes when you hear an athlete is "up," you say the adrenalin is pumping.

Wide World Photos

Pancreas gland. The pancreas gland makes a hormone called *insulin*. Insulin regulates the amount of sugar entering a cell from the blood. If insulin is lacking, a disease called *diabetes* results. Diabetics cannot burn the sugar in food for energy. But they can live a

Michael Heron/Monkmeyer

normal life by taking insulin by mouth or by injection.

Gonads. The gonads are the sex glands. In females they are the *ovaries* and in males the *testes*. They produce *sex hormones*. Male sex hormones regulate the male sex characteristics. These characteristics include a low voice, beard, body hair, and heavier muscle development. Female sex hormones regulate female sex characteristics. These include a high voice, breast development, and the menstrual cycle.

14. **Complete Table 1 on your data sheet. List the five glands discussed; list one hormone for each gland and what the hormone regulates.**

Using the information in Table 1, you are to construct a card game. We'll call the game *Hormones*.

15. **For every four players, cut 30 7.5 x 12.5 cm index cards in half across the width. You now have 60 cards.**

16. Write the name of one gland on each of four cards.

17. Repeat Step 16 for the other four glands.

18. Write the name of one hormone on each of four cards.

19. Repeat Step 18 for the other four hormones.

20. Write what one hormone regulates on each of four cards.

21. Repeat Step 20 for what the other hormones regulate.

Here are the rules for the game (for 2 to 4 players per deck):

To Start: Shuffle well and deal eight cards to each player. Place the leftover cards face down on the table. Turn the first card over next to the pile. You now have a draw pile and a discard pile.

To Play: The play starts on the dealer's left and goes clockwise. Each player picks up the top card from the draw pile *or* the discard pile. Each player must then discard one card, except when that player wins. The winner should yell, ''Hormone.''

To Win: The winner is the first person to lay down 9 cards in the following pattern:
   3 cards related to one gland (Pituitary, Growth hormone, Regulates growth)
   3 cards related to another gland
   3 cards related to another gland

To Renew: If the draw pile runs out, keep the last discard face up. Shuffle the others and place face-down.

C. THE FINAL REGULATION

What makes people fat or skinny, tall or short, bony or stocky? What makes some people slow-moving and others nervous and jumpy? What tells the heart to beat faster or slower?

22. **Define regulation.**

23. **What system in your body regulates?**

24. **What organs make up this system?**

25. **What substance do these organs make?**

26. **Explain the function of hormones.**

CONCEPT

ENRICHMENT

1. Write a paper on the work of von Mehring and Minkowski, and on what they discovered about hormones.

2. Plants produce hormones. Grow Little Marvel and Alaska pea seeds. These are dwarf and regular size pea plants. Spray some of each with gibberellic acid (100 mg gibberellic acid in 100 ml water). Measure the heights of the plants daily and write a paper based on your game plan.

3. Obtain day-old cockerels. These are baby male chickens. Take some of the cockerels and rub the tops of their heads with testosterone. This is a male sex hormone. Measure the size of the comb daily. Write a paper on your findings.

4. Construct a chart listing some of the other hormones that are produced by the endocrine glands.

Investigation 6

Creating Concepts Can Cause Consternation

The people of ancient times thought that courage and thinking were done in the heart. They thought that cowardice came from the liver. They knew very little of the brain. One of our greatest achievements has been to learn about the learning machine in our head.

There are ten things in the top drawing that are different from the bottom drawing. Can you find them?

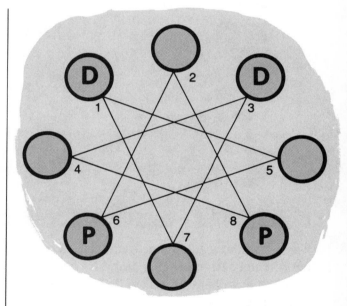

Can you reverse the positions of the dimes (D) and pennies (P)? Move one coin at a time along the lines connecting the circles. Any continuous move counts as one move. For instance, if you move a coin from 1 to 7 to 3 to 4, that is only one move. You may not move to a circle that already has a coin. It can be done in seven moves. How many did it take you?

How you feel, how you know, how you do, how you solve problems — all depend on nervous control. In the last Investigation you studied chemical control. In this Investigation you will study nervous control.

Nervous control is carried out by the nervous system. The ***nervous system*** consists of the brain, the spinal cord, and the nerve cells. Let's see how these parts function.

A. ARE YOU COORDINATED?

The millions and millions of cells that make up your body are organized into different systems. What controls all of these systems? You know that the endocrine system controls by regulation. The nervous system controls by ***coordination***. The nervous system coordinates the life activities. Coordination requires a communication network that links all of the cells together.

Fujihira/Monkmeyer

The person at a telephone switchboard coordinates. As messages come in, the switchboard operator makes decisions. These decisions are based on past experience. Action is taken to connect the people who want to communicate.

You probably take eating with a knife and fork for granted. But eating with a knife and fork takes coordination. Coordination is controlled by the nervous system.

Ken Regan/Camera 5

Maybe you've heard the phrase, "She's very coordinated." Just what does that mean?

How coordinated are you? There are 40 numbers printed on page 201.

1. **You are to touch each number in order, starting at 1. You have 30 seconds. Start when your teacher says, "Go."**

2. **What number did you reach after 30 seconds?**

Your teacher will ask you to do it again. But this time see if you can recognize a pattern. This means the numbers have been arranged in a certain way.

3. **Touch each number in order starting at 1. Start when your teacher says, "Go." Again, you will have 30 seconds.**

4. **What number did you reach after 30 seconds?**

5. **How are the numbers arranged? (Discuss this in class.)**

6. **Now that you see the pattern, do Step 3 again.**

7. **What number did you reach this time?**

8. **How do your results compare between the first and third trials?**

9. **Why did you reach a higher number each time?**

10. **What system of your body did you use to do Steps 1, 3, and 6?**

11. **How does the nervous system control?**

12. **What does the nervous system coordinate?**

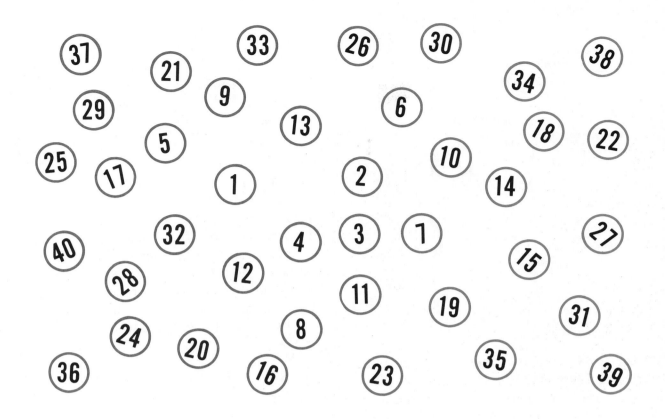

B. WHERE ARE YOUR TASTE BUDS?

Todd Friedman/Spectra Action

Being coordinated requires that you keep all the parts functioning together in harmony. This can mean being the coach on the football team, managing a store, or staying on a skateboard.

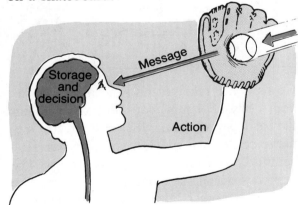

To be better coordinated, three things must happen. First, you receive messages from your surroundings. Second, your brain stores the messages and makes a decision. Third, a message goes out to your body to cause an action. The concept is simple, but the process is complicated.

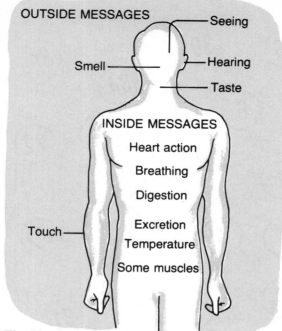

OUTSIDE MESSAGES

- Seeing
- Hearing
- Taste
- Smell
- Touch

INSIDE MESSAGES

Heart action

Breathing

Digestion

Excretion

Temperature

Some muscles

The Nervous System

There are two major ways that messages begin. There are those messages that come from inside the body. Your nervous system automatically takes care of these. You don't have to think to digest or to breathe. Then, there are those messages that come from outside the body. These are usually received by the five senses: taste, touch, smell, hearing, and seeing.

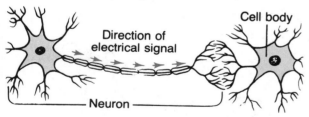

Direction of electrical signal

Cell body

Neuron

How do you receive and send messages in your body? For this, you must know about the basic part of the nervous system. It is the nerve cell or *neuron*. Each neuron has a central body from which stems branch. The branches on one side are usually short. The ones on the other side are long. The neurons line up, short side to long side, to form *nerve tissues* that run throughout the body like electrical wires. In fact, the messages that travel from one neuron to the other are electrical signals. This is how the nerves or neurons connect all parts of the body with the brain and with each other.

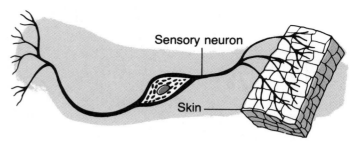

Sensory neuron

Skin

The outer ends of some of the neurons are equipped with sensitive receptors. These receptors pick up messages; they can be found on the eye, skin, tongue, nose, and ear. For instance, your tongue can distinguish four kinds of taste: salty, sweet, bitter, and sour. The receptors for each taste are at different places on your tongue. In this activity you will map the taste areas of your tongue.

13. Wipe or rinse your tongue.

14. Do not look at the labels of the four bottles provided.

15. Have your partner place one drop from Bottle 1 on the tip of your tongue with a toothpick.

16. Using a new toothpick each time, repeat a drop from Bottle 1 on the sides and rear of the tongue.

17. On your data sheet, color in the area on the tongue where you detected the corresponding taste.

18. Repeat Steps 13 to 17 with Bottles 2, 3, and 4.

There are two kinds of nerves: *sensory nerves* and *motor nerves*. You have just seen one group of sensory nerves in action, the sensory nerves on the tongue. Sensory nerves receive messages. They run from the surface of your body to the brain.

19. Define coordination.

20. What three things must happen for coordination to take place?

21. What are the two major ways that your body receives messages?

22. What is the basic unit of the nervous system?

23. What is nerve tissue?

24. Name the five senses and the organs responsible for each one.

25. What are sensory nerves?

C. LET'S COORDINATE THIS WHOLE THING

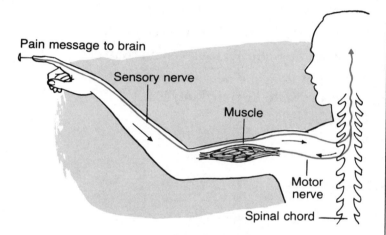

Pain message to brain

Sensory nerve

Muscle

Motor nerve

Spinal chord

You have just learned about sensory nerves. The other kind of nerves are motor nerves. They run from the brain to the glands and muscles of your body.

The muscles, in turn, are connected to bones. Thus, a message may come from the brain to a muscle. The muscle contracts or becomes shorter; the tissue or bone moves; and a body action occurs.

26. What happens when someone gently tosses a cotton ball at your face?

27. First, what organ and what sense detected the cotton ball coming?

28. Then, over what nerves did the message rush telling you of approaching danger?

29. What organ stored and interpreted the incoming message?

30. Over what nerves did the message go out telling your body to do something?

31. Explain how your eyelids close to protect you from the cotton ball.

32. In one word, what caused all of the things in Questions 27 to 31 to function smoothly?

33. What system is responsible for this?

Now that we have studied both ends of the communication network, let's take a look at the central switchboard. The brain is the central switchboard of your nervous system. It's like talking to a friend on the phone. Here you are, the two of you babbling along, taking everything that goes on in between at the phone company for granted.

The brain weighs about 1.3 kilograms and fills the cavity at the top of your head. The brain is divided into three major parts: the

cerebrum, cerebellum, and *medulla.* Each part coordinates different activities in the body.

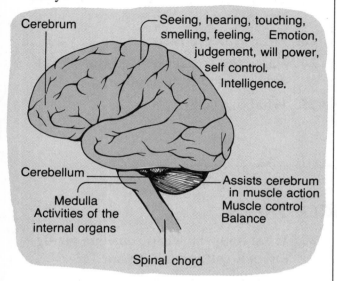

Cerebrum

Seeing, hearing, touching, smelling, feeling. Emotion, judgement, will power, self control. Intelligence.

Cerebellum

Medulla
Activities of the internal organs

Assists cerebrum in muscle action
Muscle control
Balance

Spinal chord

The spinal cord leads down from the brain. It runs down the back of your body and is protected by a set of hollow bones, the backbone. The sensory nerves come from all parts of the body and join at the spinal cord, where they travel up to the brain. In turn, the motor nerves run down from the brain to the spinal cord. Then they branch out to all the muscles in your body.

Now that all the pieces are together, let's give your coordination one last try. Quickly, repeat this sentence three times:

CREATING CONCEPTS CAN
CAUSE COORDINATED CARLOS
CONSIDERABLE CONSTERNATION

34. **How do sensory nerves differ from motor nerves?**

35. **Name the parts of the brain. Name one thing that each part coordinates.**

36. **Name the parts of the nervous system.**

37. **How does the nervous system control?**

38. **What does the nervous system coordinate in your body?**

CONCEPT

ENRICHMENT

1. How sensitive are your skin receptors? Open a paper clip to make a U out of the wire. Progressively bring the ends of the wires closer and closer together, each time gently touching your partner's skin. Your partner is not to look. What is the closest distance in which two wires cannot be detected?

2. How many marbles can you pick up in one minute with a pair of chopsticks? How many after many practices?

3. Make a chart showing the sizes or weights of the brains of various animals.

4. Research how lower animals, which do not have brains, coordinate their life activities.

The Latest Teen Drug

"Well, I have to go now, pal. It's been real nice talking to you."

If you laughed at the cartoon, you're quite normal. Everybody laughs at the lovable lush. Getting drunk and laughing at the drunk is an acceptable life style. In fact, it is all right to drink just to get drunk.

If you visit a home in the Philippines, Mexico, or Sweden, you will probably be offered food and coffee or tea. Most gracious

Switzerland Cheese Association

American hosts or hostesses, however, offer the adult a beer, wine, or liquor. Drinking is as American as apple pie.

The cocktail party is uniquely American. Some trains have bars for the people who commute. The drinking is done standing up. The alcohol is gulped down. The aim is to ''get high.''

Macha/deWys

205

"If you want a good example of widespread 'drug abuse,' take a look at the middle-class American cocktail party."

Dr. Robert Petersen
National Institute on Drug Abuse

Yes, alcohol is a drug. A *drug* is any substance taken into the body to cure or change a body function. If used as directed by a doctor, no damage is done. But if too much of a drug is taken, it is misused. This is called **drug abuse**. An example of drug abuse is **alcoholism**, which is caused by excessive drinking.

"Alcohol is the drug which should top the nation's 'most dangerous' list."

Dr. Dora B. Goldstein
Stanford University School of Medicine

A. THE LATEST TEEN DRUG: ALCOHOL

In the last Investigation you learned that the nervous system coordinates the different systems in the body. Here is an example of coordination.

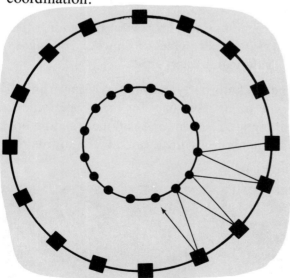

Study the drawing and notice that there are two circles. The outer circle has squares and the inner circle has dots. You are to alternately connect squares and dots. A part of the two circles has been connected as an example.

1. You will have 10 seconds to see how many squares and dots you can connect. Use Circle A on page D125. Start when your teacher says "Go."

2. Count the number of squares and dots you actually touched.

3. Repeat Steps 1 and 2. Use Circle B on page D125.

4. **What is the total number of squares and dots you touched in two trials? This is your control count.**

You are now going to play at being drunk. Ask to be excused if the next steps make you feel bad.

You can play at being drunk with any of the following methods:

a. Spin yourself around 10 times.

b. Shake your head vigorously, sideways or up and down, for 10 seconds.

c. Lower your head in front of you and shake it vigorously for 10 seconds.

Caution!

a. Watch each other to prevent falling due to dizziness.

b. Only one person in a team is to do the activity at a time.

c. Take all safety precautions. Listen to the teacher.

5. Use one of the methods described to make yourself "drunk."

6. Repeat Steps 1 and 2. Use Circle C on page D125.

7. Repeat Steps 5 and 6. Use Circle D on page D125.

8. **What is the total number of squares and dots you touched in two trials? This is your experimental count.**

9. Collect the class data in Table 1.

10. How do the control results compare with the experimental results?

11. How does a person's coordination compare when sober *vs.* drunk?

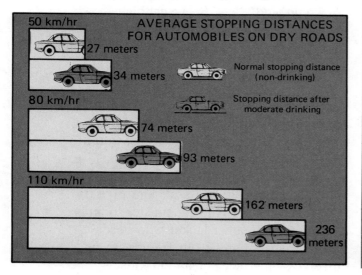

NUMBER of COCKTAILS or BOTTLES of BEER	EFFECTS ON AVERAGE PERSON
OR	Happy!
OR	Warm- relaxed
OR	Talks too much
OR	Awkward!☆ clumsy!
OR	Bombed!

12. What happens to the body as the amount of alcohol goes up?

AVERAGE STOPPING DISTANCES FOR AUTOMOBILES ON DRY ROADS

50 km/hr — 27 meters — 34 meters

Normal stopping distance (non-drinking)

Stopping distance after moderate drinking

80 km/hr — 74 meters — 93 meters

110 km/hr — 162 meters — 236 meters

13. According to the graph, who can stop a car more quickly?

The moderately drinking driver needs over 3 more car lengths than the non-drinking driver to stop at 80/km hr.

So you see, each drink makes a person more dangerous. Is it any wonder that 50,000 people are killed each year by drunken drivers? Ten thousand of these are killed by drivers between the ages of 15 and 25.

Let's face some facts:

a. 500,000 people under 20 years of age are alcoholics or are problem drinkers.

b. 95 million Americans over the age of 15 drink regularly.

c. 9 million Americans are alcoholics or problem drinkers compared with 5 million 10 years ago.

d. 1 out of 3 alcoholics is a woman compared to 1 out of 6 ten years ago.

e. About 1 million high school students (1 in 20) get drunk an average of once a week.

f. 60% of junior high students have used alcohol at least once.

g. 3 out of 4 teen-agers drink; 1 in 20 has a serious problem; and 1 in 10 will become an alcoholic.

Research has shown that alcohol can upset the nervous system's ability to coordinate. Alcohol causes the brain to function less effectively. There is less self-control. The senses are deadened. Memory, movement, accuracy, speed, and learning are all affected. In time, alcohol damages the liver and the nervous system.

14. What does alcohol do to the nervous system?

B. ESCAPE TO NOWHERE

We think you should know as much as the average pusher.

MARIJUANA (Pot, Grass)
High lasts 2 to 4 hours.
$25-50 per lid (28 grams)
50 joints per lid.
About 75¢ per joint.*

HALLUCINOGENS (Acid, Peyote, Mescaline, DMT)
High lasts up to 16 hours.
$2.00 per capsule, paper, or cube.*

HEROIN ("H," Horse)
High lasts up to 12 hours.
$60-$150 per fix.*

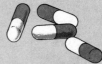

STIMULANTS (Speed, Dexies, Bennies, Ups)
High lasts 8 to 12 hours.
10 for $2.00.*
(Coke) $75-125 gram*

DEPRESSANTS (Goofballs, Redbirds, Yellow jackets)
High (or low) lasts up to 10 hours.
10 for $5.00.*

*Prices will vary.

In order to support their habits, drug addicts steal billions of dollars each year. They steal 1½ billion dollars each year in New York City alone. Most people hide the fact that they use drugs. We do not know exactly how many drug users there are in the United States. But good estimates show:

Drugs	Estimated Users
Stimulants, depressants	25 to 30 million
Marijuana	15 to 25 million
Heroin	100 to 200 thousand

With so many people using drugs, we think you should know what the average user knows. They know what marijuana smells like. Do you?

15. **Your teacher will give you an artificial marijuana wafer.**

16. **Break the wafer into two pieces. Place the larger piece on top of the smaller piece in a glass dish.**

17. **Light the top piece. Notice the odor.**

18. **Describe the odor of marijuana.**

keep off the grass

Why do people use marijuana? Table 2 shows a few of the reasons given by people who use it often.

TABLE 2 REASONS FOR USING MARIJUANA

1. To be "in"	5. To enjoy things
2. To unwind	6. To get high
3. To relax	7. To relieve sadness
4. To be sociable	8. To make friends

19. **Which reasons were used to escape from problems?**

All the others are social reasons. Most teenagers begin using drugs to get into a "cool group." The desire "to belong," to be part of an "in group," is strong. In fact, many teenagers buy "grass" and give it away. The pusher is not a sinister-looking character in a leather jacket who needs a shave. Pushers can be our friends, even ourselves—the nice, clean-cut kids.

20. Why do many teenagers give away drugs? What are they looking for in return?

21. The average teenager is not after the drugs themselves. What is he or she after?

C. COLD TURKEY IS NOT A THANKSGIVING LEFT-OVER

What can drug abuse do to the systems of the body? What is it like to be a speed or coke freak?

22. Why do speed freaks go from a few pills to many?

23. Why do speed freaks go from many pills to injections?

24. What can drug abuse do to the nervous system?

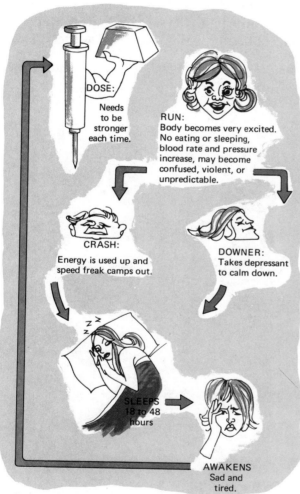

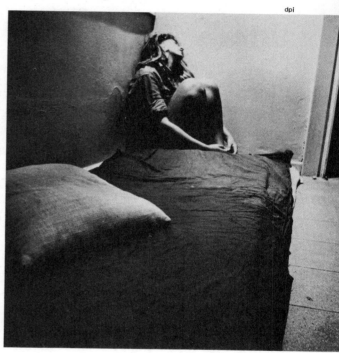

dpi

"Speed," that's just another name for methamphetamine. "Coke" is not a cola drink. It's cocaine, the "in" drug today. Speed is more dangerous than coke. Neither drug is physically addicting. The body does not have to have it. But the body can become tolerant. This means that the user needs a larger and larger dose to get turned on. With speed, you can inject it or take it as pills.

Speed or coke may not be addicting, but heroin is. This means your body must have it. And when you don't get heroin, you get cold turkey.

You get a terrible headache. You feel very cold. But you also run a high fever. You can't think straight. You vomit. You shiver and shake. You thrash around. And you do all this for three days, maybe more.

Do you want this to happen to you? Not on your life, huh? So let's talk about drugs. Because if we don't, the pusher will.

D. TURN ON NATURALLY, THE ORGANIC WAY

There are no right or wrong answers to what you are about to do. Be a free spirit. Just state your opinions. Then the class can have a rap session.

25. Do you believe that drugs are *not* harmful? If so, write your reasons in Space A. If you believe that drugs *are* harmful, write those reasons in the space.

26. Cut out an ad that tells you how a product can make you happier. Attach it to your data sheet.

27. How are these ads like turning on with drugs?

28. A part of a newspaper article is shown in Space B. Finish the article. Write some of the other things people might say about drugs.

29. Suppose you had to write a letter to the editor. What would you say about the article? Do this in Space C.

Here are two situations. What would you say?

Carl is 12 and in the 7th grade. He's been blowing a little pot lately. One day, Steve says, ''Grass is for babies. Try some coke. It's the greatest!''

Carl is not sure. He had heard that coke can cause serious illness. Steve says, ''Go on. Try it.''

30. **If you were Carl, what would you say?**

Jim has invited Beverly to the school dance. They meet Ronald and Carol there. During the dance, the four sneak out. Jim has a bottle of whiskey. Ronald and Carol are eager to begin. Beverly has never drunk alcohol before. Jim offers her a drink.

31. **If you were Beverly, what would you say?**

"THANK HEAVEN! MAYBE NOW HE'LL STAY AWAY FROM POT."

32. **Comment on the above cartoon.**

Here are some sayings for you to think about. Comment on each, if you want.

''The happy that I am when I'm straight is so much more beautiful than the happy that I seem to be when I'm stoned.

''Get high with life and turn on with sunshine.''

33. Write your own saying in Space D. Write a poem. Draw a picture. Make a collage. Be yourself.

Let's wrap this Investigation together.

34. **What is the function of the nervous system?**

35. **What can alcohol and drugs do to the nervous system?**

Combine your answers to Questions 34 and 35 to formulate your concept.

CONCEPT

WORDS TO KNOW

The following words have been used in this Idea. Carefully review the Idea and define each of them on your data sheet.

Alcoholism	Drug abuse
Breathing	Endocrine system
Chemical digestion	Hormone
Circulation	Indicator
Circulatory system	Membrane
Coordination	Nervous system
Diffusion	Regulate
Digestion	Respiration
Digestive system	Respiratory system

SUMMARY OF THE IDEA: THE SYSTEMS OF THE HUMAN BODY

In Idea 3 you studied how an organism is organized. An organism is a community of cells, communicating and working together. These cells are organized into groups called tissues. In turn, the tissues are organized into organs, and finally into systems. It's much like an army of soldiers, organized into companies, then battalions, and finally into divisions. Your body is organized in the same way. This Idea has been about the systems of the human body.

To understand a system of the body, you must also understand its function. Each human system is responsible for a life activity. It is these life activities that keep you alive. To stay alive, you need energy. This energy comes to you in the food you eat. The food is broken down in the food tube of the digestive system by a process called digestion. At the same time, gases are exchanged by the respiratory system. The exchange of gases is called breathing. During this process oxygen is inhaled and carbon dioxide is exhaled. The digested foods and the gases enter the circulatory system by diffusion. The foods and gases are transported throughout the body by circulation. At the same time waste products and gases are picked up. The exchange of foods, gases, and waste products between the circulatory system and the cells takes place by diffusion, too.

There are two systems that control the digestive system, respiratory system, and circulatory system. They are the endocrine system and nervous system. The endocrine system makes hormones which control by regulation. The nervous system uses electrical signals to keep all the systems coordinated. Drugs and alcohol can disrupt this coordination.

In this Idea you have studied the following systems and their related life activities:

Human Systems	Life Activities
Digestive System	Digestion
Respiratory System	Respiration
Circulatory System	Circulation
Endocrine System	Regulation
Nervous System	Coordination

You have studied seven concepts about human systems.

1. **State these seven concepts.**

2. **What is a system?**

3. Name the systems you studied in this Idea.

4. What is a life activity?

5. Name the life activities you studied in this Idea.

6. Re-read Questions 2 and 3. State what the body is a group of.

7. What do the systems of the body carry on?

8. Why are life activities necessary?

Combine your answers to Questions 6-8 to summarize the Idea.

IDEA SUMMARY

ENRICHMENT

1. Interview people of another culture or who know of other cultures. Find out what they offer visitors to their homes. If your parents or neighbors offer liquor, find out why they do it.

2. Cigarettes carry a warning on their packages. What does this warning say? What would you design to be placed on bottles of liquor?

3. Visit an Alcoholics Anonymous meeting. Write a report on what you observed.

4. Research and write a paper on what alcohol does to the liver.

5. There are some systems which were not covered in this Idea. They include the excretory system, muscular system, and the skeletal system. Draw pictures of any of the systems. Explain how each system functions. Name and explain the life activity each is responsible for.

Investigation 1

The Goose Tree

No one knows when life first originated on earth. Modern day scientists believe that life on earth may have originated more than a billion years ago. Many theories have been suggested to explain where living things come from. At times, there were almost as many theories as scientists. Some of the earliest recorded explanations date back more than 2,000 years. The early Greeks believed that the different parts of the body came together suddenly. They believed that fire, water, air, and earth were joined in some mysterious way to do this.

Frogs, toads, rats, and mice were believed to come from mud and slime. Worms were

born in rotten cheese and meat. The hairs of animals that fell into ponds became worms and eels.

Goose trees were special trees that produced geese at special times. Sounds silly, doesn't it? Some people didn't think so 700 years ago. In fact, some people still believed in the goose tree 250 years ago.

People in the Orient talked about another kind of tree. This tree had fruits that looked like melons. These melons were said to contain full-grown lambs.

Most of these ideas had one thing in common. They suggested that living things came from non-living matter. This idea was

generally known as the theory of
spontaneous generation.

1. **How did people generally explain the origin of living things?**

2 **What was this idea known as?**

The theory of spontaneous generation was accepted for thousands of years. Finally, in the late 1600's, a simple experiment revealed the truth. There was no magical energy. There was no mysterious force. Using pieces of meat and several containers, the Italian scientist, Francesco Redi, disproved the theory of spontaneous generation.

The Bettmann Archive, Inc.

You can perform a similar experiment and arrive at your own conclusions.

A. INVESTIGATING FRUIT FLIES

In Idea 2, you learned that living things grow. You also learned that organisms change as they grow. This is especially true of many insects. Very young flies do not look like adult flies. They look like tiny worms. These worms are called maggots.

3. **Get 3 plastic base vials.**

4. **Place a slice of banana in each vial.**

5. **Place a piece of gauze over the mouth of one vial. Snap on a vial connector.**

6. **Place a piece of cellophane over the mouth of a second vial. Snap on a vial connector.**

7. **Do not cover the last vial. Snap on a vial connector.**

8. **Fold the cardboard base. Your teacher will show you how. Label the base.**

9. **Place the 3 base vials in the cardboard base.**

Your teacher will give you three vials of fruit flies. **Do you like bananas? Fruit flies do!** They also like to fly! Keep the vials covered.

10. Hold a vial of flies near the top of the uncovered base vial.

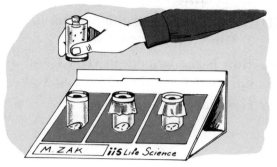

11. Loosen the cover. But do not let any flies escape.

12. Quickly remove the cover and snap the upper vial onto the vial connector.

13. Number this vial 1.

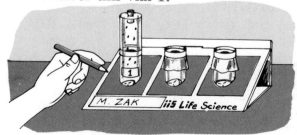

14. Observe the flies. What are they doing?

15. Why do you think they are doing this?

16. Hold another vial of flies over the gauze-covered base vial.

17. Loosen the cover.

18. Quickly remove the cover and snap the upper vial onto the vial connector.

19. Number this vial 2.

20. Observe the flies. What are they doing?

21 Why do you think they are doing this?

22. Where are most of the flies?

23. What is the gauze doing?

24. How many flies have gotten through the gauze?

25. Hold the last vial of flies over the cellophane-covered base vial.

26. Loosen the cover.

27. Quickly remove the cover and snap the upper vial onto the vial connector.

28. Number this vial 3.

29. What are the flies doing?

30. Where are most of the flies?

31. How can you explain this?

32. How many flies have gotten through the cellophane?

33. What is the cellophane doing?

34. Store your experiment for 2 days. Do not disturb.

B. RESULTS AND EXPLANATION

35. After 2 days, examine your vials.

36. Carefully observe the banana in vial 1. Describe what you see.

37. How has the banana changed?

38. Explain what you think caused this change.

39. Carefully observe the banana in vial 2. Describe what you see.

40. How has the banana changed?

41. How many flies go through the gauze?

42. What do you think caused the change in the banana?

43. Describe how you think this happened.

44. Carefully observe the banana in vial 3. Describe what you see.

45. How is the banana in vials 1 and 2 different from the banana in vial 3?

46. How can you explain this?

C. REDI'S RESULTS AND YOURS

The experiment conducted by Redi was very similar to the one you have just completed. One basic difference is that Redi used meat, whereas you used slices of banana. At the conclusion of Redi's experiment, maggots appeared on the meat in the open containers. No maggots appeared on the meat in the sealed containers. The results of this experiment presented strong evidence against the theory of spontaneous generation. From this, Redi formed his own theory. He suggested that all life originates from other living things.

47. How do your experimental results compare with those of Redi?

48. Based upon your results, what would you conclude?

Let's review your results to see if they support your conclusion.

49. How many maggots can you see on the banana in vial 1?

50. Where do you think these came from?

51. How many maggots can you see on the banana in vial 2?

52. Where do you think these came from?

53. How did they reach the banana?

54. How many maggots can you see on the banana in vial 3?

55. How can you explain this?

56. Based upon Redi's experiment, where do living things come from?

57. Based upon your experiment, where do living things come from?

Re-read your answers to Questions 56 and 57. State the concept.

CONCEPT

ENRICHMENT

1. Research and report on various theories which attempt to explain the origin of life on earth. In your opinion, which theory appears to present the most valid argument? Explain why.

2. Research and report on the work of Louis Pasteur. How were his experiments different from those performed by Redi? How did his work disprove the theory of spontaneous generation?

Investigation 2

One Form of Reproduction

It is not difficult to understand why the theory of spontaneous generation remained unchallenged for so long. During the Middle Ages most people were more hungry for food than for knowledge. They saw flies and maggots growing near decaying food. They thought that these living things came from the non-living material. People never made the whole connection between flies and maggots.

The findings of Francesco Redi were only the beginning of scientific awakening. Redi's discovery increased the curiosity of other scientists. Such people as Lazarro Spallanzani and Louis Pasteur were now probing the mysteries of life.

Each of these men studied **_bacteria_**, microscopic, one-celled plants, and the part these play in the process of decay. Using bacteria, these scientists also disproved the theory of spontaneous generation. It was now widely accepted that living things come from other living things.

A. MICROSCOPIC BOWLING PINS

The downfall of the theory of spontaneous generation raised many new questions. It also failed to answer some already existing ones. For example, the question of how life first originated on earth still remains unsolved. Scientists are still investigating this problem. Among the questions which were raised was how one living thing produces another.

Louis Pasteur   **Lazarro Spallanzani**

217

"Produce" means "to make." So "to make again" would be "to reproduce." That's what it's all about: *reproduction*. Organisms making more organisms. But making organisms of the *same kind*. Like people making more people. Or flies making more flies. In other words, organisms reproduce their own kind.

And how it all happens is the subject of this Investigation.

Within the several types of reproduction by living things, one process is shared by all — division. During all processes of reproduction, division of some kind takes place. You've worked with yeast before. Yeast cells are one-celled microscopic plants. Let's examine how the yeast cell reproduces.

1. **Get a jar containing yeast mixture.**

2. **Use your dropper. Place a drop of yeast mixture on a clean microscope slide.**

3. **Add a cover slip.**

4. **Examine the slide under low power with your microscope.**

5. **In Space A on your data sheet, draw some of the yeast cells.**

6. **What shape do most of the yeast cells have?**

7. **Examine the slide carefully. You may have to move it. Try to find a cell that looks like a bowling pin.**

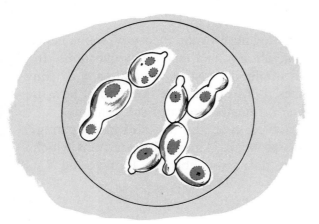

8. **In Space B, draw one of these cells.**

9. **How is this cell different from the ones you drew in Space A?**

Look at the cell you drew in Space B. The larger part of the cell is the parent cell. The smaller part is the new, developing organism. It is called a **bud. Budding** is a process by which yeast cells reproduce. During budding, the developing organism remains attached to the larger, parent cell. In time, the bud will separate from the parent cell completely. Budding in yeast is a form of reproduction in which the original cell divides or splits into two *unequal* sized cells.

10. **What is the new organism attached to?**

11. **In time, what happens to the bud?**

12. **By what process do yeast cells reproduce?**

Budding as a form of reproduction is limited not only to yeast. A complicated form of budding takes place in Hydra, a tiny water animal. During budding in Hydra, a small organism develops along the main body of the parent. In time, this organism will separate from the parent.

Carolina Biological Supply Co.

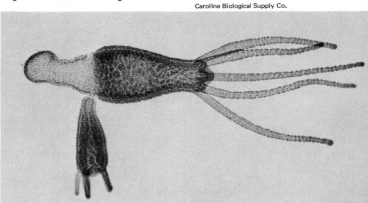

13. **How can reproduction take place in some living things?**

14. **How many parent cells are needed for reproduction in yeast?**

15. **How many organisms are needed for reproduction in Hydra?**

B. THE ORGANISMS ARE BREAKING UP

Budding is not the only process by which organisms reproduce. In Idea 3, you studied one-celled animals. Like other living things, they reproduce. A process by which ameba and paramecium reproduce is called **_binary fission_**. Study the following illustrations.

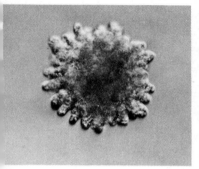
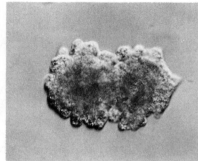

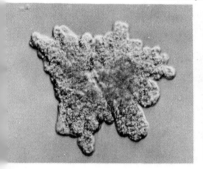
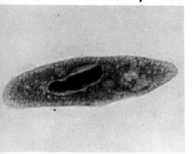

Carolina Biological Supply Co.

Binary Fission in Ameba

Binary Fission in Paramecium

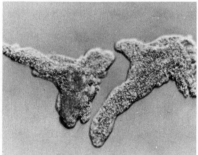
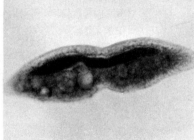

Carolina Biological Supply Co.

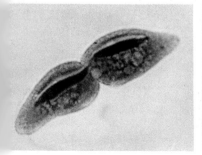
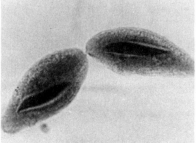

Binary fission is similar to budding in that cell division takes place. However, unlike budding, the parent cell divides or splits to produce two smaller cells of *equal* size. Each of these new cells is called a **_daughter cell_**. The daughter cells are about one-half the size of the original parent cell. In time, each of these daughter cells will grow and reproduce in the same way as the original parent cell.

16. **How is binary fission similar to budding?**

17. **How is binary fission different from budding?**

Binary fission represents a type of reproduction which takes place in many one-celled organisms. These organisms may be either plant or animal.

18. **How many parent cells are needed for reproduction during binary fission?**

19. **How many cells does the parent cell produce?**

20. **How are the daughter cells different from the parent cells?**

21. **How do the daughter cells compare with each other in size and shape?**

22. **In time, what happens to the daughter cells?**

23. **By what process do many one-celled organisms reproduce?**

C. CAN CELLS MULTIPLY?

As many-celled organisms carry on their life activities, cells that make up tissues normally wear out and die. Other cells may be injured. When you cut yourself, the cut heals. Cells that are injured, worn out, or dead are replaced. In many-celled organisms, the process by which most new cells are produced is called cell division or **_mitosis_**. Like binary fission, mitosis results in the formation of two new cells.

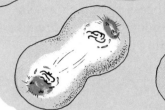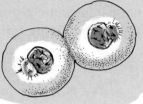

24. **By what process do cells reproduce in many-celled organisms?**

25. **How many parent cells are involved in this process?**

26. **How many new cells are produced?**

Steps in Animal Mitosis

D. AND NOW THERE ARE TWO

In this Investigation, you have studied several processes of reproduction. People raised many questions about these processes. The German scientist, Rudolf Virchow, encouraged many of these questions with the statement that cells must come from cells. The big question was *how*.

The Bettmann Archive, Inc.

The kind of reproduction in which there is only one cell or organism is known as *asexual reproduction*.

27. **By what process does reproduction take place in yeast cells?**

28. **By what process does reproduction take place in Hydra?**

29. **By what process does reproduction take place in many one-celled organisms?**

30. **By what process do most cells reproduce in many-celled organisms?**

31. **How many parent cells are involved in each of these processes?**

32. **What kind of reproduction are each of these examples of?**

33. **How do many cells and organisms reproduce?**

Re-read your answer to Question 33. Write the concept.

CONCEPT

ENRICHMENT

1. Research and report on several advantages and disadvantages of asexual reproduction.

2. Research and explain the meaning of *vegetative propagation*. Remove the eyes or buds from a white potato. Plant these in soil. Report on your results.

3. Research and report on the methods of reproduction in bacteria.

Investigation 3

A Special Kind of Reproduction

At times, there appear to be no limits to what an organism can do. An outstanding example of this is reproduction. In the last Investigation, you studied asexual reproduction. You learned that budding and binary fission are processes by which one-celled organisms reproduce. You also learned that mitosis is a process by which individual cells in many-celled organisms reproduce. There is still another aspect of asexual reproduction which is little understood. It can be observed, and even predicted; but much of what happens is still a mystery.

Carolina Biological Supply Co.

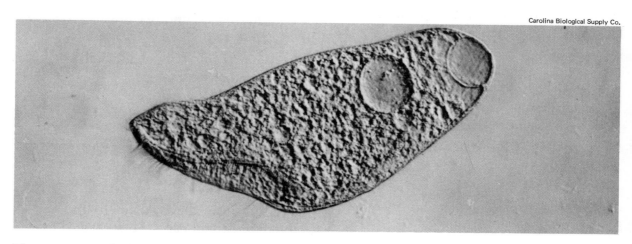

The structure, function, and organization of cells are outstanding cellular features. But there is evidence that cells and organisms are capable of more than what we might normally suspect. An example of this can be seen in Blepharisma.

Blepharisma is a one-celled animal. One of the interesting features of Blepharisma is its ability to replace injured parts. This can be demonstrated using a weak acid. Most acids are harmful to skin and other body tissues. When a weak acid is added to a microscope slide containing Blepharisma, the plasma membrane disappears. This is not surprising, since acids destroy tissues. But if fresh water is added, the acid is washed away and a new plasma membrane appears.

The ability of an organism to reproduce new parts is known as ***regeneration.*** A complex type of regeneration takes place in Planaria, a freshwater flatworm.

Carolina Biological Supply Co.

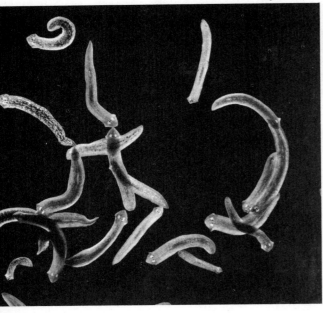

Experiments with Planaria have shown that different types of regeneration take place in this organism. The type of regeneration depends upon the way the organism is injured. For example, a Planaria cut like this,

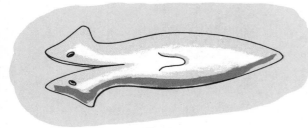

will regenerate two complete heads, one from each of the injured ones.

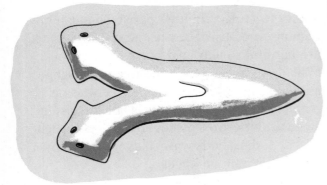

If cut this way,

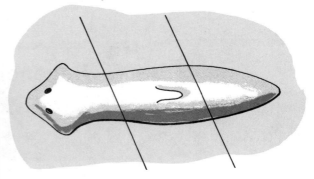

each section regenerates a complete new organism.

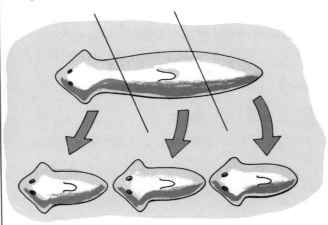

1. **What do certain organisms have the ability to do?**

2. **What is this type of asexual reproduction called?**

B. SKIN, SPONGES, AND STARFISH

Many organisms have the ability to reproduce certain parts. Some lizards have the ability to regenerate a lost tail. Many reptiles are able to regenerate lost teeth within several days. And snakes actually grow out of their old skin and into a new one.

What an organism can regenerate is often limited; and it appears that the more complex an organism is, the less is its power to do this. This is especially true in people. Once baby teeth have been replaced, there are no more. Skin cells are worn out and washed away daily, but new ones take their place. Even a cut heals itself; but much more than this is too much for the body to handle. Let's take a look at regeneration in some other living things.

Florida News Bureau

Did you know that a sponge is an animal? Sponges can even be grown and farmed. Sponge farmers cut large sponges into many small pieces. These pieces are then planted in shallow water. When the pieces grow large, they are harvested.

Carolina Biological Supply Co.

The starfish is another animal that has the capacity for regeneration; but, as with Planaria, it is a very special type. When one

of the arms of a starfish is removed, it can be replaced. Even more amazing is the fact that the arm itself can reproduce a complete new starfish.

Starfish feed on oysters. Many years ago, angry fishermen who caught starfish would cut them up. Then they threw them back into the sea. They thought this destroyed the animal.

3. **Based upon what you have just read, why was this an unwise thing to do?**

4. **What process allows some one-celled organisms to form a new plasma membrane?**

5. **How may regeneration take place in Planaria?**

6. **How does regeneration take place in some reptiles?**

7. **What process allows people to replace worn or damaged skin cells?**

8. **What is special about the types of regeneration that take place in starfish and Planaria?**

9. **What special kind of asexual reproduction have you studied in this Investigation?**

10. **What is regeneration?**

Re-read your answers to Questions 9 and 10. State the concept.

CONCEPT

ENRICHMENT

1. Define autonomy. How is this word used to describe regeneration?

2. Research and describe the processes involved in the healing of a wound. Include drawings.

3. Obtain a culture of Planaria. Design an experiment which illustrates the regenerative properties of this organism. Include accurate drawings in your research.

4. Research regeneration in lobsters and crabs. Explain how regeneration in these organisms may be considered protective.

5. Design an experiment which illustrates regeneration in a carrot.

Investigation 4

Getting Together

One of the most obvious features of reproduction is its results. In the case of asexual reproduction, the results may be two cells formed by the division of one. Asexual reproduction may also produce a complete, new, many-celled organism, as in the case of Hydra. No matter how simple a description of reproduction may be, the process involves a series of complex events. In some instances, it has taken many years to understand these events. Much has been learned through research and experimentation. Yet, there are still unsolved mysteries.

In spite of the complicated changes that take place, asexual reproduction is referred to as the simplest type of reproduction. Our planet is home for billions of organisms, each unique in its own way. With this diversity of life, you might think that there is an equal diversity in types of reproduction. However, this is not so. There are only two known types of reproduction. In the type you have already studied, the process is division. This is called asexual reproduction. In the type you are about to study, the process is one of joining. It is called ***sexual reproduction***. In sexual reproduction, two special reproductive cells join to produce a new organism. Sexual reproduction usually takes place in many-celled organisms.

By the way, you are a many-celled organism.

A. BUILDING A BRIDGE

Sex is the difference between male and female organisms. In people and in most other animals, it is not difficult to tell male from female. However, in plants this is not always the case. The sex of many plants is often difficult to determine. This is especially true in Spirogyra.

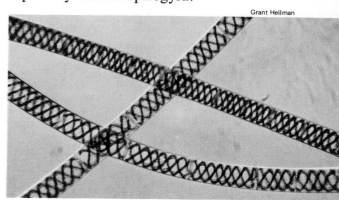

Grant Heilman

Spirogyra is a freshwater plant. During the summer, water in many ponds looks green. This is often due to the presence of Spirogyra. Spirogyra resembles long pieces of fine, green sewing thread. The cells of this plant are attached end to end, forming a thread.

Spirogyra reproduces sexually. Let's examine some pictures and see how this happens.

During the early stages of reproduction, two threads line up alongside one another.

1. **How are the threads arranged?**

2. **How are the cells in each thread arranged?**

In time, small projections begin to develop along the facing edges of each of the lined up cells.

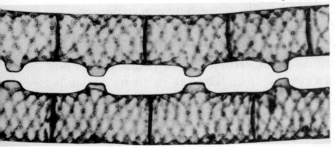

As these projections continue to grow outward, they meet, forming a bridge between each of the two cells. The walls separating each of the bridges dissolve, forming a continuous tube called a *conjugation tube*.

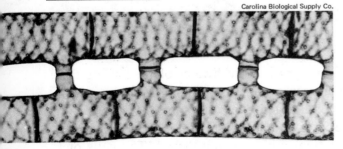

3. **What happens along the facing edges of each of the lined up cells?**

4. **What forms as these projections meet?**

The conjugation tube serves as a passageway. The cell contents of one cell, called the active cell, flow through the conjugation tube into the other cell, called the passive cell. Generally, all of the cells in one thread are either active or passive. This basic difference between active and passive cells is believed to be a sexual one.

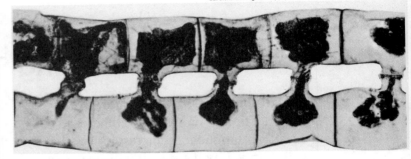

5. **What does the conjugation tube serve as?**

Active and passive cells in Spirogyra function as specialized reproductive cells. These special reproductive or sex cells are called *gametes*. When gametes join, the cytoplasm and nuclei of each cell combine. The result of combination is the formation of a *zygote*.

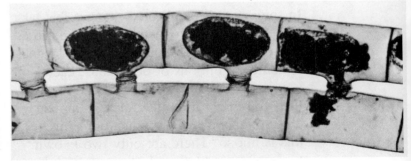

6. **What moves through the conjugation tube?**

7. **What occurs as a result of this movement?**

8. **What do active and passive cells in Spirogyra function as?**

9. **What are these cells called?**

10. What forms when gametes combine?

In time, the zygote develops into a new Spirogyra cell. This cell will divide several times to form a new thread. Then sexual reproduction will begin again.

11. How many parent cells are needed during sexual reproduction in Spirogyra?

12. How many new cells are formed during sexual reproduction?

Spirogyra is only one of many plants that reproduce sexually.

13. How may Spirogyra reproduce?

14. How do you think some plants reproduce?

B. THE MYSTERY OF HOMUNCULUS

Sexual reproduction in animals has been a subject of scientific study for more than 300 years. There is even evidence to suggest that the role of male and female reproductive cells may have been known thousands of years ago. However, it was not until 1676 that the first major discovery was made. Using the simple microscope made by Leeuwenhoek, a medical student discovered the male gamete, *sperm*.

Carolina Biological Supply Co.

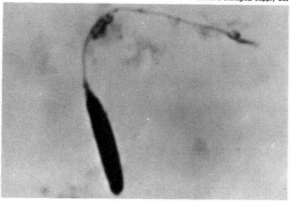

After its discovery, the role of the sperm cell was the center of confusion for more than 200 years. It was not until the 1880's that the sperm cell was actually observed joining with the female gamete, the *egg*.

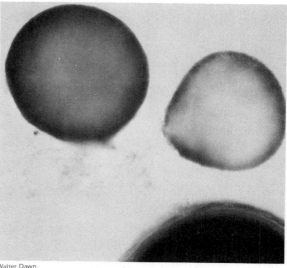

Walter Dawn

Beyond this, little was understood. Some explained the function of human sperm as containing a tiny human form, a *homunculus,* curled up inside it. In time, this miniature human was supposed to grow into a fully developed human being.

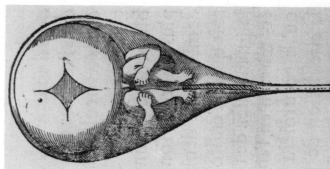

National Library of Medicine

Experiments with male and female plants and animals have led scientists to an understanding of the structure and function of gametes. Reproduction in fish represents the basic process of sexual reproduction involving gametes. Let's examine the process.

In one-celled organisms, different sexes are not found. There is no male. There is no female. This is not true in most many-celled organisms. Fish, frogs, dogs, horses, and people are examples of many-celled organisms. In each group, there is a male and a female. The male organism produces special reproductive cells, called sperm. Sperm cells are tiny and contain very little cytoplasm. The cell is composed of a head containing a large nucleus, and a tail which enables the cell to move.

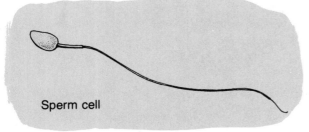

Sperm cell

Female organisms also produce special reproductive cells, called eggs. Egg cells are larger than sperm cells and are not able to move. They contain a nucleus, cytoplasm, and a food supply or *yolk*.

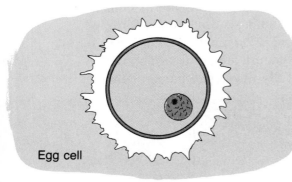

Egg cell

Sexual reproduction in fish usually begins when the female lays her eggs. In some fish, thousands or even millions of eggs may be dropped at one time.

The male fish swims over the eggs and deposits millions of sperm to cover them. Using their tails, the sperm cells approach the eggs.

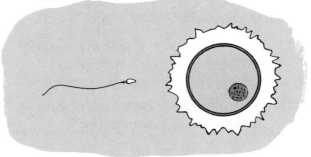

When a sperm cell enters an egg cell, the tail becomes detached and remains outside the egg. The nucleus of the sperm cell joins with the nucleus of the egg cell.

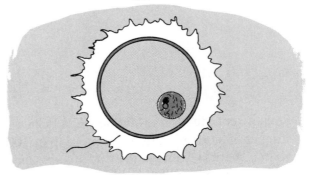

A thick, protective cover now forms around the cell. The function of this cover is to prevent the entrance of other sperm cells. The process whereby sperm and egg nuclei join is known as *fertilization*. The new cell formed as a result of fertilization is called a zygote.

15. **What happens to the tail of a sperm cell as it enters an egg?**

16. **What happens to the nucleus of a sperm cell as it enters an egg?**

17. **What is this process called?**

18. **What prevents other sperm from entering the egg?**

19. **What is a zygote?**

The zygote undergoes a series of rapid divisions which bring about many changes. Each division and change is a further development of the zygote toward the formation of the new organism. The developing organism is called an *embryo*.

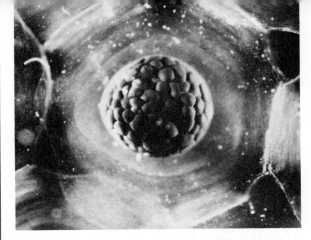

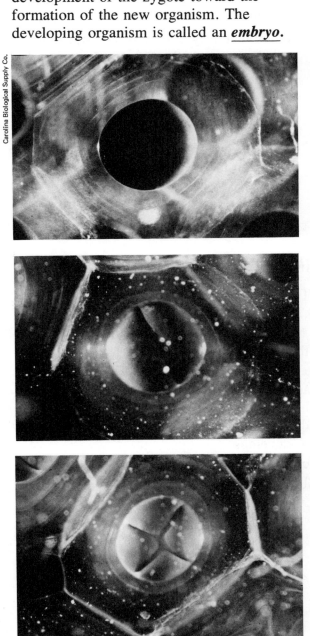

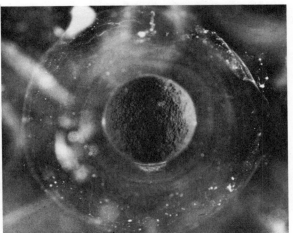

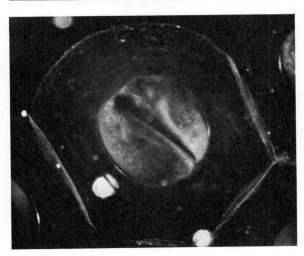

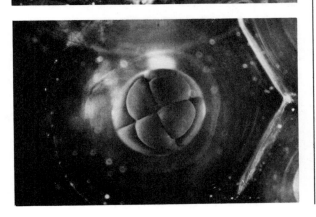

229

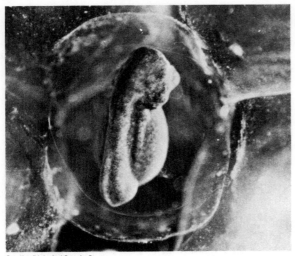

Carolina Biological Supply Co.

20. How many parent cells are needed during sexual reproduction in fish?

21. How many new cells are first formed during sexual reproduction?

22. How may fish reproduce?

23. How do you think many animals reproduce?

Re-read your answers to Questions 14 and 23. Write the concept.

CONCEPT

ENRICHMENT

1. Discuss the function of yolk for a developing embryo. Do all animal egg cells contain yolk? Explain.

2. Carefully examine frog eggs. Notice the jelly-like cover. What is its function? Are the eggs the same color throughout? How can you explain this?

3. What is an incubator? Make an incubator. Obtain some fertile chick eggs from a farm or hatchery and place these in the incubator. Wait at least three days. Carefully open an egg each day. Examine the embryo as it develops.

4. Explain why the eggs of different animals differ as they do.

5. What is an egg tooth? Do all animals have one? What is its function?

IDEA 7 Genetics

Investigation 5

Genes Are The Thing

The series of events which takes place during reproduction is not yet fully understood. This is especially true of the processes which occur after gametes combine. Some of the same questions that were asked more than 100 years ago are still being asked today. The development of the electron microscope has helped solve many mysteries, and many of the questions have been answered; but there is still much to learn.

Scientific learning may come about in many different ways. Observation is one of the most important single processes. It was just this process that led to the development of a new field of science more than 100 years ago.

For centuries people had observed that children look like their parents. That offspring resemble their parents is not only limited to people. It is true of all plants and animals.

Forsyth/Monkmeyer

arma/dpi

Grant Heilman

231

How and why offspring resemble their parents was not understood until the late 19th century. Two things were known, and from these would come the answer. First was that all organisms resemble their parents. Second was that only sperm and egg were responsible for the offspring. Can you make any predictions based upon this information?

A. GREGOR MENDEL'S PEA PLANTS

To help you make your predictions, it might be helpful first to make some careful observations. To do this, you will be given a package of dried peas.

1. **Carefully pour the peas on the table in front of you.**

2. **Examine the peas carefully. Try to identify as many differences as you can.**

3. **What differences do you notice in your pea seeds?**

4. **Compare your results with those of your classmates.**

5. **What differences did they find?**

6. **Enter your results in Table 1 on your data sheet.**

The differences, features, or characteristics of organisms are referred to as *traits*. You identified several traits for pea seeds.

7. **What traits did you identify? Refer to Table 1 if you need some help.**

All plants and animals have traits. Examples of traits in plants may be height, size, and shape of the leaves, or the color and odor of the flowers. Examples of traits in animals are body size and shape, the presence or absence of horns or antlers, and the type of fur an animal may have. Hair color, eye color, and the shapes of eyes, nose, and ears are examples of traits in people.

One of the first people to single out and study traits was an Austrian monk, Gregor Mendel.

Culver Pictures, Inc.

From his studies, Mendel concluded that traits are handed down from parent to offspring. The handing down or passing on of traits from parent to offspring is known as *heredity*. In other words, the traits of an offspring are inherited from its parents.

Genetics is the scientific study of heredity.

8. **List several examples of traits in plants.**

9. **List several examples of traits in animals.**

10. **List several traits in people.**

11. **Who was one of the first people to study traits?**

12. **From his studies, what did Mendel conclude?**

13. **What is heredity?**

14. **What is genetics?**

B. COLOR AT ITS BEST

The **work of Mendel** was not widely known for more than 25 years after his death. But during those 25 years, other scientists proved that Mendel's conclusions were valid. The focus of genetics now turned toward those factors which control heredity. It was known that sperm and egg combine to form a single cell. It was assumed that heredity was controlled by some factors within this cell. Let's see if you can determine what these factors might be.

You will be given two slides of onion root tip cells. One of the slides is marked ''N'' for normal; the other is marked ''D'' for dividing.

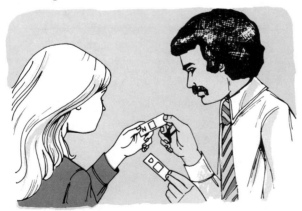

15. **Examine slide ''N'' under low power with your microscope.**

16. **In Space A, carefully draw what you see.**

17. **Identify and label the nucleus.**

18. **Describe the shape of the nucleus.**

19. **Examine slide ''D'' under low power.**

20. **In Space B, carefully draw what you see.**

21. **Identify and label the nucleus.**

22. **Describe the shape of the nucleus.**

The bands or chains that you have just described are called ***chromosomes***. Chromosomes are thread-like structures found in the nucleus of cells. When a cell is not dividing, the chromosomes are packed closely together and appear as a solid, rounded nucleus. However, as you have seen, they are most visible when a cell is dividing. During a cell division, the nucleus divides. Each daughter cell receives an equal number of chromosomes from the parent cell. In sexual reproduction, sperm and egg nuclei containing chromosomes join. Thus the zygote contains chromosomes from each parent. In 1903, Walter Sutton, a biologist, suggested that chromosomes contain the hereditary factors studied by Mendel.

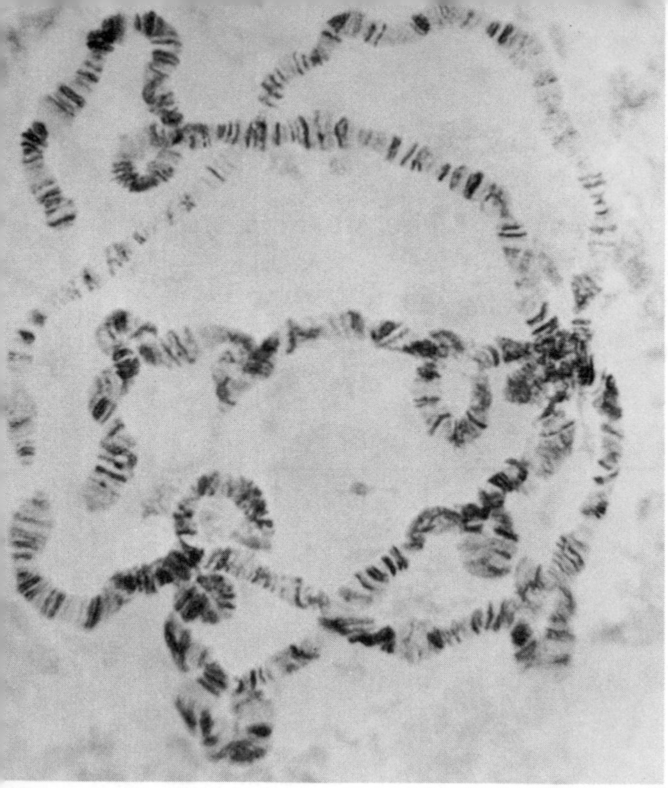

Carolina Biological Supply Co.

Fruit Fly Chromosomes

At first glance, chromosomes appear to resemble a coiled spring. However, photographs of chromosomes show them to be made of a series of dark colored bands called ***genes***.

Scientists Studying Human Chromosomes

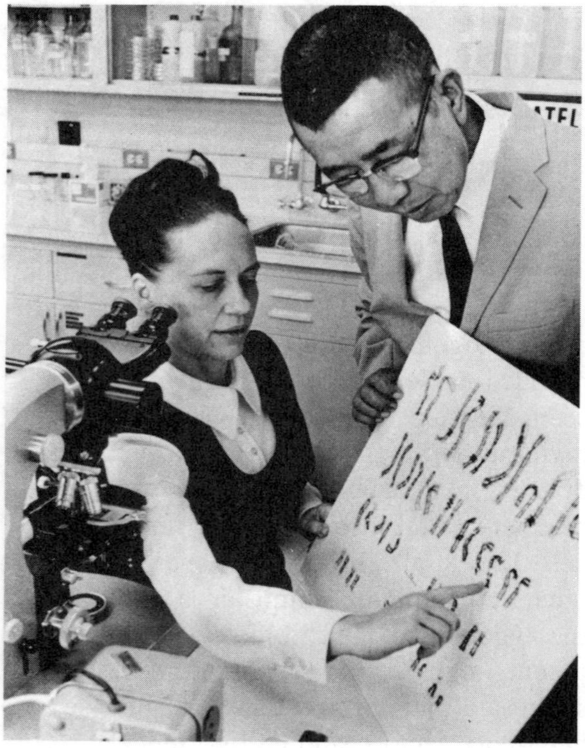

UPI

Scientists strongly believe that genes are the factors which control inherited traits.

Experiments have shown that genes occupy definite places on the chromosome; and that each gene controls a specific trait.

23. What are chromosomes?

24. How does a daughter cell receive its chromosomes?

25. Explain how a zygote receives its chromosomes.

26. What did Sutton's theory suggest?

27. What are these hereditary factors called?

28. What do genes control?

29. What is heredity?

30. What controls heredity?

Re-read your answers to Questions 28-30. Write the concept.

CONCEPT

WORDS TO KNOW

The following words have been used in this Idea. Carefully review the Idea and define each of them on your data sheet.

Asexual reproduction	Genetics
Bacteria	Heredity
Binary fission	Mitosis
Bud	Regeneration
Budding	Reproduction
Chromosome	Sexual reproduction
Conjugation tube	Sperm
Daughter cell	Spontaneous generation
Egg	Trait
Embryo	Yolk
Fertilization	Zygote
Gamete	
Gene	

SUMMARY OF THE IDEA: PROCESSES IN REPRODUCTION

Well done! You've pulled yourself through fire, water, air, and earth; you've climbed through mud and slime, and even up a goose tree or two. But you have survived and have completed still another Idea. This Idea has been about reproduction, its processes and results. Of all the life processes, reproduction is unique. It is the only life process which organisms do not have to carry on daily to stay alive. Yet, without reproduction, all life on earth would eventually end. Reproduction insures the continuation of life.

The origin of life on earth still puzzles scientists. The earliest recorded theories suggested that life and therefore living things took shape from air, earth, fire, and water. As ideas changed, so did theories; thus the theory of spontaneous generation. Mud, slime, hairs, and even trees were thought to be responsible for the existence of various animals. Then, in the late 1600's, Redi's experiments disproved the theory of spontaneous generation. Living things do not arise from nonliving matter. The new question then, was *how*.

The invention of the microscope helped answer many questions concerning the processes involved in reproduction. Soon division was identified as a process common to all types of reproduction. Thus, asexual reproduction was soon recognized as a simple type of reproduction. It involved the splitting of a cell to produce two cells. The discovery and observation of the behavior of sperm and egg enabled scientists to conclude that reproduction may also begin with the joining of two cells to form an organism.

One of the more outstanding features of reproduction is the similarity between parent and offspring. Attention was soon focused on why this occurred. Thus, the science of genetics, the study of inherited traits, came into being. The structure and function of genes and chromosomes have been the subjects of study for many years. Scientists believe that these factors hold the answers to many unsolved questions, including those involved in the processes of regeneration.

In this Idea on reproduction, you have studied five concepts.

1. **State these five concepts.**

2. **Redi was the first to disprove the theory of spontaneous generation. What did Redi conclude?**

3. **By what process are plants able to continue their own kind?**

4. **By what process are animals able to continue their own kind?**

5. **Why is it important for living things to reproduce?**

IDEA SUMMARY

ENRICHMENT

1. Research and report on the work performed by Mendel. Explain the meaning of dominant and recessive traits.
2. Prepare a list of traits that you share with one or both of your parents.
3. DNA molecules are considered to be the building blocks of genes. What is DNA? Who are James D. Watson, Francis C. Crick, and Rosalind Franklin?
4. Research and prepare a model of the structure of DNA.
5. Describe how sex is inherited in human beings.
6. Research and report on the work of Thomas Hunt Morgan.
7. How would you explain the fact that more men than women are color blind?
8. What is a chromosome map?

Investigation 1

Water and the Environment

In Idea 7 you studied how living things reproduce. Before living things reproduce, they must first grow. Growth and reproduction depend upon the conditions found in the ***environment***. The environment is defined as the surroundings of living things. These surroundings include physical factors such as light and temperature. The environment also includes biological factors such as the organisms that live in the environment. Both physical and biological factors determine how successful an organism is within any environment.

Cactus plants are found in the desert. The most important biological factors around

cactus plants are the desert animals that use them for water, food, and shade. The most important physical factor in the desert environment that affects **the cactus is the** scarcity of water. You will learn more about how a cactus survives in it's environment in Idea 9.

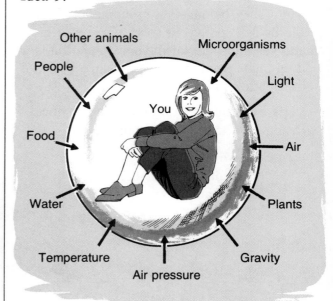

The environment is like a bubble surrounding you. Your surroundings include such physical factors as light, temperature, air, water, air pressure, and gravity. The biological factors include food, people, plants, other animals, and microorganisms you can't even see.

Van Campen/dpi

237

This Idea is about the environment. You will investigate how the factors in the environment affect living things.

A. A CONTROLLED MOLD

Grant Heilman

You have probably seen **molds**. They are small plants that grow on bread, cheese, or fruit. They belong to a group called **fungi**. Molds can spoil your food. They also give cheeses their special flavors. Penicillin is a drug made from molds; it can save your life by fighting infection.

Let's experiment with one of the physical factors in a mold's environment.

1. Get two jars. Label one jar "Control." Label the other "Experiment."

2. Place a small piece of bread in the control jar.

3. Place an equal size piece of bread in the experiment jar. Add 10 drops of water to it. Do not place any water in the control jar.

4. Give both jars to your teacher. Your teacher will shake a dusty rag over both jars to insure that mold falls on the bread. Both jars will then be sealed and stored for a few days.

5. This is a controlled experiment. What conditions were kept the *same* for both pieces of bread?

6. What is the only difference in how the bread was treated?

7. What physical factor in the mold's environment are you controlling?

Molds are like animals in that they cannot make their own food. They must grow on living or dead plants and animals. What they grow on decays into simple forms of matter. Organisms that cause decay are called **decomposers**.

Molds reproduce by *spores*. Spores are similar to seeds, but very much smaller. They consist of one or just a few cells surrounded by a thick, hard coat. Spores are very hardy. They can float around for years, waiting to fall on some suitable material. They can survive extreme heat, cold, and dryness.

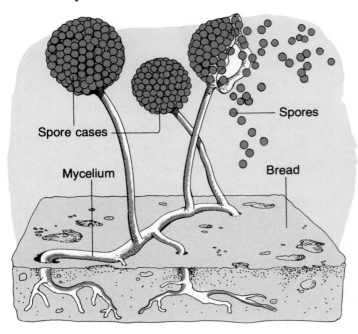

A typical mold is shown in the drawing. The fuzzy growth seen on moldy bread is made up of a tangle of threads called the *mycelium*. The mycelium grows into the bread. Certain threads extend upward and develop round bodies at the tip. The round bodies are spore cases inside which spores grow. The spores develop from protoplasm and several nuclei. They form tough cell walls and then burst free to drift in the air.

8. After a few days, examine both jars. Do not open them. Try to locate the spore cases and the mycelium.

9. What do you observe in the control jar?

10. What do you observe in the experiment jar?

11. How are the pieces of bread different?

12. What caused this difference?

13. Besides a source of food, what must the environment provide molds before they can grow?

14. What do you think happens to molds if the environment doesn't supply water?

15. What might happen to all living things if the environment didn't supply the water they need?

B. A SUBSTITUTE FOR WATER?

Ambler/National Audubon Society

You've found out that water is an important physical factor. Do you think there is a substitute for water?

16. Your teacher will give you a petri dish. It is divided into 4 parts.

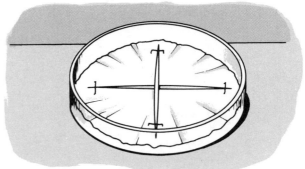

17. Label each part as shown.

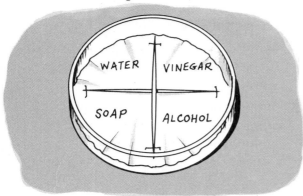

18. Wet the paper in the petri dish.

19. Get 5 water-soaked radish seeds. Place them in the part of the dish marked "Water."

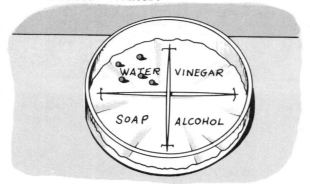

20. Use your forceps. Rinse off 5 vinegar-soaked seeds.

21. Place them in the part of the dish marked "Vinegar."

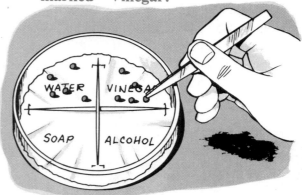

22. Rinse off 5 soap-soaked seeds. Place them in the part of the dish marked "Soap."

23. Rinse off 5 alcohol-soaked seeds. Place them in the part of the dish marked "Alcohol."

24. Cover the seeds with a wet paper towel circle.

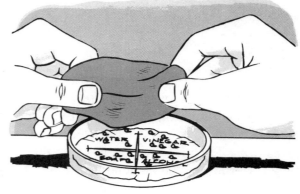

25. Cover and label your petri dish.

26. Store your experiment for a few days.

27. **What were the four environments of your seeds?**

28. **Which seeds do you predict will not grow?**

29. **Which seeds do you predict will grow? Explain your answer.**

30. After a few days, examine your seeds.

31. **What happened to the vinegar-soaked seeds?**

32. **What happened to the soap-soaked seeds?**

240

33. **What happened to the alcohol-soaked seeds?**

34. **What happened to the water-soaked seeds?**

35. **Suppose you had placed 5 dry seeds in a dry petri dish. What would have happened and why?**

36. **What must the environment provide seeds before they can grow?**

37. **What must molds, seeds, and all living things obtain from their environment?**

C. DRINKING IT ALL

Myers/Black Star

38. **Why do you think these animals are here?**

Massar/Black Star

39. **Why do you think nothing has grown here?**

Bernheim/Woodfin Camp & Assoc.

40. **Why do you think this scientist is testing the village water supply?**

Water is an essential physical factor in the environment of all living things. From the environment must come the water that makes up most of the protoplasm of cells. The life activities of circulation, excretion, respiration, and photosynthesis would be impossible without water. Inside your own body water must carry food, air, and waste materials. Water helps digest your food, lubricate your joints, and keep you cool.

41. Besides the ways listed on page 241, how else do you use water?

42. What must the environment supply for molds, seeds, and people?

43. What factor in the environment can affect all living things?

CONCEPT

ENRICHMENT

1. Grow a mold garden. Place various foods such as fruits, cheese, crackers, cereal, and baby food into a disposable container. Expose to the air for a few hours. Add some water and cover with a sheet of clear plastic. Examine after a few days. CAUTION! For safety's sake, inspect your molds through the plastic. Let your teacher dispose of the container for you.

2. Set up a controlled experiment using different brands of bread. Find out which bread gets moldy the soonest.

3. Slime molds are molds that can move. Try to obtain and grow some slime molds.

4. Find out whether insects prefer a damp or a dry environment. Place some insects in a box where one side is damp and the other dry.

5. Make a display of the many ways people use water.

Investigation 2

Environmental Temperature

In the last Investigation you studied how living things are affected by water in the environment. Water is only one of the physical factors in the environment. Another important physical factor is temperature.

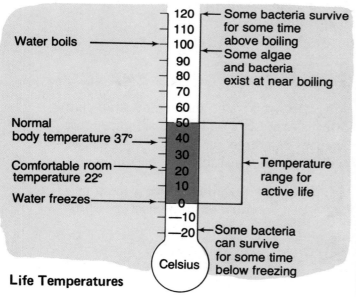

Life Temperatures

120 — Some bacteria survive for some time above boiling
110
100 — Water boils
90 — Some algae and bacteria exist at near boiling
80
70
60
50
40 — Normal body temperature 37°
30
20 — Comfortable room temperature 22°
10
0 — Water freezes
—10
—20 — Some bacteria can survive for some time below freezing

Celsius

Temperature range for active life

Temperatures in our solar system can range from millions of degrees to 250 degrees below zero Celsius. Here on earth the temperature can range from 80°C in the desert to -88°C in the Antarctic. Generally, life on earth is limited to temperatures between -1°C and 50°C. These liveable temperatures can be found over most of the earth's surface and beneath the oceans.

Plants such as corn die when the temperature falls much below freezing. Some plants, such as pine trees, can withstand temporary temperatures well below freezing. Some bacteria can exist for long periods of time at temperatures well above boiling or well below freezing. Active animals must have temperatures between -1°C and 50°C if they are to survive.

DO YOU KNOW...?
LIVING THINGS CANNOT STAND TOO MUCH HEAT.
THEY CANNOT STAND TOO MUCH COLD.
THEY CAN ONLY LIVE WITHIN A NARROW TEMPERATURE RANGE.

You are different from other active animals. You can protect yourself from temperature extremes by the use of proper clothing and shelter. You are also ***warm-blooded***. This means that your body can keep a constant temperature of 37°C regardless of the environmental temperature. You can maintain the same temperature whether you are at the Equator or the South Pole. You share being warm-blooded with mammals and birds. Fish and lizards, on the other hand, are **_cold-blooded_**. This means that they take on the temperature of their environment.

Let's investigate how fish respond to environmental temperature changes.

A. GILL MOVEMENTS

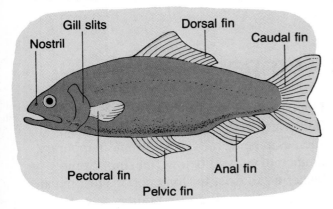

Nostril
Gill slits
Dorsal fin
Caudal fin
Pectoral fin
Pelvic fin
Anal fin

1. Get a jar of water containing a fish.
2. Use the diagram to help you identify the various parts of your fish.
3. Observe the gill slits of your fish.
4. **What are the gill slits doing?**

Fish breathe through **_gills_**. Water moves into the mouth and out through the gill slits. The gills of a fish are like your lungs. Your lungs take oxygen from the air you breathe. A fish's gills take oxygen from the water.

You are going to count the number of gill movements of your fish. You will count for one minute. The number of gill movements in one minute is the breathing rate. Your fish will be moving, so watch closely.

5. Read the temperature of the water. Enter this temperature in Table 1 on your data sheet.
6. Count the number of gill movements of your fish. Remember to count for 1 minute. Enter this count in Table 1.
7. Gently place 2 ice cubes in the water.

8. Wait 2 minutes. Read the temperature. Enter it in Table 1.
9. Count the number of gill movements in 1 minute. Enter this in Table 1.
10. **What was the breathing rate of your fish in water with no ice cubes?**
11. **What was the breathing rate of your fish after ice cubes were added?**
12. **How much did the water temperature change?**
13. **How much did the breathing rate of your fish change?**
14. **What change in the fish's environment caused the breathing rate to slow down?**
15. **What do you predict would happen to a fish's breathing rate if you warmed, instead of cooled, the water?**
16. **Besides water, what physical factor in the environment might affect living things?**

B. DO YEAST CELLS CHANGE?

In Part A, you found that temperature can affect a fish. Let's find out what temperature changes can do to yeast cells. Your teacher will give you a test tube of yeast mixture.

17. **Use your dropper. Place a drop of yeast mixture on a microscope slide.**

18. Add a cover slip.
19. Examine the yeast cells under low power with your microscope.
20. **What color are the yeast cells?**

21. Add 5 drops of red dye to the yeast mixture.

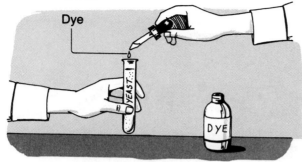

Dye

DYE

YEAST

22. Shake the tube gently.

YEAST

23. Rinse your dropper. Place a drop of the red yeast mixture on a slide.

24. Add a cover slip.

25. Examine the mixture under low power.

26. **What color are the yeast cells?**

27. **What color is the water around the yeast cells?**

THINK ABOUT...

IN YOUR HOUSE, YOU CAN OPEN AND CLOSE THE DOOR. YOU CAN CONTROL WHO COMES IN.

CAN A CELL DO THE SAME THING? CAN IT CONTROL WHAT MATERIALS COME IN?

IF YOU ARE NOT HOME, SOMEONE CAN BREAK IN.

IF THE CELL IS DEAD, CAN ANYTHING BREAK IN?

You have learned that materials diffuse in and out through the cell membrane. Does this mean *anything* can move into and out of the cell?

28. Use your test tube holder. Heat the mixture of yeast and dye until it begins to bubble.

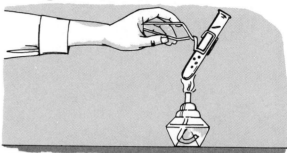

CAUTION! REMEMBER TO USE SAFETY GOGGLES

29. Rinse your dropper. Place a drop of mixture on a slide.

30. Add a cover slip.

31. Examine under low power.

32. **What color is the water around the yeast cells?**

33. **What color are the yeast cells?**

34. **What color were the yeast cells before heating?**

The red dye is an unwanted material. As long as the yeast is alive, its cell membrane can keep the red dye out. When the cell dies, materials are free to enter it..

35. **What is the job of the cell membrane?**

36. **What was able to pass through the cell membrane after the yeast cells were heated?**

37. What did the boiling temperatures do to the yeast cells?

38. What might extreme temperatures do to living things?

C. WHAT'S THE TEMPERATURE?

Henderson/Rapho-Guillumette

Stouffer Productions, Ltd./Bruce Coleman, Inc.

Life does exist on earth despite wide temperature variations. These temperature variations, however, affect all living things. You've discovered how temperature changes affect fish and yeast cells.

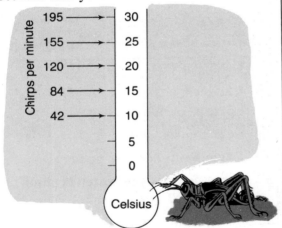

Chirps per minute	Celsius
195 →	30
155 →	25
120 →	20
84 →	15
42 →	10
	5
	0

Temperature vs. Cricket Chirps per Minute

Temperature changes can even affect how crickets chirp. Next time you hear a cricket, count the chirps in one minute and compare the rate to this scale. For example, at 15°C a cricket will chirp about 84 times a minute.

Some animals hibernate when the temperature falls too low. This bear will sleep during much of the winter. During its sleep, the bear's fat reserves are slowly used up. The fat is burned to provide the body heat needed to stay alive.

39. How do temperature changes affect crickets?

40. What do bears do during the cold winter?

41. Explain the difference between warm-blooded and cold-blooded animals.

42. What happens to the breathing rate of fish when their water environment gets colder?

43. Explain how boiling temperatures can kill yeast cells.

44. Besides water, what physical factor can affect all living things?

CONCEPT

ENRICHMENT

1. How are plants affected by temperature extremes? Set up controlled experiments to find out.
2. Do other animals, besides bears, hibernate? Report your findings to the class.

Investigation 3

Light and Survival

You've learned that water and temperature are two environmental factors that affect life. Light is another physical factor that can determine the survival of living things.

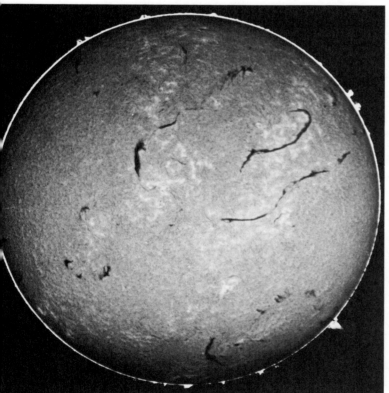

High Altitude Observatory, Boulder, CO

This is a close-up view of our sun. From the sun comes the heat energy that warms the earth. From the sun comes the light energy that makes it possible for plants to carry on

photosynthesis. With few exceptions, sunlight is the ultimate source of all the energy that we use on earth. Coal, oil, and gas all started out millions of years ago as sunlight energy trapped by plants. Even the energy from this morning's breakfast came indirectly from sunlight. The cereal may have come from wheat that ripened in sunlight. The milk came from a cow that ate grass that grew in the sunlight. The egg came from a chicken that was fed corn that grew in the sun. The orange came from a tree that drew its energy from sunlight. Can you think of something you ate that cannot be traced back to sunlight energy?

A. TRAPPING SUNLIGHT

1. **Get 2 thermometers and 2 envelopes from your teacher.**

Notice that one envelope is made from white paper. The other is made from dark green paper. The green color is similar to the green color of leaves that capture sunlight.

2. **Read the temperature of one of your thermometers. Slip it into the white envelope. Record the temperature in Table 1 as "Beginning Temperature."**

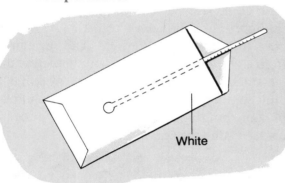

White

3. **Read the temperature of the other thermometer. Slip it into the green envelope. Record the temperature in Table 1.**

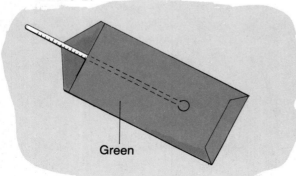

Green

4. **Place both envelopes outside so that they receive equal amounts of sunlight. If there is no sun, you can place them under a lamp.**

5. **Wait 12 minutes. After 12 minutes, read the temperatures of both thermometers. Record them in Table 1 as "Final Temperature."**

6. **Subtract the "Starting" from the "Final" temperature for each and record as "Change in Temperature."**

7. **Which thermometer had the greatest increase in temperature?**

8. **What was the only difference in how the thermometers were treated?**

Sunlight is a form of energy. As you have learned, sunlight energy can be converted to food energy during photosynthesis. Sunlight can also be converted directly into heat energy. When you stand in the sun, you can feel the light warming your body. In this experiment, you have exposed a light and a dark material to the sun. Now you should know which converts the most light to heat.

9. **Which envelope must have absorbed the most light energy?**

10. **Which envelope must have converted the most light energy into heat?**

11. **Based upon this experiment, do you think light or dark colored objects convert more light to heat? Explain your answer.**

Leonard Lee Rue/Bruce Coleman, Inc.

The roadrunner is a bird that is found in the deserts of the western United States. In deserts the days are very hot and the nights are very cold. Just like you, all birds are warm-blooded. Scientists wondered how the roadrunners managed to maintain their constant body temperature in the desert environment. As they observed roadrunners they found one of the answers. Early every morning, roadrunners stand with their backs to the sun. Their feathers are ruffled up to expose the skin on their backs. The back skin is black.

12. Explain how roadrunners warm themselves on cold mornings.

The desert sunlight can help roadrunners, snakes, and lizards keep warm. The light from the sun can affect the height and shape of trees in a forest. The sunlight that penetrates the ocean can affect the kinds of life that live at each depth. Sunlight can even affect where you go on your vacation.

13. What is the source of most of the energy on earth?

14. Do light or dark objects convert more sunlight to heat?

15. Besides water and temperature, what physical factor can affect how plants grow?

16. What environmental factor can affect living things?

B. WATER AND LIGHT

Most of the photosynthesis in the world is carried on by ocean plants. Let's find out how a water plant is affected by environmental light conditions.

17. Get two test tubes. Label one tube "Light" and the other "Dark."

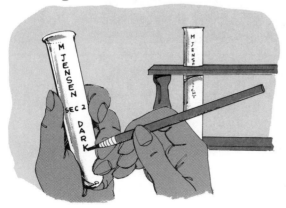

18. Fill both tubes 2/3-full with bromthymol yellow. As you know, bromthymol yellow shows the presence of carbon dioxide. If carbon dioxide is removed, it turns blue.

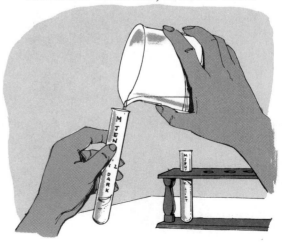

19. **Place a piece of Elodea in each tube. The pieces should be the same size.**

20. **Stopper both tubes.**

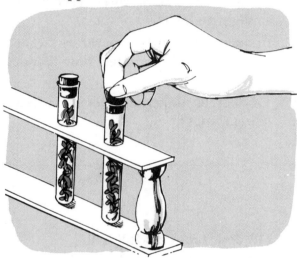

21. **Give the "Dark" tube to your teacher for storage.**

22. **Place the "Light" tube under a strong light.**

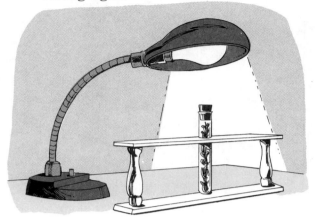

23. **Wait 1 day. After 1 day, observe both tubes.**

24. **What is the only difference in the environment of the two pieces of Elodea?**

25. **What color is the liquid in the "Dark" tube? Explain what this means.**

26. **What color is the liquid in the "Light" tube? Explain what this means.**

THINK ABOUT...
THE ELODEA IN LIGHT MUST HAVE TAKEN IN CARBON DIOXIDE.
AND THE CARBON DIOXIDE TURNED BROMTHYMOL BLUE.

27. **What physical factor must be present if Elodea is to carry on photosynthesis and take in carbon dioxide?**

28. **What physical factor can affect plants?**

29. **What factor in the environment might affect living things?**

C. LIGHT AND ANIMAL BEHAVIOR

Light conditions in the environment affect living things in many ways. The moth's attraction to light may cause it harm.

Some plants turn to face the sun as it moves in the sky. The bending and growth of a green plant toward light is called *phototropism*. A tree adjusting its leaves so that each leaf gets the maximum sunlight is an example of phototropism.

Rue/Monkmeyer

The owl is a *nocturnal* animal. Nocturnal animals are normally active during the night.

The migration of Canadian geese to the south in winter is triggered by the amount of daylight. Some plants will not bloom until they get over 12 hours of light each day. Even many of your habits and activities are determined by the absence or presence of light.

30. In what ways are you affected by light?

31. Why is an owl called a nocturnal animal?

32. A sunflower turns slowly to face the sun. Why is this an example of a phototropism?

33. What environmental factor can affect Elodea?

34. Water and temperature are two physical factors in the environment. What is a third factor in the environment?

35. What factor in the environment might affect living things?

CONCEPT

ENRICHMENT

1. Grow radish seeds in darkness and in light. Compare them after four days to see the effect of lack of light.
2. Construct a simple plant maze to find if a young plant can find its way toward light.
3. The length of time that light falls on an organism can regulate its life activities. This is called *photoperiodism*. Research the subject and report your findings back to the class.
4. Can sunlight heat water? Paint a soda pop can black. Fill it half full of water. Check the water temperature before and after placing it in the sun.
5. Solar energy is being captured directly in many devices. Research some of these devices and try to build a model of one.

Investigation 4

The Food Supply

You've learned that water, temperature, and light can affect life. These ancient people are hunting for something else in their environment. They, and all other living things, must find a source of food to survive.

Our hunters may have lived in 8000 B.C. At that time there were only 5 *million* people estimated to be on earth. The number of people, or the number of any organism, is called the **_population_**. The population of the earth is now about 4 *billion* people. By the year 2000, the population may be 5½ *billion*.

TABLE **1** WORLD POPULATION

Year	Population in Millions
8,000 B.C.	5
1 A.D.	250
1650	1,000
1930	2,000
1960	3,000
1975	4,000
2000	5,500 (estimated)

Every minute about 235 more people are born. In that same minute, only about 95 people die. This adds up to 75 million more people added to the earth's population each year. Finding food to feed this growing population is one of the world's most serious problems. It is estimated that 20 million people starve each year. And millions more barely survive in a weak and unhealthy condition.

The food supply available can limit the size of the human population. It can also influence the size of the population of all living organisms. Let's find out how the food supply can affect bacteria and mold populations.

A. BACTERIAL GROWTH

1. **Your teacher will give you 2 petri dishes. Do not open them.**

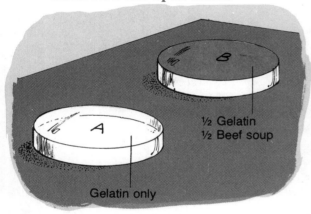

½ Gelatin
½ Beef soup

Gelatin only

These dishes are marked A and B. Dish A contains gelatin which has little or no food value. Dish B contains about half gelatin and half beef soup. Beef soup has much food value. You will try to grow bacteria and molds in each dish.

2. **Label each dish. Open them both.**

3. **Press a finger gently in the center of Dish A.**

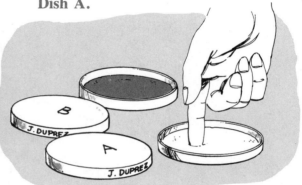

4. **Press a *different* finger in the center of Dish B.**

5. **Place a little saliva near the edge of each dish.**

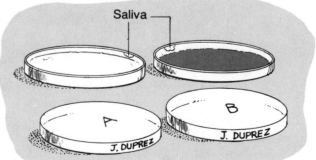

Saliva

6. **Sprinkle dust over both open dishes.**

7. Cover your dishes and tape them shut. Give them both to your teacher for 2 or 3 days' storage.

THINK ABOUT...
BACTERIA AND MOLDS MUST BE EVERYWHERE. HOW DO YOU KNOW THEY ARE THERE IF YOU CANNOT SEE THEM?

PERHAPS YOU CAN SEE THEM AFTER THEY GROW IN PETRI DISHES.

8. What two kinds of organisms are you trying to grow?

9. What is the only difference between the two dishes?

10. Which dish do you predict will have the greatest population of organisms? Explain your prediction.

You studied molds in the first Investigation of this Idea. Besides molds, you will be observing bacteria on your dishes. You can't actually see individual bacteria with your unaided eye. Some are so small it would take 10,000 of them to line up across one centimeter. What you will see are spots containing millions of bacteria. Each spot is called a *colony*. The number of bacteria in any one colony is its population.

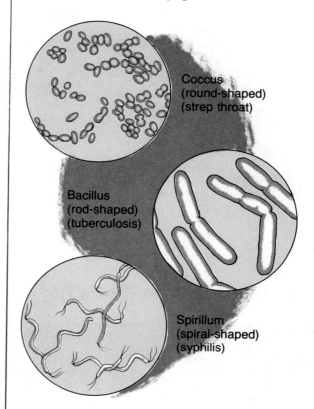

Coccus (round-shaped) (strep throat)

Bacillus (rod-shaped) (tuberculosis)

Spirillum (spiral-shaped) (syphilis)

Individual bacteria are found in the three general shapes shown in the drawing. Most bacteria are harmless. Some are even helpful as decomposers because they decay dead matter into rich soil. Some bacteria are harmful and can cause diseases in people and other living things. These harmful bacteria are called *pathogenic*.

Bacteria have cell membranes and cell walls. Some have slime layers around the cell walls. They do not have a nucleus, but they do contain the hereditary material needed for cell division. Reproduction for most bacteria involves simply splitting into two cells. The splitting in two can take less than thirty minutes when conditions are right.

When observing bacteria colonies, look for differences in color, size, shape, and texture. Your mold colonies will have a fuzzy look due to the mycelium. Bacteria colonies generally have a smooth, shiny surface.

11. Get your petri dishes. *Do not open them*. Make all your observations with the dishes closed.

12. What do you observe in Dish A?

13. What do you observe in Dish B?

14. Which dish had more growth?

15. Which dish had more food?

16. Each colony is a population of millions of organisms. Which dish had the greater population? Why?

17. What do populations of bacteria and molds need to grow?

18. What is needed to support large human populations?

19. What do populations of living things need for growth?

B. PROTEIN AND GROWTH

Nancy Palmer

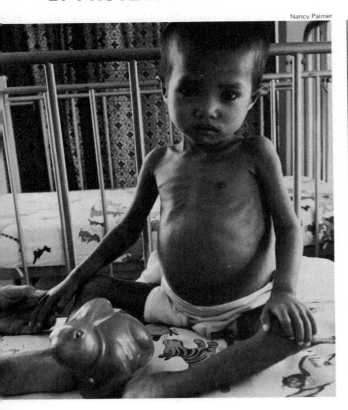

This child is sick. He has a disease common in some less developed countries that are overpopulated. His diet consists mainly of starch. Starch foods can give you energy, but you need another kind of food to help you grow. The kind of food that builds strong muscles and helps you grow is called **_protein_**. If this child could obtain protein foods, he might grow normally.

But didn't you just study that the more food, the more population? Perhaps certain foods are better for population growth?

You've already learned how to test food for starch and sugar. Now let's test food for protein.

20. Pour a small amount of water into a test tube.

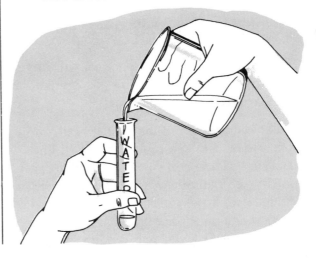

21. **Pour an equal amount of milk into another test tube.**

22. **Add 4 drops of protein test solution A to each tube.**

23. **Add 5 drops of protein test solution B to each tube.**

24. **What change did you observe with the water?**

25. **What change did you observe with the milk?**

The violet color shows that protein is present. If the violet color does not appear, protein is not present. Now try some other foods.

26. **Pour a little egg white into a test tube.**

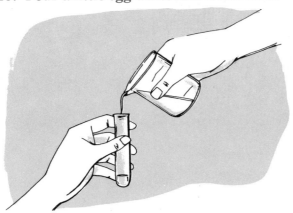

27. **Add 4 drops of protein test solution A. Then add 5 drops of protein test solution B.**

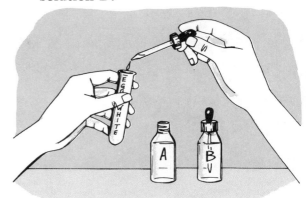

28. **What change do you observe?**

29. **What type of food is in egg white?**

30. **If time permits, test other foods for protein. All the foods should be in liquid form.**

31. **Besides milk and eggs, what foods did you find that contain protein?**

32. **Why is protein necessary for your body?**

33. **What is missing in the diet of the sick child on page 256?**

34. **What could happen to populations of people that do not get enough protein food?**

35. **What might happen to populations of organisms that do not get enough food?**

C. FEEDING MORE POPULATIONS

The earth's population cannot continue to grow unless the food supply increases. Many new ways have been discovered to increase the food supply. New varieties of wheat and rice have been developed to provide triple the grain of the old varieties. Imitation meat with high protein value has been made from easily grown soy beans. A product called

FPC (for fish protein concentrate) is being made from fish. FPC powder is 81% protein, is cheap, and can be added to enrich various foods.

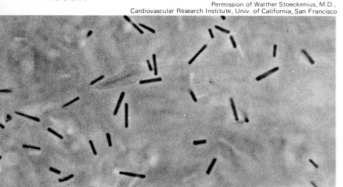

Halobacteria, 1850 X

These organisms are a special kind of bacteria called *halobacteria*. Halobacteria are unique. Unlike other bacteria, they can make their own food. They contain a purple pigment which uses sunlight energy to make food. Without the chlorophyll that green plants have, halobacteria still carry on a process similar to photosynthesis. It is possible that they may be used to help relieve the world's food shortage.

36. **Why is FPC an important food product?**
37. **What can halobacteria do that other bacteria cannot?**
38. **What is needed if the earth is to support a growing population?**
39. **How did the amount of food affect your bacteria and mold populations?**
40. **What do populations of living things need to grow?**
41. **What factor can influence the size of a population?**

CONCEPT

ENRICHMENT

1. Plant 5 seeds in a small planter. Plant 50 seeds in another planter of equal size. Find out what happens to the population of seedlings when they are crowded.
2. Fertilizer is like protein to a plant. Try a controlled experiment, growing one plant with and one plant without fertilizer.
3. Human populations need vitamins as well as proteins. Find out how to test foods for vitamins.
4. Make a display of protein foods.
5. One bacterial cell can reproduce and become two in ½ hour. If the bacteria kept reproducing at the same rate, how large a bacteria population would you have at the end of 5 hours?

Investigation 5

Change in the Environment

Jeff Foott, Bruce Coleman, Inc.

Pro Pix/Monkmeyer   Leonard Lee Rue/Bruce Coleman, Inc.

Tidal creatures undergo rapid environmental changes. Some environmental changes are seasonal. This snowshoe rabbit changes colors as the environment changes. How do you think the snowshoe rabbit's color change helps it to survive?

This oil drilling rig is in the frozen north of Alaska. Oil was made millions of years ago by tiny organisms that lived in warm tropical

Bojilova/dpi

These organisms live where the ocean meets the land. Their environment is constantly changing. Every few minutes they are battered by a wave. About every 12 hours they go through a cycle of high and low tides. The high tide may submerge them, while the low tide can leave them exposed to the air. The water, temperature, light, and food factors in their environment are not constant.

oceans bathed in sunlight. North Alaska must once have had a warm, tropical climate. The oil is evidence that over millions of years the Alaskan enviornment has changed.

From moment to moment, from day to day, and from season to season, the environment is changing. These changes can affect paramecia, plants, polar bears, and people.

A. RAINFALL

Werner Stoy/Camera Hawaii/dpi

This mountain environment is in Hawaii. Over 1200 centimeters of rain may fall here each year. That is about 8 times your height.

This desert environment is in Death Valley, California. Only about 10 centimeters of rain fall here each year.

Frank/Rapho-Guillumette

Study Table 1. It shows the monthly rainfall (or snowfall) in New York City for a recent year.

TABLE 1 MONTHLY RAINFALL (OR SNOWFALL) IN NEW YORK CITY

Month	Rainfall In Cm
January	2.8
February	7.9
March	9.4
April	10.2
May	6.9
June	8.1
July	18.8
August	6.4
September	21.1
October	5.1
November	9.1
December	18.0

1. **Which month had the most rain?**

2. **How much rain fell in that month?**

3. **Which month had the least rain?**

4. **How much rain fell in that month?**

5. **How much difference in rainfall was there between the wettest and the driest months? (Subtract your answer to Question 4 from your answer to Question 2.)**

6. **How many months had exactly the same amount of rain?**

7. **The spring months are March, April, and May. How much rain fell during the the spring?**

8. **The summer months are June, July, and August. How much rain fell during the summer?**

9. **How much difference in rainfall was there between summer and spring? (Subtract your answer to Question 7 from your answer to Question 8.)**

10. **What factor in an environment can change from season to season?**

11. **What can you say about the amount of rain in any one environment?**

260

B. TEMPERATURE

The amount of rainfall in an environment isn't the only thing that can change. Study Table 2. It shows the average monthly temperature in Los Angeles for a recent year.

TABLE 2 AVERAGE MONTHLY TEMP-ERATURE IN LOS ANGELES

Month	Average Temperature °C
January	14
February	16
March	16
April	16
May	19
June	21
July	23
August	24
September	22
October	20
November	17
December	13

12. **Which month had the highest average temperature?**

13. **What was the average temperature for that month?**

14. **Which month had the lowest average temperature?**

15. **What was the average temperature for that month?**

16. **What was the difference in average temperature between the hottest and coldest months? (Subtract your answer to Question 15 from your answer to Question 13.)**

17. **How many months had the same average temperature?**

18. **Besides rain, what factor in the environment can change from month to month?**

Study Table 3. It shows the highest daily temperature in Chicago for one month.

TABLE 3 HIGHEST DAILY TEMPERA-TURE IN CHICAGO DURING JULY OF A RECENT YEAR

July	Highest Temperature °C	July	Highest Temperature °C
1	29	17	24
2	27	18	28
3	32	19	22
4	35	20	28
5	30	21	30
6	31	22	32
7	33	23	27
8	30	24	26
9	26	25	29
10	27	26	22
11	22	27	24
12	30	28	24
13	33	29	22
14	28	30	20
15	29	31	23
16	33		

19. **Which date had the highest temperature?**

20. **What was the temperature on that date?**

21. **Which date had the lowest temperature?**

22. **What was the temperature on that date?**

23. **How much difference in temperature was there between these two dates? (Subtract your answer to Question 22 from your answer to Question 20.)**

24. **How many dates had the same 30° temperature?**

25. **What factor in the environment can change from day to day?**

26. **What can you conclude about the temperature in any one environment?**

C. DOES EVERYTHING CHANGE?

You can be sure that the environment will change. These changes will affect you and all other living things. Living things themselves cause environmental changes. A growing oak tree may change the light conditions for the plants beneath it. A gopher digging its holes may change the soil environment for earthworms. A beaver dam may affect the supply of water available downstream. People cause most environmental changes. Some of those changes have endangered the survival of over 600 different kinds of warm-blooded animals. Millions of passenger pigeons once thrived in America. When people cut down their forest environment, they died out.

27. **This is the same tree in summer and winter. What environmental changes could have caused these differences?**

28. **How can a tree affect its environment?**

29. **How do people cause environmental change?**

30. **What can you conclude about the amount of rain in any one environment?**

31. **What can you conclude about the temperature in any one environment?**

32. **What can you conclude about all the physical and biological factors in an environment?**

33. **What is constantly happening to the environment?**

CONCEPT

Grant Heilman

Grant Heilman

ENRICHMENT

1. Make a display of local and national weather maps.
2. Set up a weather station. Collect daily data on temperature, humidity, and air pressure.
3. Take the outdoor temperature each day at the same time and place. Display your daily results to the class in a data table.
4. Collect and display pictures of animals and plants whose appearances change with the seasons.

Investigation 6

Where on Earth Is Life?

NASA

This is the earth as seen from space. Earth is the environment for billions of organisms. Living things must obtain water and food from this environment. They need proper light and temperature conditions. They must find protection from harmful environmental changes.

No trace of life has been discovered on any other planet. The environments on other planets do not seem to have what living things need.

Can life exist everywhere on the earth?

Parker/National Audubon Society

A. THE BIOSPHERE

The *biosphere* is a thin layer of life around the earth. We find life only in the biosphere. Conditions are not right for life above and below the biosphere.

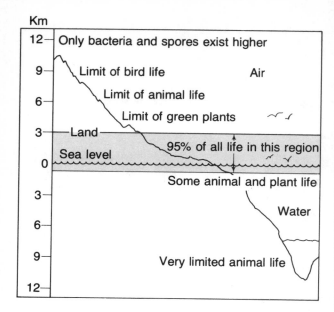

Km
12 — Only bacteria and spores exist higher
9 — Limit of bird life   Air
6 — Limit of animal life
        Limit of green plants
3 — Land
      Sea level   95% of all life in this region
0
                          Some animal and plant life
3
                                              Water
6
9
                          Very limited animal life
12

William H. Amos

This hatchet fish can live many kilometers below the ocean surface. It feeds on dead materials that fall from above. Very few fish can live at these great depths. The deep environment cannot supply their needs.

1. **What part of the ocean supports the most life?**

2. **Why isn't there much life deep in the ocean?**

Burpee/dpi

Few plants grow high in the mountains.

3. **What factors in a mountain environment might affect plant growth?**

4. **If few plants grow on mountain tops, how would this affect animal life?**

5. **Why are most birds found close to the earth's surface?**

6. **How high above sea level does the biosphere extend? (See the biosphere chart for help.)**

7. **How far below the sea surface does the biosphere extend?**

8. **Why wouldn't you expect to find much life at the upper and lower limits of the biosphere?**

9. **What is the narrow band of life around the earth called?**

Ninety-five out of 100 organisms on the earth live in the shaded area. This extends just three kilometers above sea level. It reaches only 90 meters below the water's surface.

A few organisms can be found higher than three kilometers. Birds have been spotted at eight kilometers. Some bacteria have been found eleven kilometers above sea level. Some spiders survive high on mountain tops.

Most fish are found just below the water's surface. They are dependent upon plants for food. Plants cannot get enough light to exist beyond 90 meters depth.

This strange looking creature was photographed 5 km deep in the ocean. It looks like a plant but it is actually an animal. The food-gathering tentacles are at the end of a meter-long stem.

Walter H. John /NORDA

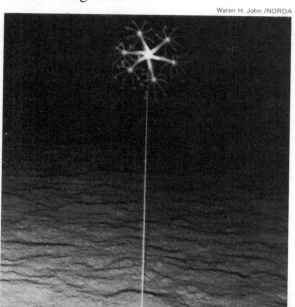

B. LIFE IN THE BIOSPHERE

There are many unfriendly environments in our biosphere. Some are in hot, dry deserts. Some are near the frigid North and South Poles.

Information Canada Phototeque

William Mares/Monkmeyer

Few people live in the Sahara Desert. It is an environment with little water. The days are hot and the nights cold. Hot winds may blow sand for hours and even days.

The Bedouins survive by leading a wandering life. They move their camels from oasis to oasis in search of water. The camels supply them with food, clothing, and transportation.

A camel can go over 30 days without water. Camels don't sweat much. They can use their own tissues for water when needed. The camel's hump is made of fatty tissue which serves as stored food. Their eyes and noses have special protection against sandstorms. Their feet are protected from the sand by heavy pads. Few other animals could survive in this part of the biosphere.

Only a few Eskimos live in the far north. Their part of the biosphere is very cold. They live in darkness for months at a time. A tree is a rarity in their environment.

Eskimos are short and stocky. This shape helps them retain their body heat. Tall thin people would have trouble surviving cold climates. Eskimos eat fatty foods which build up fatty tissue under their skin. The fat layer also helps keep them warm.

Penguins are birds that swim but do not fly. They live in the frigid environment of the Antarctic. Thick layers of fat under their skin protect them from the cold. So do their oily, waterproof feathers.

Like all birds, penguins lay eggs. Eggs normally wouldn't hatch in this cold part of the biosphere. Penguins solve the problem by placing the eggs on their feet. Then they cover the eggs with their fat bellies.

dpi

265

10. **Besides Eskimos and penguins, what animals might you find in a very cold environment?**

11. **Besides Bedouins and camels, what animals might you find in a desert environment?**

12. **Why are there few living things near the North Pole?**

13. **Why are there few living things in the desert parts of the biosphere?**

Camels could not live at the North Pole.

Penguins could not survive in the desert. Only people seem to be able to exist throughout the biosphere.

14. **Why are there so few organisms living near the North Pole?**

15. **Why are there so few organisms living in the Sahara Desert?**

16. **What must the biosphere provide for living things?**

17. **What is the biosphere?**

C. DIFFERENT ENVIRONMENTS

Environments are not all the same. The amount of light, heat, water, and food changes from place to place.

It would be difficult to change the environment of Eskimos and camels. It should be easy to change the environment of pond creatures, though.

18. **Place a few drops of pond water on a slide. Do not use a cover slip.**

19. **Examine your slide under low power with the microscope.**

20. **Describe what you see.**

21. **Remove the slide. Place it on the table. Allow the pond water on this slide to dry out. You'll view it again later.**

22. **Place 2 full droppers of pond water in a small test tube.**

23. **Your teacher will heat it gently over a flame.**

24. **Place the heated pond water on a fresh slide. Add a cover slip and examine under the microscope.**

25. **Describe what you see.**

26. **What factor has changed for this pond life?**

27. **What effect did raising the temperature have on pond life?**

28. **What would you predict very hot temperatures might do to living things?**

29. **Get some frozen pond water from your teacher. It was frozen overnight and then melted.**

30. **Place a few drops of this pond water on a slide. Use a clean dropper. Add a cover slip and examine under the microscope.**

31. **Describe what you see.**

32. **What factor has changed for this pond life?**

33. **What effect did lowering the temperature have on pond life?**

34. **What do you predict very cold temperatures might do to living things?**

35. **Using your microscope, examine the dried pond water from Step 21.**

36. **Describe what you see.**

37. **What factor has changed for this pond life?**

38. **What effect did lack of water have on pond life?**

39. **What would you predict lack of water would do to living things?**

40. **What kinds of environments might harm or destroy living things?**

41. **Why aren't many living things found outside of the biosphere?**

D. WRAPPING UP THE BIOSPHERE

Here's what the environment looks like on the moon. There is no water, no air, and no food. The nights are as long as two of our weeks on earth. These moon nights are very dark and very cold. Life cannot exist on the moon without water, food, air, light, and proper temperatures.

NASA

42. **Why wouldn't you expect to find a biosphere on the moon?**

43. **What liquid that life requires is missing on the moon?**

44. **How would a plant be affected by two weeks of darkness?**

45. **How would living things be affected by two weeks of below freezing temperatures?**

46. **Why wouldn't you expect to find food on the moon?**

47. **What factors are found in the earth's environment that make life possible?**

48. **What are the surroundings of living things called?**

49. **What is the narrow band of life around the earth called?**

Re-read Questions 41 and 49. State the concept.

CONCEPT

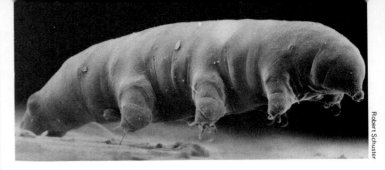

Robert Schuster

The following words have been used in this Idea. Carefully review the Idea and define each of them on your data sheet.

Biosphere	Mycelium
Cold-blooded	Nocturnal
Colony	Phototropism
Decomposer	Population
Environment	Protein
Fungi	Spore
Gill	Warm-blooded
Mold	

SUMMARY OF THE IDEA: FACTORS IN THE ENVIRONMENT

Living things are surrounded by certain conditions of life. Some are physical factors and some depend upon the presence of other living things. Together, these factors make up the environment. The environment of an organism must provide all the conditions necessary to maintain life.

The environment sets limits for the growth, development, and reproduction of living things. The food and water available set certain limits. Some limits are set by the temperature and light conditions. Still other limits are set by the populations of organisms in the environment that may compete for the food or light available. Within any particular environment, many factors work together to make survival possible.

The biosphere is a narrow band around the earth in which life exists. Most life is found toward the center of the biosphere, just above the land surface and just below the water surface. There is some life at the fringes of the biosphere which has adjusted to the physical and biological factors present there.

Here's our Tardigrade again. It's less than 1 millimeter in size. It lives in the same biosphere that you do. Yet Tardigrades can survive environmental factors that will kill practically all other organisms. When conditions are not right, Tardigrades can go into a form of hibernation. They have been known to remain in an inactive state for as long as 120 years.

Tardigrades can tolerate temperatures that range from way below freezing to way above boiling. They can be dried until they lost 85% of their body water. They can be placed in a high vacuum and exposed to atomic radiation. They can even be kept in an environment with no oxygen. Yet they can survive all these extreme physical factors and return to an active life.

In this Idea on the environment, you have studied six concepts.

1. **State these six concepts.**
2. **What are some of the extreme physical factors that Tardigrades can survive?**
3. **What are some of the physical factors in the environment of a fish?**
4. **What are some of the biological factors in the environment of a fish?**
5. **What do organisms depend upon the environment for?**
6. **Define the environment.**

Re-read this section. Then summarize the entire Idea.

IDEA SUMMARY

ENRICHMENT

1. Give a class report on polar bears, seals, penguins, or Eskimos.
2. Build a model of a moon city or a South Pole Base.

Investigation 1

Things Change

Scientists have many reasons to believe that the environment is constantly changing. These changes take place in a variety of ways; and all parts of the environment, both living and non-living, are affected. Time is a part of all changes. Sometimes the changes are slow. They may take place over thousands or even millions of years. What may once have been this,

Dr. Edward J. Kormondy

may in time change and become this.

Dr. Edward J. Kormondy

But all changes are not slow. Sometimes they are sudden.

Bill Males/National Severe Storms Laboratory, NOAA

269

While some changes may last for long periods of time,

Davis/dpi

others may last for only a short time.

THINK ABOUT...
HOW THE ENVIRONMENT CHANGES.
WHAT HAPPENS TO THE ORGANISMS LIVING THERE?
THEY MANAGE TO STAY ALIVE.
MAYBE SOME OF THEM CHANGE WITH THE ENVIRONMENT.

Many organisms do change with the environment. Sometimes these changes are simple and quick. Other times, the changes are complex and take a long time. But change is the important thing. Organisms must be able to sense changes. They must also be able to adjust to these changes. Life may depend upon adjustment. In this Investigation, you will study some simple changes in organisms. You will first set the stage, then you will create the change and observe the response.

A. DANCING SHRIMP?

J.A.L. Cooke/Bruce Coleman, Inc.

Brine shrimp are tiny, salt water animals that respond to light in an interesting way. Your teacher will give you a covered bottle containing brine shrimp. Do not uncover the bottle until you are ready to begin your experiment. You are going to study how these animals behave in dim and in bright light. To do this, you must begin your experiment with the room as dark as possible.

1. Light a candle and melt the bottom into one half of a petri dish. The candle will help you observe the shrimp.

2. Place the candle about 60 cm from the covered bottle.

3. Uncover the bottle of shrimp.

4. Slowly move the candle closer to the bottle. Stop when there is just enough light for you to see the shrimp.

5. Study the movements of the shrimp.

6. **What are the shrimp doing?**

7. **In what direction are the shrimp moving?**

8. **Move your hand up and down very slowly between the bottle and the candle. What happens?**

9. Carefully move the candle to the other side of the bottle. Do not move the candle closer to the bottle.

10. **What are the shrimp doing?**

11. **In which direction are the shrimp moving?**

12. **Did the shrimp respond quickly? Explain.**

13. Cover your bottle of shrimp.

14. Store the shrimp in a dark place. Do not disturb for one day.

B. WATCH THIS STEP

The room will be made dark again.

15. Uncover the bottle of shrimp.

16. Place your flashlight against one side of the bottle. Switch it on.

17. Study the movements of the shrimp in the beam of light.

18. **In which direction are the shrimp moving?**

19. **After a while, where are most of the shrimp?**

20. **Why do you think this happens?**

21. Turn off the flashlight for about 3 minutes.

22. **After 3 minutes, explain the response of the shrimp to the absence of light.**

23. Shine your flashlight into the bottle from the top.

24. **How do the shrimp respond?**

25. **Why do you think the shrimp respond as they did?**

26. What change did you make in the environment of the shrimp?

27. How do you know that the shrimp were able to sense this change in their environment?

28. In your opinion, was the adjustment of the shrimp a slow one or a rapid one?

29. How did the shrimp adjust to the change in their environment?

C. A CHANGE FOR THE BETTER

Shrimp are not the only organisms that can adjust to changes in the environment. Many organisms can do this, including you.

In Idea 2, you learned that the eye responds to changes in the environment. This response is another example of adjustments that organisms make as their environment changes.

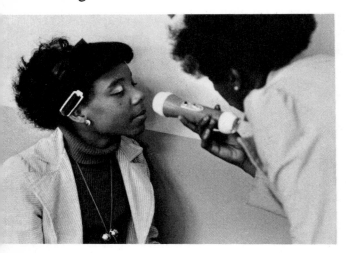

30. What happened to the iris in the experiment you did in Idea 2?

31. What change in the environment caused this adjustment?

32. Was the adjustment a slow one or a rapid one?

33. What is always happening to the environment?

34. What adjustment do brine shrimp make to light changes in their environment?

35. What adjustment do your eyes make to light changes in the environment?

When you are hot, you perspire. Perspiring helps your body cool off. This is an adjustment to heat. When you are cold, you shiver. Shivering helps keep your body warm. This is another adjustment. Your body constantly adjusts to changes in the environment.

36. What does your body do as the environment changes?

37. What do you think most organisms do when their environment changes?

Re-read your answers to Questions 29, 36, and 37. Write the concept.

CONCEPT

ENRICHMENT

1. Repeat your experiment with the brine shrimp. Substitute a tuning fork for the light. Touch the base of a vibrating tuning fork to the bottle. How do the shrimp respond to the vibrations?

2. Repeat your experiment using an assortment of colored filters. How do the shrimp respond to different colored lights?

3. Prepare a bulletin board display illustrating sense receptors in a variety of organisms.

4. Research and report on the sense receptors on the skin of sharks.

Investigation 2

A Self-Regulating Machine

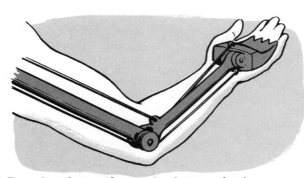

People often refer to the human body as an amazing machine. If you think about it, it is not difficult to understand why. The brain is more complex than any computer. And you don't have to call a service person every few weeks to check it out.

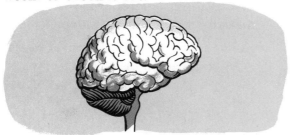

Leo deWys, Inc.

What about the heart? Think about how many times this amazing pump works over a lifetime.

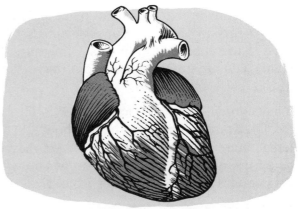

Masterflex is a reg. tm. of Cole Parmer Instrument Co., Chicago, Ill.

It rests only between beats. There are many kilometers of tubes that carry blood and other body fluids. No company can offer a guarantee to match the heart's performance.

The eye functions like a camera. Muscles burn fuels and move bones. Special cells in the nose and tongue allow you to smell and taste. And there's so much more. But you get the idea. The body is truly an amazing machine.

In the last Investigation, you learned that organisms can adjust to changes in the environment. You have seen how quickly the eye adjusts to changes in light. You have also seen how quickly shrimp adjust to light. These adjustments to changes in the environment are important. They work to protect the organism.

A. WHAT'S YOUR TEMPERATURE?

The adjustments that organisms make are not always easy to see. Sometimes scientists have to use special instruments to measure them. You are going to use one of these instruments now.

Your normal body temperature is 98.6°F (37°C). Some people may have a body temperature that is a bit higher; others may be a bit lower. What happens to your body temperature when the weather is cold?

What happens to your body temperature when the weather is hot?

Does your body adjust to temperature changes in the environment? Does your body temperature change when the temperature of the environment changes? Can you make a prediction?

Be patient and perform each of the following Steps carefully. You will use two different kinds of thermometers. Your teacher will review how to use each.

Work in groups of four for this experiment. One student will be the subject. One student will take the subject's oral body temperature. The third student will take the water temperature. And the last student will record the data.

1. **Which thermometer will you use to measure body temperature?**

2. **Which thermometer will you use to measure water temperature?**

3. Fill a large container with cold water. Add ice. The colder the better.

274

4. Take the body temperature of the subject. Enter your data in Table 1 on your data sheet.

5. Take the temperature of the ice water. Record this in Table 1.

B. TAKE A DIP

Now that you have recorded the body temperature of the subject and the temperature of the ice water, it's time to test your prediction.

6. The subject should place as much of one hand and arm as possible into the water.

7. Place the oral thermometer in the subject's mouth.

8. **What time is it now?**

9. **What time will it be 4 minutes from now?**

10. After 4 minutes, the subject should remove the hand and arm from the water. Dry the arm.

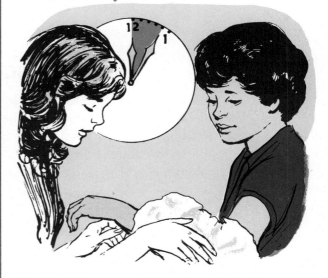

11. **Feel the arm. How does it feel?**

12. Read the subject's body temperature. Record the temperature in Table 1.

13. Take the temperature of the water. Record this in Table 1.

C. KEEPING STEADY

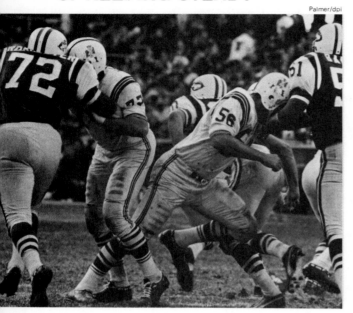

Palmer/dpi

Keeping a steady inside environment is not always easy, especially when the outside environment changes. But that amazing machine of yours can do many things. Just look at your experimental results.

14. What was the subject's body temperature at the start of the experiment?

15. What was the subject's body temperature at the end of the experiment?

16. How much did the subject's body temperature change?

17. What was the temperature of the water throughout the experiment?

18. What effect did this have on the subject's arm?

19. What effect did this have on the subject's body temperature?

20. What do you think happens to the inside body temperature in people when the outside temperature changes?

21. Why do you think this is important?

22. From your experiment, what do you predict *some* organisms do when the outside environment changes?

Re-read your answers to Questions 20 and 22. Write the concept.

CONCEPT

ENRICHMENT

1. Repeat your experiment. This time, take the skin temperature of the subject in addition to the other temperature readings. How does the skin temperature compare with the body and water temperatures? Explain.

2. What is a thermostat? Upon what principle does it operate? Compare the function of a thermostat to what you have learned in this Investigation.

3. Prepare a report on Claude Bernard and homeostasis.

4. What is an enzyme? How is the work of an enzyme affected by temperature changes?

5. Explain why either mercury or colored alcohol is used in thermometers when colored water is less costly.

6. How and why does sweating affect skin temperature? Experiment by allowing such liquids as water, alcohol, and acetone to evaporate on your arm. Explain your results.

Investigation 3

Seeing Is Believing

Courtesy of the American Museum of Natural History

Plants and animals have existed on earth for millions of years. Although there are no written records to prove this, there is much other evidence to suggest that this is the case. You will study some of this evidence in Investigation 4.

Throughout the earth's history, many changes have taken place in the environment. Some of these changes may affect the amount of rainfall. Thus, some environments are wet,

while others may be dry.

Schlecker/dpi

Other environmental changes may affect temperature. Thus, some environments are hot,

Frank/dpi

Wells/dpi

while others are extremely cold.

With all these changes, life goes on. In one way or another, most living things manage to survive. An interesting question is, *how?* You will examine this question in this Investigation.

A. THE DEEP FREEZE

In the last Investigation, you learned that some organisms keep a steady inside environment when the outside environment changes. As you might imagine, this is not so with all living things. We can use body temperature to illustrate this again.

Van Campen/dpi

Looking at a lake such as this may suggest many things. The water at the top is frozen; the water beneath is icy cold. How could anything survive in this freezing environment? Yet, there is life in the

freezing waters beneath the ice. The lake is a home for frogs, fish, and salamanders. These organisms are cold-blooded; they are able to adjust to temperature changes around them. If the temperature in the lake drops, the body temperature of these organisms decreases. In summer, when the lake becomes warm, the body temperature of these organisms increases.

In desert regions, there are dramatic temperature differences from day to night. During the day, temperatures may rise to over 40°C. At night, the temperature can drop below freezing. The body temperature of some desert lizards can rise to more than 35°C in the sun and drop to almost 0°C at night. That's a temperature change of about 35 degrees. In people, if body temperature rises or falls more than 3 or 4 degrees, we may die.

1. **How do people react to temperature changes in the environment?**

2. How do frogs, fish, and salamanders react to temperature changes in their environment?

3. What happens to the inside environment of some desert lizards as the outside environment changes?

4. What can happen to the inside environment of some organisms as the outside environment changes?

B. COUNTING HEARTBEATS

Your teacher will give you a jar containing water and Daphnia, a water flea.

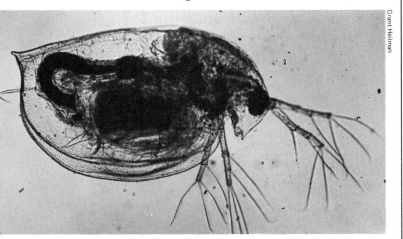

Daphnia are small water organisms. They belong to the same group of animals as shrimp and lobsters. Daphnia are interesting little animals because you can see through them.

5. With your dropper, place a Daphnia on a clean microscope slide.

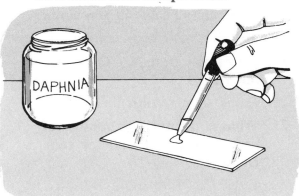

6. Place a small amount of cotton on the water drop. This will keep the Daphnia from moving around too much.

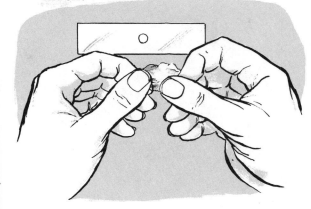

7. Gently add a cover slip. Try not to injure the Daphnia.

8. Use a paper towel. Blot away any water that seeps out from under the cover slip.

9. Focus under low power with your microscope.

10. Find the Daphnia's heart. It is just behind the eye.

The heartbeat rate of Daphnia is very rapid. This makes it very difficult to count. You can use pencil and paper to help you.

Use a sharp pencil and work on a hard surface. You will have to set up a rhythm of pencil tapping. This means you will use your pencil to tap on a piece of paper. You must tap at the same rate as the Daphnia's heartbeat. After you have counted and tapped for 15 seconds, all you have to do is count the pencil marks. It will be easier to count your marks if you make them in a straight line. Practice this several times before going on to Step 11.

You may want to cut down the amount of light on your slide. This will help you see better. It will also cut down the amount of heat.

11. Count the number of heartbeats in 15 seconds.

12. **How many beats did you count?**

13. Multiply your answer by 4. This will give you the number of heartbeats in 1 minute.

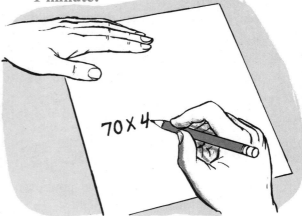

14. **How many beats are there in 1 minute?**

15. Write this number in Table 1 on your data sheet.

16. Count the number of heartbeats in another 15 seconds.

17. **How many beats did you count?**

18. Multiply your answer by 4.

19. **How many beats are there in 1 minute?**

20. Enter your data in Table 1.

21. **What is the average number of heartbeats per minute for your Daphnia?**

22. Enter this number in Table 1.

C. SLOWING IT DOWN

Your teacher will give you a bottle containing a liquid that will change the Daphnia's environment. Make sure that the liquid moves under the cover slip. The results may amaze you.

23. **Use a clean dropper. Place a drop of the liquid at the edge of the cover slip.**

24. **Wait at least 20 seconds.**

25. Count the number of heartbeats in 15 seconds. Use the same tapping system as before.

26. Multiply the number by 4.

27. **How many beats are there in 1 minute?**

28. Enter your data in Table 1.

29. Count the number of heartbeats in another 15 seconds.

30. Multiply your answer by 4.

31. **How many beats are there in 1 minute?**

32. Enter your data in Table 1.

33. **What is the average number of heartbeats per minute for your Daphnia?**

34. Enter this number in Table 1.

D. WHAT DOES IT MEAN?

In many instances, survival depends upon the ability of organisms to adjust to changes in the environment. In this Investigation, you have studied adjustment of body temperature and heartbeat rate. In each instance, organisms adjusted to changes in the outside environment.

35. **Look at Table 1. What was the average heartbeat rate of your Daphnia in water?**

36. **What was the average heartbeat after you added the liquid?**

37. **What is the difference in average heartbeats?**

38. **What do you think caused this change?**

39. **What happened to the Daphnia's inside environment when the outside environment changed?**

40. What happens to the inside environment of cold-blooded animals when the outside environment changes?

41. What do you think happens to the inside environment of some organisms when the outside environment changes?

Re-read your answers to Questions 4 and 41. Write the concept.

CONCEPT

ENRICHMENT

1. Repeat the experiment you did in this Investigation. Use other liquids, such as dilute alcohol or vinegar.
2. Some newborn babies are placed into an incubator. Report on how and why the incubator is used to control the environment.
3. Heating systems are used to warm homes. Research and report on some of the ways that people are able to change their environment.
4. Insecticides are substances used to control insect pests. Explain why insecticides can lose their effect in controlling certain insects.
5. Many animals hibernate during winter months. What is hibernation? How does hibernation help animals conserve energy during the cold winter months of the year?
6. Before Olympic competition at high altitudes, athletes often spend several weeks in training at these altitudes. What is the purpose of this?
7. Adrenalin is a chemical substance produced in the body. Where is adrenalin produced? What effect does it have on the inside environment? Why is this important?

Investigation 4

Footprints in the Sands of Time

The origin and diversity of life is one of the great mysteries of science. For millions and millions of years, organisms have been living and dying on and under the surface of the earth. A similar cycle of life and death has also been taking place in the earth's waters. The story of early life cannot be found in any books. There are no written words or pictures to describe it; yet scientists have an understanding of the story.

Thousands of bits and pieces are added to the story each year. These bits and pieces are uncovered in mines,

at building sites,

283

by scuba divers,

and by people digging in their backyards.

The bits and pieces are fossils. *Fossils* are the remains or evidence of plants and animals that lived millions of years ago. The story they tell is one of change.

A. HOW FOSSILS FORM

Most organisms are eaten by other organisms. Many organisms may die a natural death and are then eaten, or they decay. Under the proper conditions, a small number are preserved as fossils. Of this small number, only a few are actually discovered. Let's examine some of the conditions necessary for fossil formation.

Your teacher will give you two petri dishes and two pieces of meat.

1. **Fill the dishes with water.**

2. **With your forceps, place a piece of meat in each dish.**

3. **Cover both dishes. Label each.**

There will be two large trays set up in the room. One of the trays is marked "Freezer." The other is marked "Room Temperature."

4. **Place one dish on the tray marked "Freezer."**

5. Place the other dish on the tray marked "Room Temperature."

6. Do not disturb your experiment for 2 days.

7. After 2 days, examine the meat in each dish.

8. **What happened to the meat in the freezer?**

9. **What happened to the meat left at room temperature?**

10. **What effect did freezing have on the meat?**

11. **What effect did room temperature have on the meat?**

Bacteria are responsible for food decay. Under the proper temperature conditions, bacteria cause foods to change and decay. One of the most common methods of preserving foods is to refrigerate them. This is especially true of foods which contain

water. Frozen foods cannot be changed by bacteria.

Novosti/Sovfoto

This huge, hairy creature is a wooly mammoth. It lived thousands of years ago. Scientists believe that it was frozen while still alive. Thus, it was preserved as a fossil.

12. **What modern animal does it look like?**

13. **How did freezing affect this animal?**

B. PRESERVED IN AMBER

Freezing is not the only method by which fossils are preserved. Tar is also an agent of fossil formation. Natural pools of tar often trapped such animals as the saber tooth tiger.

Courtesy of the American Museum of Natural History

Courtesy of the Natural History Museum of Los Angeles County

A more recent nomination for becoming a fossil is this rabbit, which was trapped in tar. Animals that sink into tar are protected from decay and thus may be preserved as fossils.

Let's see another way in which fossils are preserved.

14. Place several small pieces of resin in a test tube.

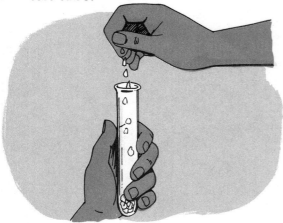

15. Hold your test tube with a test tube clamp.

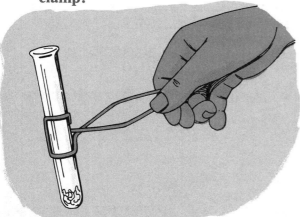

16. Carefully melt the resin over a low flame. Do not let the resin boil. Keep the mouth of the test tube pointed away from everyone.

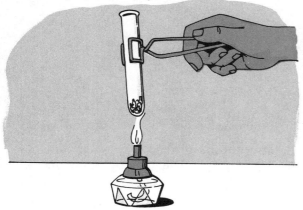

Your teacher will give you a small cardboard box and some insects.

17. Carefully pour the melted resin into the cardboard box.

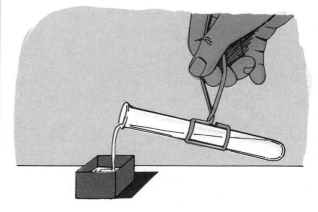

18. With your forceps, place an insect in the resin.

19. Let the resin cool at room temperature.

20. After the resin hardens, peel off the paper.

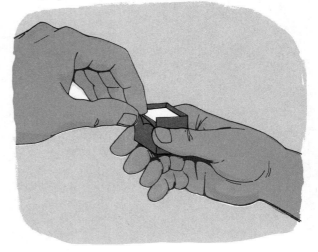

Congratulations! You have made an insect fossil. Ants and flies were trapped in resin which dripped down the bark of trees. As the resin hardened, it changed into a clear plastic-like material called *amber*. Amber preserved the insects for millions of years.

C. THE STORY TOLD BY FOSSILS

Scientists often find fossils of animals that lived millions of years ago.

By putting the bones of these animals together, scientists can learn many things. In other words, fossils are clues to the kinds of plants and animals that lived in a region. For example, the bones of a 20-meter dinosaur were found in Wyoming. In the same rocks were found other animals, insects, and plants that live in swamps. By putting all of the details together, scientists learned about the dinosaur, its friends and neighbors, and where they all lived. Today, those Wyoming swamps have dried up. The climate has changed; it has become much cooler. New types of plants and animals have replaced the old. Indeed, many changes have taken place.

Here is another example. One of the most complete fossil records is that of the horse. Horse fossils date back about 70 million years. Can you find any evidence of change?

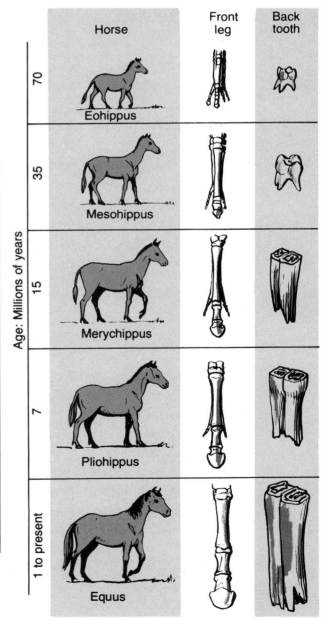

287

21. **Which horse is the oldest?**

22. **Which horse is the smallest?**

23. **How many toes does Eohippus have?**

24. **How do the teeth of Eohippus compare with the teeth of the other horses?**

25. **What appears to have happened to the horse over millions of years?**

Eohippus was a horse that lived about 70 million years ago. It stood only about 45 cm tall, had small teeth, and had 4 toes on its front legs. The home of Eohippus was a region now called Nebraska. During the time of Eohippus, the Gulf of Mexico reached westward and then curved north into Nebraska. The land in Nebraska was soft, and rich in plants.

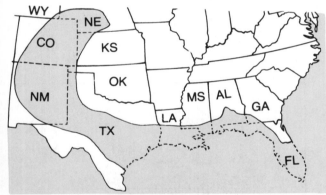

The teeth and toes of Eohippus were well suited to the climate. The horse could move easily in the moist soil and could feed well. However, over millions and millions of years, many changes took place. The climate changed; it was no longer moist, but became drier. The land changed; the waters of the Gulf of Mexico no longer reached as far north. The land hardened and the food supply changed. As all of these changes took place, what happened to the horse?

26. **As the type of plants changed, what happened to the teeth of the horse?**

27. **As the soil hardened, what happened to the number of toes?**

28. **What happened to the size of the horse over millions of years?**

29. **What happened to the appearance of the horse over millions of years.?**

The wooly mammoth pictured on page 285 no longer exists, yet there are still elephants.

30. **What happened to the appearance of the elephant over millions of years?**

31. **What evidence is there that the tiger has changed?**

32. **What do you think can happen to living things over millions of years?**

Review Questions 25-32. Write the concept.

CONCEPT

ENRICHMENT

1. What is a paleontologist? Why is his or her work important? Research the qualifications necessary for becoming a paleontologist.

2. Research and prepare a report on the origin and development of humankind.

3. Prepare a bulletin board display illustrating differences between prehistoric organisms and their living relatives.

4. Press a small object into a flat surface of clay. Describe a method you might use to make a mold of your impression. How do paleontologists make molds or casts of dinosaur footprints?

Investigation 5

The Mystery of Change

Early in this Idea, you studied adjustments that organisms make to changes in their environment. In the first three Investigations, the adjustments were temporary, rather than permanent. Although these adjustments were necessary, they lasted for a limited period of time. In the last Investigation, you studied fossil evidence of changes in the horse. These changes were permanent. Whether temporary or permanent, all of the changes studied have something in common; they give the organism an *advantage* in the environment. Scientists refer to change which gives an organism an advantage in the environment as **adaptation**.

Several years ago, doctors at various New York City hospitals became puzzled and alarmed. Patients under their care, some on their way to recovery, were suddenly and mysteriously dying. At first, tests revealed nothing, and the cause of these deaths was unknown. Were the patients being treated properly? Were the wrong medicines being given? Were sudden heart attacks responsible for the deaths? These and many other questions were raised. Finally, through more laboratory tests and research, the answer was found. Nothing really new had taken place, but the doctors were concerned. A new form of bacteria had developed.

These new bacteria were responsible for the deaths. How can this happen? What does it mean? That will be the subject for this Investigation.

A. CACTUS ADAPTATIONS

Van Campen/dpi

The cactus is among the oldest flowering plants. This may seem strange, since flowers are rarely seen on cacti. The flower of the cactus plant blossoms only during periods of heavy rain; and in the desert, this is rare.

Evidence suggests that cacti may have first developed about 100 million years ago. During this period of the earth's history, the climate was moist and warm. Conditions were ideal for the development of flowering plants. Probably the cactus was originally a plant with large leaves. Over millions of years, the climate began to change. It became cooler; and as the amount of rainfall decreased, it became drier. Plants which could not adapt to the changing environment could not survive. Let's examine some of the adaptations of the cactus plant.

1. **When do scientists believe that the cactus first developed?**

2. **Describe the climate during this period of the earth's history.**

3. **What kind of leaves did the cactus probably have?**

4. **Over millions of years, what changes in climate took place?**

5. **What is adaptation?**

6. **What did the cactus have to do in order to survive?**

You will be given two small sections of cardboard tubing and two large metal jar covers.

7. **Remove the inside material from each of the jar covers. Set the covers aside.**

8. **Carefully melt some wax in a tin can. Do not allow the wax to boil.**

9. **Use tongs to remove the can from the ringstand.**

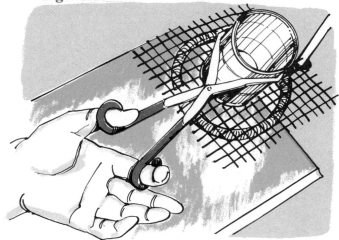

10. **Shut off the flame.**

11. **Insert a piece of string through one of the pieces of cardboard tubing.**

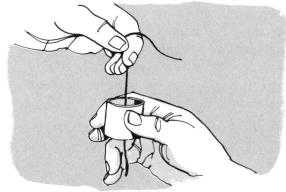

12. **Dip the tubing into the wax so as to completely coat it.**

13. Allow the wax on the cardboard tubing to cool and harden. Cut off the string.

14. Use the tongs. Carefully fill each of the jar covers about ½-full with melted wax.

15. Place a piece of cardboard tubing into each jar cover. Allow the wax to harden.

16. In what way are each of the pieces of cardboard tubing different?

17. Which piece of tubing is the experimental piece?

18. Which piece of tubing is the control?

19. Carefully fill each of the pieces of tubing almost to the top with water.

20. Set your experiment aside. Do not disturb it for about 20 minutes.

Cacti are commonly found in desert regions. Few other plants are able to survive in these regions. Deserts are generally hot and dry, and do not favor the growth of many plants. However, the cactus is well adapted for survival. One of its many adaptations is a coating of wax over the surface of the stem. Your experiment will help demonstrate the advantage of this wax coating.

21. After 20 minutes, observe each of the pieces of cardboard tubing.

22. What are your observations?

23. How can you explain this?

24. From your experiment, what can you conclude about one adaptation of cactus for preventing water loss?

Cacti possess other adaptations for preventing water loss. The needles or spines of the cactus are actually leaves.

These spines have such a small surface that water loss is greatly reduced. Even the stomates are sunk deep into the skin, and these are further protected by tiny hairs to prevent water loss. Some cacti have the amazing ability of being able to seal punctures, much like sealing an inner tube of a tire. If the plant is punctured, a sticky juice seals the hole almost instantly to prevent a loss of water.

A waxy stem, small leaves, sunken stomates, and a self-sealing system are examples of structures developed by the cactus. Each of these structures gives the cactus an advantage in its environment. Thus, each of these is an adaptation to their environment.

25. What are a waxy stem, small leaves, sunken stomates, and a self-sealing system examples of?

26. What do these structures give to the cactus?

27. Thus, what may we call these structures?

B. ANIMAL ADAPTATIONS

As you learned in the last Investigation, adaptations are by no means limited to plants. Indeed, the horse has had its share of adaptations, but so have all plants and animals. In fact, every living organism on earth has adapted in some way to its environment. It's a matter of survival. Organisms that do not adapt vanish from the earth forever; they become *extinct*.

The diversity of animal adaptations is staggering. Here are several examples.

Body color is an outstanding feature of living things. As an adaptation, it serves many purposes. Many organisms blend in so perfectly with their surroundings that they are often difficult to see; especially by their enemies. Thus, coloration may be protective; it may be a sort of camouflage.

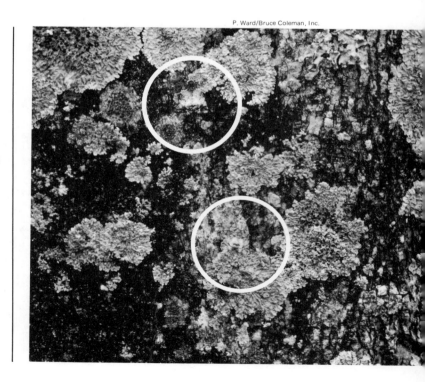

P. Ward/Bruce Coleman, Inc.

Bob Campbell/Bruce Coleman, Inc.

Some organisms use their color to hide and thus surprise their prey. One such organism is the African mantis. This insect conceals itself among the leaves of a plant. The insect waits patiently for the proper moment to strike. How successful do you think this hunter is?

Still other insects use patterns to fool their enemies and thus survive. The bumblebee moth is a harmless insect which feeds on the nectar of flowers. However, the bumblebee at the bottom has a stinger that can cause pain or death to other insects and birds. The type of adaptation where one organism looks like another is known as *mimicry*. What advantage does mimicry give to the bumblebee moth?

Lilo Hess

The feet of birds show a variety of adaptations which give them an advantage in their environment. Birds that spend much of their time in water have webbed feet adapted for swimming. Other birds have feet adapted for wading, walking, or running. Can you identify the feet of the hawk, which is a hunting bird? Or the feet of the woodpecker, which clings to the bark of trees?

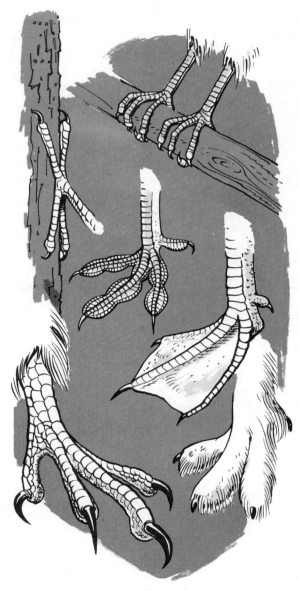

Similarly, the beaks and bills of birds are closely related in shape and structure to their diets. The hawk is a flesh eater. It uses its beak to tear meat apart. Some birds may feed on fish, insects, or the hard seeds of plants.

Can you identify the type of food a bird eats by its beak or bill?

organs that produce unpleasant odors,

Leonard Lee Rue/Bruce Coleman, Inc.

and poison are also important adaptations for survival.

J.R. Simon/Bruce Coleman, Inc.

Speed,

Animals, Animals

28. **What adaptations for survival have some insects developed?**

29. **What structures have birds developed to give them an advantage in their environment?**

30. **What do all of the structures studied offer the organism?**

31. **What do we call structures which give an organism an advantage in the environment?**

C. RESISTANT BACTERIA

At the beginning of this Investigation, you read about a new form of bacteria that developed. Very often, doctors use drugs to treat diseases caused by bacteria. These drugs are selected because they are known to be effective in destroying bacteria. During treatment with drugs, some bacteria remain alive. These bacteria may reproduce new forms. Some of these new forms may not be affected by the drug being used. In other words, the new bacteria are *resistant*. Through adaptation, resistant forms of bacteria gain an advantage in their environment. They survive and reproduce more of their own kind.

32. **How do resistant forms of bacteria gain an advantage in their environment?**

33. **What adaptations has the cactus made to its environment?**

34. **How have some insects adapted to their environment?**

35. **What structures have birds developed as adaptations to their environment?**

36. **What is adaptation?**

37. **What do we call structures which give organisms an advantage in their environment?**

Re-read your answers to Questions 27, 31, and 37. State the concept.

CONCEPT

WORDS TO KNOW

> The following words have been used in this Idea. Carefully review the Idea and define each of them on your data sheet.
>
> | | |
> |---|---|
> | Adaptation | Mimicry |
> | Extinct | Resistant |
> | Fossil | |

SUMMARY OF THE IDEA: ADAPTATION AND THE ENVIRONMENT

You've done it again! You've had to work in the dark, tap like a woodpecker (are you adapted for that?), and chase horses through Nebraska. But it had to be worthwhile because you've completed still another Idea. This Idea has been about adaptations, the adjustments or changes that organisms make to gain an advantage in their environment.

Adaptations can and do occur in a variety of ways. They may be simple things, like the adjustment of the eye to light; they may be complex, like the development of totally new structure. They may take place rapidly, like the response of heartbeat rate; or they may come about over millions of years, as with the cactus. Fossils are often important evidence of these adaptations. Fossils of the dinosaur, horse, and people support this idea.

All adaptations share a common purpose. They may be quick or slow; they may be simple or complex. But adaptations give an organism an advantage in its environment, an advantage geared toward survival. This was the case with the bacteria you learned about earlier in this Investigation. Organisms that cannot adapt eventually become extinct. They vanish from the earth, never to return.

In this Idea on adaptation, you studied five concepts.

1. State these five concepts.

The adaptations of organisms help them survive.

2. What must organisms adapt to?

3. What is adaptation geared towards?

4. How do organisms survive?

Re-read your answer to Question 4. Summarize the Idea.

IDEA SUMMARY

ENRICHMENT

1. How can doctors treat diseases caused by bacteria if resistant forms of these bacteria develop?

2. What danger might there be in giving too much of a certain drug in fighting a bacterial disease?

3. Plan a trip to a hospital bacteriology laboratory. How do bacteriologists determine what drugs are to be used in treating bacterial diseases?

4. The appendix is a vestigial structure. List some other vestigial structures in people and explain why these are vestigial.

5. How are fish adapted for a life in water?

6. Explain how and why intelligence may be considered an adaptation for survival. How does this apply to people?

Investigation 1

Count, Kind, Place, and Time

There are many kinds of relationships in the world. Some familiar relationships are a family, a girl and her dog, and a bird and a tree.

Leonard Lee Rue/Bruce Coleman, Inc.

Paul Conklin/Monkmeyer

Some other examples of relationships are a mosquito and a person, a forest, and a city.

Bannett/dpi

Leo deWys, Inc.

297

Lizabeth Corlett/dpi

Greenberg/dpi

In what way do all of these pictures show relationships? That will be the subject of this Idea.

You have already studied some relationships. A group of cells having the same structure and function is a tissue. A group of similar tissues is an organ. A group of organs working together is a system. And the life activities of all the systems contribute to the life of an organism. But that is not the end of relationships. A group of similar organisms is a population.

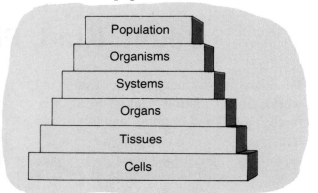

Look around your classroom or where you live. There are different kinds of living things. There are people, of course. Then, there may be goldfish, cats, dogs, geranium, and ivy. If we take each of these as separate groups, we begin to deal with populations.

A. ROLL CALL

As you begin this Investigation, your teacher may have just taken attendance. Your teacher keeps a record of the attendance each day. The attendance record is an example of a population. The *population* is the number of one kind of organism in one place at one time. To say that the class count is 28 is not enough. The study of a population also requires information on place and time. For instance, when the attendance is taken, your

teacher records the
number of students in
room 7 at 3rd period on March 1.

(count • kind • place • time)

1. **What is the student population of your science class this period? Complete the top line of Table 1.**

2. **Determine the student population the next two days. Enter the data in Table 1.**

3. **When you look at a population, what four things must you consider?**

The word *population* comes from the Latin word for *people*. It can mean the number of people living in a place. But all populations are not made up of humans. There are also populations of other animals and of plants.

U.S. Army Corps of Engineers

Salmon swim upstream to spawn. When a dam is built, steps are built to allow the salmon to swim up and around the dam. This person is counting the different kinds of salmon as they pass the John Jay Dam on the Columbia River. This will help to establish the population in the area.

U.S. Army Corps of Engineers

Bradford Island Fish Count

SPECIES	TODAY	YEAR TO DATE
Chinook	3805	62122
Coho	168	5951
Jacks	182	3448
Sockeye	157	5371
Steelhead	470	9742
Shad	4834	12682

4. **What was the population of Chinook salmon passing Bradford Island on the day of the photograph?**

5. **What is a population?**

B. IT'S GETTING CROWDED

GRAPH 1 The population of red salmon in Bristol Bay, Alaska, from 1966 to 1975

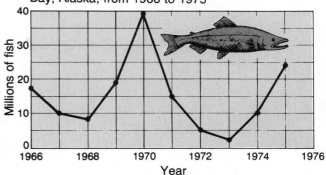

6. **What kind of population is described in the graph?**

7. **Where was the population counted?**

8. **Between what times were the counts taken?**

9. **What was the population in 1968? 1970? 1973?**

10. **What happened to the population between 1966 to 1975?**

One characteristic of populations is that they can change. The numbers can go up and down. We say that populations show *fluctuation*.

There is one population that has shown change, but not fluctuation. Its change has been steady growth. This is the world human population.

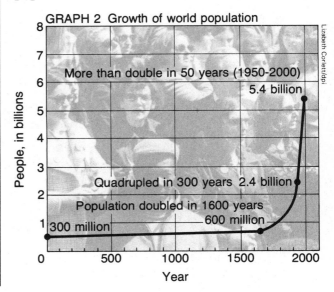

GRAPH 2 Growth of world population

More than double in 50 years (1950-2000)

5.4 billion

Quadrupled in 300 years 2.4 billion

Population doubled in 1600 years

600 million

300 million

Lizabeth Corlett/dpi

11. **What was the world population in 1600?**

12. **What was the world population in 1950?**

13. **What may the world population be in 2000?**

Imagine that your classroom is 10 meters by 12 meters. A diagram of this room is shown on page D180 of your Data Book. The classroom has been divided into 1-meter squares.

14. **How many squares are in the diagram?**

15. **What is the student population of your classroom?**

16. **Pretend that each student has a space of 1 square meter. For each student, draw an "X" in 1 square. The number of "X's" should equal the number of students.**

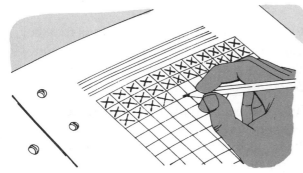

Imagine that the student population doubles in one year.

17. **How many students would there be in 1 year?**

18. **How many more "X's" would you have to draw to equal the population?**

19. **Draw the additional "X's" needed to equal the population increase.**

Imagine that the student population doubles again in one year. Remember to double the new population.

20. **How many students would there be in 2 years?**

21. **How many more "X's" would you have to draw to equal the population?**

22. **Draw the additional "X's" needed to equal the population increase.**

Imagine that the student population doubles again in one year. Again, remember to double the new population.

23. **How many students would there be in 3 years?**

24. **How many more "X's" would you have to draw to equal the population?**

25. **Draw the additional "X's" needed to equal the population increase. You must place all the "X's" in the spaces.**

26. **If you ran out of spaces, where did you place the extra "X's"?**

27. **What is a population?**

28. **A population can show a fluctuation. What does this mean?**

29. **Name one population that has shown steady growth so far.**

30. **What is overpopulation?**

C. POPULATION DENSITY

Another characteristic of a population is *density*. Density is the number of individuals in a space at a given time. The density of wheat in the field is great compared to the birds on the beach at the top of the next page.

Taylor/dpi

Sabarese/dpi

Lukas/Rapho-Guillumette

Manhattan, New York City

TABLE 2 POPULATION DENSITY OF SELECTED AREAS

Area	Density Persons per sq. km
Belgium	318
Brazil	12
Canada	2
China	83
Egypt	35
France	95
Hong Kong	3,924
India	172
Japan	287
Kenya	21
Manhattan, New York City	26,487
Mexico	27
USSR	11
USA	22

Look at the clock and count the seconds. Do you know how long it would take you to count 1 billion seconds? 30 years. Yes, 30 years!

31. How long would it take to count 5 billion seconds?

The world population is expected to be more than 5 billion by 2000. If you started counting *now*, you couldn't even count that many people! And the world's population is expected to double again 35 years later!

Today, 70 percent of the world's population lives on less than 4 percent of the land.

32. There are 100 squares in the diagram on page D181 of your Data Book. Draw 70 "X's" in 4 of the squares. Then spread out 30 "X's" in the other squares.

The density of the world's population is not evenly spaced out. It is more crowded in some places than in other places.

33. Where is the human density the greatest?

34. Name one place where the human density is not great.

35. What is the population density of the United States?

36. What is population density?

37. How do you think the density of New York City differs from a Kansas farm?

38. Population density varies. Explain this statement.

D. COUNT IT

You have been studying some characteristics of populations.

39. You've learned that populations show fluctuation. What does that mean?

40. You've also studied population density. What is population density?

41. Finally, you studied overpopulation. What is overpopulation?

42. What is every organism a part of?

43. What four things must you know about a population?

44. In summary, what is a population?

Re-read Questions 27 and 44. Then state the concept.

CONCEPT

ENRICHMENT

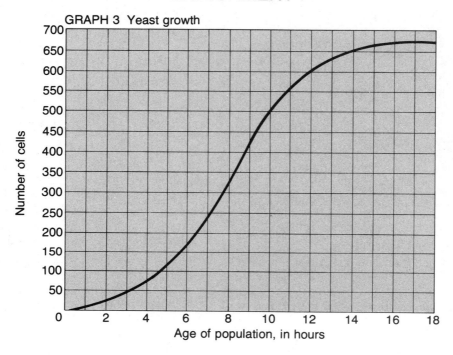

GRAPH 3 Yeast growth

Number of cells (y-axis), *Age of population, in hours* (x-axis)

1. This graph shows the growth of a yeast population under laboratory conditions. The graph of such a growth is called a *population growth curve,* or S-shaped curve. Explain what a graph of this shape tells you.

2. What environmental conditions control population size and growth?

3. Look up the two words: *natality* and *mortality.* What do they mean and what do they have to do with population?

4. Populations can be distributed in three ways: random, uniform, and clumped. Explain and give examples of each.

5. Make a map of your school. Check to see how many students are in each classroom. Show how they are distributed at different times such as recess, classtime, or lunch hour.

6. Find out your school population for the last 10 years. Chart this on a graph.

Investigation 2

Types of Communities

In the last Investigation, you learned that each organism is part of a population. A population tells you how many there are of something. A population also tells you where the organisms are found and when. For instance,

(a) There were 560,000 people in San Jose, California, in 1976.

(b) I counted 40 dandelions in a square meter of my lawn on May 15.

(c) There were 8 goldfish in my aquarium last week. There are 7 today.

R.W. Young/dpi

Leonard Lee Rue/Bruce Coleman, Inc.

acha/deWys

Weldon/deWys

No organism lives alone. Organisms usually live grouped together. People can be found living in cities. Elephants are found in herds, ducks in flocks, and redwood trees in a grove. A group of similar organisms is called a population.

No population lives alone, either. Populations live grouped together. They live next to each other and need each other. A group of populations living in an area is a *community*. Putting it all together, this is how the relationships are organized.

Community
Populations
Organisms
Systems
Organs
Tissues
Cells

A. COUNTING POPULATIONS

The aquarium is an example of a community. There are several populations in an aquarium.

1. **Observe the aquarium in your room.**

2. **Observe the different kinds of organisms in the aquarium. List each kind in Table 1 on your data sheet.**

3. **Count each population. Record your data in Table 1.**

4. **How many different populations did you find in the aquarium?**

5. **What is in a community?**

6. **What do you call a group of populations living in an area?**

That was easy, wasn't it? Now you're going to make a population count of another community. Only you'll have to find a community of your own. This may mean going outside.

7. **Find a small community where you can make a population count.**

It isn't hard to find a community.

Heiniger/Rapho-Guillumette

Look under a rock.

Dr. Harold R. Hungerford

Turn over a log.

Look over, under, and around the rocks at the seashore.

M. Woodbridge Williams

Study the cracks in the cement.

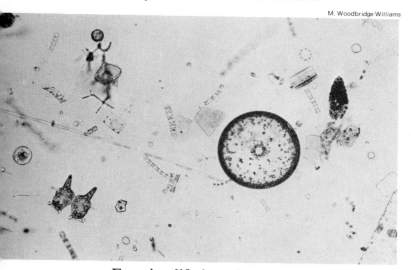

Examine life in a drop of pond water.

Observe the life around a city building.

Get down on your hands and knees. What do you find in a square meter of lawn?

8. Complete the title to Table 2. Then record the rest of the data in the table.

9. How many kinds of organisms did you find?

10. Each kind of organism is a population. How many different populations did you find?

11. Does each population live by itself? Explain.

12. What is a community?

B. DIFFERENT BIOMES

A pond is a community. So is a lake, cave, forest, or town. But communities do not always have nice, neat names. You usually name a community by where you find it. For instance, there can be a community under your fingernail, on the back of a dog, or in a pile of hay.

305

There is a larger kind of community. It is called a *__biome__*. A biome usually covers a large geographical area. It usually has a certain type of climate because of where it is located. A biome near the equator differs from a biome near the pole; a biome in a valley differs from a biome at a mountain top. This map shows the location of the six major land biomes of the earth.

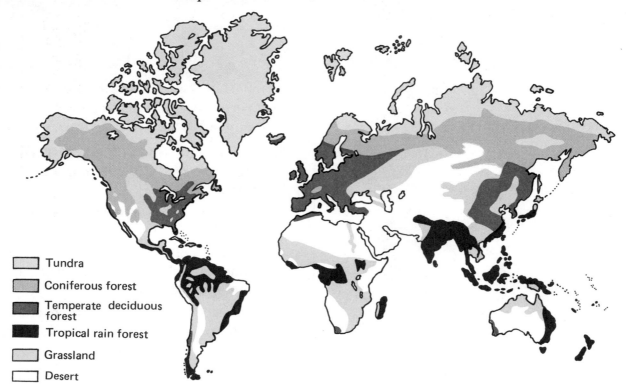

- Tundra
- Coniferous forest
- Temperate deciduous forest
- Tropical rain forest
- Grassland
- Desert

Leonard Lee Rue/National Audubon Society

Tundra Biome

The *tundra* is found near the north pole. Here the earth is permanently frozen 1 or 2 meters below the surface. Therefore, only mosses and shrubs can be found. The animal population includes mosquitoes, mice, snowshoe rabbits, polar bears, and reindeer.

South of the tundra are the great forests of trees which have cones. This is why they are called the *coniferous forests*. Common animals include black bears, beavers, squirrels, and foxes.

Coniferous Forest Biome

American Stock Photos/Bruce Coleman, I

Temperate deciduous forests are located in areas with definite seasons. A deciduous forest is one in which the leaves fall from the trees in the autumn. Such trees include the maple, elm, and poplar. Deer, rabbits, birds, and insects live here.

emperate Deciduous Forest Biome

Werner Stoy/Camera Hawaii/dpi

Tropical Rain Forest Biome

The *tropical rain forests* are found at the equator. There is no major type of tree there. There are many trees that grow 30 to 40 meters tall. The branches form a cover which is so thick that the forest floor can be dark during the day. The forest is alive with many insects, spiders, birds, and monkeys.

Grasslands are areas where very few trees are found. This is because there is not enough rain to support large plants such as trees. The area is covered by many different kinds of grasses. The lion, zebra, and giraffe roam the grasslands of Africa. In America, the grassland populations include prairie dogs, snakes, grasshoppers, and hawks.

Grassland Biome

Grant Heilman

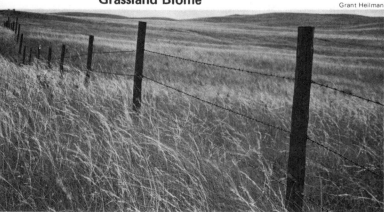

Van Campen/dpi

Desert Biome

Deserts are the very hot, dry areas of the earth's surface. The major form of plant life is the cactus. The camel, kangaroo rat, many insects, reptiles, and birds can be found here.

In addition, there are two other biomes: the *ocean biome* and the *fresh water biome*.

13. **Name the six land biomes.**
14. **What populations would you find in the tundra?**
15. **What populations would you find in the coniferous forests?**
16. **What populations would you find in the temperate deciduous forests?**
17. **What populations would you find in the tropical rain forests?**
18. **What populations would you find in the grasslands?**
19. **What populations would you find in the deserts?**
20. **Name the two water biomes.**
21. **How does a biome differ from a community?**
22. **What is a community?**

C. LET YOUR FINGERS DO THE WALKING

You have just learned that the climate, geography, and environment can determine what is in a community. Let's see if you can describe a community without seeing it.

23. You will be given a telephone book.

You can describe a certain kind of community from the data given in a telephone book. To help you get started, plan ahead! Don't just thumb through the telephone book. Know what you are looking for. For instance, here are some questions and suggested places to look for the answers.

(a) Is it a city or a rural community? (Look up "Farm Equipment.")

(b) Are there any Greek people living in the community? (Look up "Restaurants — Greek.")

(c) Is the community religious? (Count the number of churches and synagogues listed.)

(d) Is the community near water? (See if there are any "Boat Dealers.")

(e) Is the community rich or poor? (Count the number of doctors.)

(f) What other populations live in this community? (Look up "Pet Stores.")

24. **List some other questions you may want to ask.**

25. Work in small groups. Write your answers on page D185 of your Data Book. Then report to the class.

A community is more than a place on the map. A community is a living unit. The telephone book is just one way to tell what's happening in a community. What else could you use to tell what's happening?

D. WE NEED TO LIVE TOGETHER

Let's put everything together from the last two Investigations.

26. **What is a population?**

27. **"A community is a living unit." What does that mean?**

28. **What is a biome?**

29. **What is a community?**

Re-read Questions 22 and 29. Then state the concept.

CONCEPT

ENRICHMENT

1. Construct a community of your own. Build a terrarium or aquarium.

2. Repeat Steps 7 and 8 over a longer period of time. For instance, make observations and counts every week or every month. What happens to the community over a period of time?

3. The ocean biome is usually divided into four areas or zones: the intertidal, littoral, pelagic, and benthic zones. Find out what these mean and write a report on the ocean biome.

4. The fresh water biome has two major subtypes: flowing waters and standing waters. What kinds of populations are in each?

5. Visit your local city hall or community center and write a paper on the things that must go on to keep a community alive.

Investigation 3

Predator and Prey

Suva/dpi

Leonard Lee Rue/Monkmeyer

Why do organisms live in a community? In the next five Investigations, you will try to answer one question: What is the function of a community?

All living things need energy. This is why living things live close to other living things. The other living things may be a source of food. Some organisms make their own food. They are called *producers*. Green plants are producers.

Other organisms eat or *consume* other organisms for their food. Animals, non-green plants, and many microorganisms are ***consumers***. All consumers directly or indirectly need green plants for their food.

309

Humans are consumers. So are grass-hoppers, goldfish, and amoeba. Each is a special kind of consumer, depending on it's source of food. As you studied in Idea 2, consumers are either:

(a) Herbivores. These animals eat only plants. Examples include the grasshopper, deer, and giraffe.

(b) Carnivores. These animals eat only other animals. The hawk, dog, and tiger are in this group.

(c) Omnivores. These animals eat both plants and animals. Humans, bears, and most fish are omnivores.

All of these terms refer to *food* or *nutritional relationships*. Organisms live in communities because of their relationship to food.

1. **What is a producer?**

2. **What is a consumer?**

3. **Name three kinds of consumers.**

4. **What is a food or nutritional relationship?**

5. **Why do living things live in communities?**

A. HYDRA VS. DAPHNIA

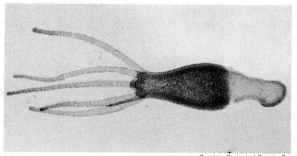

Hydra   Carolina Biological Supply Co.

It looks like a monster, but it isn't. This animal is called a Hydra. It spends its life under lily pads in a pond. You have to look hard to find it. It is about 8 mm long and almost clear. You studied budding in Hydra in Idea 7.

6. Your teacher will give you a Hydra in a test tube. Do not shake the tube or disturb the Hydra. Observe it for about 3 minutes.

7. **Describe everything you see.**

8. Use your dropper to catch a Daphnia.

9. Add the Daphnia to the test tube. Do not disturb the Hydra. Be very patient. Observe for five or more minutes.

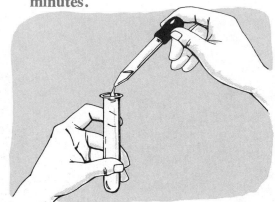

10. **Describe everything you see happen between the Hydra and the Daphnia.**

11. **In a community, what may one organism do to another?**

12. **Why do living things live in communities?**

An animal that catches and eats other animals is a *predator*. A predator is a consumer. The animal that is caught and eaten is the *prey*.

13. **Is the Hydra or the Daphnia the predator?**

14. **Which one is the prey?**

Treat Davidson/National Audubon Society

Leonard Lee Rue/National Audubon Society

15. Which is the predator and which is the prey?

16. Which is the predator and which is the prey?

17. Give another example of a predator-prey relationship.

18. What is a predator?

19. What is a prey?

B. HAWK VS. FIELD MOUSE

Keep one question in mind. What is the function of a community? To help you answer this question, you will play a game.

Pretend that you are looking at a community with two populations. They are the hawk and field mouse populations. The hawk is the predator and the field mouse is the prey. These two populations represent a food or nutritional relationship in a community. Your teacher will give you hawk cards and field mouse cards.

20. Mark an area 60 cm square on the floor. This is the community where the hawk and field mouse populations live.

21. Drop 5 field mice in the community, one at a time.

22. Stand back from the community 1.5 meters.

23. Throw a hawk into the area. Try to make it land on as many mice as possible. If a mouse is touched, the hawk has caught it.

24. Pick up the hawk card. Also remove any field mice caught.

Before you learn how to keep score, it will help to learn a new word. The new word is *generation*.

When parents have offspring, the offspring are the next generation. A generation is the next group of offspring.

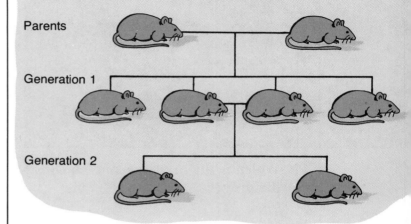

You will play this game for 20 generations. Keep a record of each new generation in Table 1. Follow these rules:

(a) The field mice left will double each generation. If you have 3 mice left after Generation 1, throw in 3 more mice. You will then have 6 field mice for Generation 2.

(b) In order to live, a hawk has to land on 4 field mice. For each 4 mice caught, the hawk will reproduce another hawk. If your hawk catches 4 to 7 mice, add another hawk for the next generation. If it catches 8 mice, add 2 more hawks.

(c) If a hawk does not catch 4 field mice, it dies from lack of food. Do not let the hawk population drop below 1. Pretend that a new one flies into the area looking for food. Start with one again in the next generation.

(d) Do not rush this game. Ask your teacher to help you keep score.

25. Which population reaches higher numbers? Why is this?

26. As the field mouse population gets bigger, what happens to the population of hawks?

27. **Notice that as the hawk population rises, the field mouse population falls. Why?**

28. **Why do populations rise and fall?**

29. **What do predators do to the size of a prey population?**

The sizes of predator and prey populations are related to each other. The size of each population is determined by the size of the other. If the number of prey is large, this leads to an increase in the number of predators. As predators feed upon the prey, the number of prey begins to fall. The number of predators also decreases, since they have a smaller food supply. As the number of predators decreases, the number of prey begins to increase. This food relationship of predator-prey creates a "cycle."

The populations of both predator and prey change, depending upon the size of the other.

30. **If the population of prey increases, what happens to the population of predators?**

31. **If the population of prey decreases, what happens to the population of predators?**

32. **If the population of predators increases, what happens to the population of prey?**

33. **If the population of predators decreases, what happens to the population of prey?**

34. **What relationship helps to determine the size of a population?**

35. **Why do living things live in a community?**

C. WHEN IS A PREDATOR A PREY?

The hawk was the predator in the game you just played. The field mice were the prey. But almost every organism is preyed upon by some other organism. So the hawk could become the prey. Can you think of an organism that would be the predator to the hawk? The field mice could become the predator in another food relationship. What could they feed on? These questions will be discussed further in Investigation 5.

36. **What is a predator?**

37. **What is a prey?**

38. **What does a predator-prey relationship determine?**

39. **What is a food or nutritional relationship?**

40. **Why do living things live in a community?**

CONCEPT

ENRICHMENT

1. Construct a bulletin board display showing different predator-prey relationships.

2. Write a paper explaining what would happen to the hawk and field mouse populations if the game in Part B were to be continued for 20 more generations.

3. Prepare a bulletin board display showing different kinds of herbivores, carnivores, and omnivores.
4. What is a saprophyte? What kind of food relationship does it have?
5. What is a decomposer? What kind of food relationship does it have?
6. A mosquito or flea is not a true predator. Explain why.

Grant Heilman

Investigation 4

Symbiotic Relationships

Compton's Encyclopedia

Crocodile and Crocodile bird

Here's a real teeth cleaning job. It may look like dinner time for the crocodile, but it's not. The crocodile is probably enjoying it. The crocodile bird cleans the teeth of the crocodile. It picks out small pieces of meat. In return for this service, the crocodile does not harm the bird. Everybody's happy! A free cleaning for the crocodile; a free meal for the crocodile bird. Both animals depend upon one another.

Here are two other happy neighbors, the tick bird and the rhinoceros. The tick bird picks insects out of the skin of the rhinoceros. Again, a free cleaning and a free meal.

Rhinoceros and Tick bird

Mark Boulton/National Audubon Society

315

The crocodile and the crocodile bird; the rhinoceros and the tick bird; they are examples of a special relationship between organisms. In a community, some organisms live in close relationship with one another. Relationships of this type are called **symbiosis**, which means *living together*. In symbiosis, where an organism lives depends upon other organisms.

1. **What does the crocodile bird get from the crocodile?**

2. **What does the crocodile get from this relationship?**

3. **Why do you think the crocodile and crocodile bird make good neighbors?**

4. **What does the tick bird do for the rhinoceros?**

5. **What does the tick bird get from this relationship?**

6. **Why do the tick bird and rhinoceros make good neighbors?**

7. **What is symbiosis?**

8. **In symbiosis, where does an organism live?**

A. ALL ABOUT ALGAE

Plants may also live together as good neighbors. Each neighbor helps the other. Sometimes plants depend upon other plants. Sound strange?

Walter Dawn

Not all plants can make food. Only green plants can. The simplest of all green plants are the *algae*. Almost all algae live in water. Many are microscopic.

Algae
Spencer/National Audubon Society

Not all algae are microscopic. Seaweed is another form of algae.

Seaweed
Jane Burton/Bruce Coleman, Inc.

9. **What are algae?**

10. **Where do algae live?**

11. **How do algae get food?**

B. FUNGI

You have done several experiments with yeast. Yeast cells are non-green plants. They do not contain chlorophyll.

Bread mold

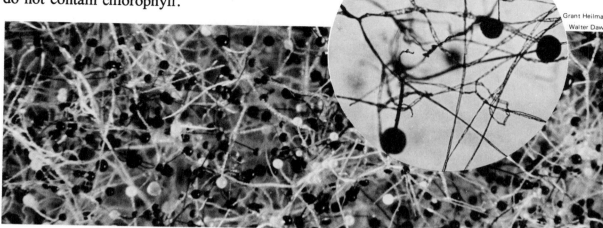

Grant Heilman
Walter Dawn

Bread mold is another example of a non-green plant. The photograph on page 238 would look like this under the microscope.

12. Where do you think yeast and bread mold get their food from?

Yeast and bread mold belong to a group of plants called *fungi*. Other examples of fungi include mushrooms, ringworm, and athlete's foot. Fungi do not contain chlorophyll. They cannot make their own food. They must get their food from what they grow on.

13. What do fungi depend upon for food?

14. Why must fungi live where they can get food?

C. LICHENS

John H. Gerard/National Audubon Society

Lichen

Algae and fungi sometimes grow and live together. Each organism has an important job. Each helps the other.

Your teacher will give you a small piece of plant material.

15. With your forceps, carefully place some of the plant material on a clean microscope slide.

16. Add 2 drops of water to the material.

17. Hold the material in place with your forceps.

18. Gently try to pull the material apart with a needle.

19. Add a cover slip.

20. Examine under low power with your microscope.

21. In Space A, draw what you see.

22. What part of the plant do you think is the algae?

23. How can you tell?

24. What part of the plant do you think is the fungi?

25. How can you tell?

26. What part of the plant makes food?

27. How do you know?

28. What does the fungi look like?

The plant you are studying is called a *lichen*. Lichens are made up of algae and fungi. The algae make the food and the fungi take in water and hold the plant in place.

29. How do the fungi depend upon the algae?

30. How do the algae depend upon the fungi?

31. How does the one organism help the other?

32. Why do some organisms live together?

33. What do you call this relationship?

34. In symbiosis, where does an organism live?

D. TYPES OF SYMBIOSIS

Knowledge about symbiosis has been around for many hundreds of years. The Chinese wrote about worms that lived in the eyes of horses and camels. The Greeks and Romans knew about worms in people and domesticated animals. The word *symbiosis* was coined in 1879 by Heinrich DeBary in Germany. He used it to describe how algae and fungi live together to form lichen.

The meaning of symbiosis has now been expanded. There are three types of symbiotic relationships: *mutualism, commensalism,* and *parasitism.*

In **mutualism**, both organisms benefit from the relationship. Lichens are an example of mutualism. The relationship between insects and flowering plants is another example. The insects get nectar from the flower; the flowers are able to reproduce because the insects carry pollen from flower to flower.

Termites eat wood for their energy. However, they cannot digest the wood. This is done by one-celled organisms that live in the termite's digestive tract. Both organisms benefit from the relationship. No one is hurt.

One-celled organisms from termite intestine

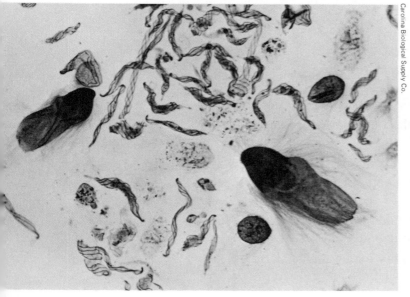

In *commensalism*, only one organism benefits from the relationship. The other is not affected at all. For example, sharks may have small fish called *remoras* attached to them. As the shark feeds, the remoras pick up the scraps. The remora benefits from this relationship. The shark is not affected at all.

Shark and Remora

The relationship between the clown fish and the anemone is another example of commensalism. The anemone feeds by stinging its prey with its tentacles. The clown fish is not affected because of a protective layer of liquid on its body. By living in and near the tentacles of the anemone, the clown fish gets food and protection. The anemone gets nothing from the relationship.

Clown fish and Anemone

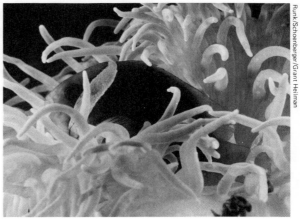

In *parasitism*, one organism lives at the expense of the other. The organism that benefits is the *parasite*. The organism that is harmed is the *host*. Parasites cannot live alone. They must live on a living host. Some parasites do slight harm to their host. Others can kill their host; these must quickly find a new host or die themselves.

Examples of parasite-host relationships are the mistletoe and a tree, a flea and a dog, and a tapeworm and a human.

Mistletoe and Oak tree

35. Name three kinds of symbiosis.

36. Explain and give an example of mutualism.

37. Explain and give an example of commensalism.

38. Explain and give an example of parasitism.

39. What is symbiosis?

40. In symbiosis, where does an organism live?

CONCEPT

ENRICHMENT

1. Visit a veterinarian and find out about worms in dogs.

2. Prepare a bulletin board display showing different kinds of symbiosis.

3. Some parasites require more than one host. The fish tapeworm is an example of such a parasite. Diagram the different hosts that it lives on in its life cycle.

4. You can buy milk that has had acidophilus added to it. What is this and what may it do for your body?

5. Write a paper or prepare a display explaining malaria.

Investigation 5

Food Relationships

Herd of Ibex

Wenzel/Black Star

You have been studying about relationships, how living things are related to each other. You have seen that an organism normally does not live alone. It lives in a group. This allows it to breed with its own kind and

produce offspring, which is necessary for continuing the species. Groups of similar organisms are called *populations*.

UPI

Populations do not live alone either. The relationship of different populations living togther in an area is called a *community*.

321

Grant Heilman

THINK ABOUT...

YOU LEARNED THAT THE HAWK EATS FIELD MICE.

THE HAWK IS THE PREDATOR AND THE FIELD MICE ARE THE PREY.

BUT WHAT DO THE FIELD MICE EAT ?

In the last two Investigations, you saw that a community is a group of organisms living in a *food relationship*. Some organisms produce their own food. Others consume the food that is produced. Others live in a predator-prey relationship. In another food relationship, organisms may live together in symbiosis.

Lettuce, carrots, celery, corn, and green food pellets. They are all the same. They are all parts of green plants. Plants are eaten by field mice. Thus,

$$\text{Plants} \xrightarrow[\text{by}]{\text{eaten}} \text{Field mice} \xrightarrow[\text{by}]{\text{eaten}} \text{Hawk}$$

A. EATING FOR ENERGY

We all eat because we need energy. Food gives us energy. Hawks eat field mice because field mice mean energy. Field mice eat plants because plants mean energy.

1. **Where do green plants get their energy?**

2. **Complete the diagram on your data sheet.**

Some animals eat plants. Some animals eat other animals that have eaten plants. Thus, food passes from plants to animals to other animals. This food relationship is like a chain. By itself, each link is not useful. Put the links together and you have a chain. Living things are related to each other by what they eat. We call this relationship a **food chain**.

Leo deWys, Inc.

Here are some examples of food chains:

(a) Algae ⟶ Daphnia ⟶ Hydra

(b) Grass ⟶ Cow ⟶ Human ⟶ Mosquito

(c) Grass ⟶ Mouse ⟶ Snake ⟶ Hawk

(d) Seeds ⟶ Rat ⟶ Cat ⟶ Flea

(e) Corn ⟶ Chicken ⟶ Human

Look at the food chains carefully. They all have one thing in common.

3. **What do they all start with?**

4. **Where do green plants get their energy?**

5. **Food passes from one organism to another in a food chain. What else passes along a food chain?**

6. **Therefore, what is a food chain?**

B. COMPLETING FOOD CHAINS

Can you find the food chains in these pictures?

7. **Complete the food chain on your data sheet.**

8. **Complete the food chain on your data sheet.**

9. **Complete the food chain on your data sheet.**

10. **Suppose you had some bread for lunch. Draw a food chain which traces the energy back to the sun.**

11. **Why do plants need the sun?**

12. **Why do animals need plants or other animals?**

13. **When does a predator become a prey?**

14. **What is passed along a food chain?**

15. **To whom is energy passed in a food chain?**

16. **What is a food chain?**

C. POISONS IN THE FOOD CHAIN

The Bettmann Archive

In the 19th century, mercury was used to make hats. Some of this mercury got into the body, causing brain damage. Many hat-makers went mad. Lewis Carroll wrote about this problem with his character, the Mad Hatter, in *Alice In Wonderland*.

© 1970 by The New York Times Company.
Reprinted by permission.

F.D.A. Checking Tuna Fish For High Levels of Mercury

DAILY NEW

Mercury in Tuna Leads to Recall

A $3.9 MILLION SUIT IS FILED IN MERCURY POISONING

Mercury found high in 89% of Swordfish tested

Energy may not be the only thing passed along in a food chain. You may have seen newspaper articles about mercury poisoning. For many years you could not fish in Lake St. Clair, which is near Detroit. The fish in this lake had 14 times the safe level of mercury. How did these fish get so much mercury? To answer this question, let's look at the world's most tragic case of ocean pollution.

Minamata is a city in southern Japan. Like most Japanese people, the people of Minamata lived on the products of the sea. They lived in a food relationship with the sea. The fishing boats, which used to fish the area, now lie abandoned. The fishermen no longer proudly talk of their catches.

One day in 1953 a young girl suddenly collapsed from a mysterious disease. During the next years many people died. Those who survived lost the use of their arms and legs and suffered great pain. At first, the mysterious disease was called the "cat dancing" disease. This was because many of the cats in Minamata began to go mad and died in twisting agony.

The source of the problem was soon located. A large fertilizer plant had been dumping waste containing mercury into the sea for years. The fish and the shellfish in the area built up mercury in their bodies. Some fish ate other fish. Then the people ate the fish and shellfish. Since mercury is not eliminated by the body, it builds up in the body. When it reaches a high level, death or damage result. There is no cure for mercury poisoning once it reaches a high level in the body. The fertilizer plant is no longer dumping mercury into the sea.

17. **What was the source of the mercury in Minamata?**

18. **What organisms picked up the mercury first?**

19. **What got the mercury next? How did they get this mercury?**

20. **Who finally got the mercury in the food chain relationship?**

Let's look at another example of how a poison can be passed along in a food chain. The peregrine falcon is an endangered species. This means that very few of them are alive. As recently as 25 years ago, there were many of them. Now peregrine falcons lay eggs that have thin shells which are easily broken during nesting. The problem is DDT, an insect spray. Study the diagram to see how DDT got into the peregrine falcon population.

21. **On what was DDT sprayed?**

22. **What ate the grain sprayed with DDT?**

23. **What eats the field mice?**

24. **What happened to the peregrine falcon?**

25. **What material is passed along in the food chain?**

DDT is presently banned from use in North America and much of the world. Here's one reason. Late in the 1960's, milk was found to have small amounts of DDT in it.

26. **Draw a food chain relationship showing how DDT could get into a person drinking the milk.**

Since DDT was banned, no other insect spray has been invented which is as cheap or as effective. When it was used, DDT saved billions of dollars of crops from insect attack. It also saved millions of human lives from diseases carried by insects. Here's something to think about and discuss.

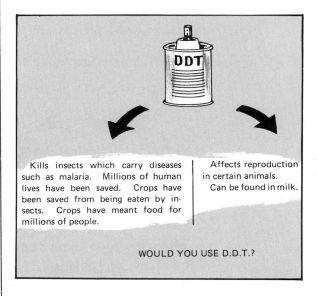

Kills insects which carry diseases such as malaria. Millions of human lives have been saved. Crops have been saved from being eaten by insects. Crops have meant food for millions of people.

Affects reproduction in certain animals. Can be found in milk.

WOULD YOU USE D.D.T.?

D. DON'T BREAK THE CHAIN

You have been doing very well. You have studied food chains. You can even look at a community and find a food chain. Now, we are going to put together some food chains. This will be done with a card game.

Here are the rules of the game (for 2 to 4 players per deck):

To Start: Shuffle well and deal five cards to each player. Place the leftover cards face down on the table. Turn the first card over next to the pile. You now have a draw pile and a discard pile.

To Play: The play starts on the dealer's left and goes clockwise. Each player picks up the top card from either the draw pile or the discard pile. Each player must then discard one card, except when he or she wins. The winner should yell, "Food Chain."

To Win: The winner is the first person to lay down six cards belonging to one food chain.

The cards must be placed down in the correct order. There are five food chains in the deck.

To Renew: If the draw pile runs out, keep the last discard face up. Shuffle the others and place face-down.

E. LINK IT UP

Try to pull yourself away from the game. Let's see what you know.

27. What is passed along in a food chain?

28. What is a food chain?

CONCEPT

Sun → Algae → Shrimp → Small fish → Tuna → Human

Sun → Grass → Insect → Frog → Snake → Hawk

Sun → Seed → Insect → Turtle → Raccoon → Mountain Lion

Sun → Algae → Daphnia → Sunfish → Human → Mosquito

Sun → Leaves → Deer → Wolf → Vulture → Mite

ENRICHMENT

1. The brown pelican almost became an endangered species. Like the peregrine falcon, it too laid eggs with thin shells. How did DDT get into the brown pelican?

2. Prepare a bulletin board display showing some food chain relationships.

3. Describe a food chain relationship in your neighborhood.

4. Research the Minamata disease case. To what degree is the fertilizer plant responsible to the people who have the disease? What should be the government's role?

Investigation 6

Combining Food Chains

Vancouver

Lake Tahoe

Vancouver is a community. Lake Tahoe is a community. Even the park nearest where you live is a community. But Vancouver, Lake Tahoe, and your local park are not just places on a map. Each is a living unit, as alive as you are alive. A community is a living unit which keeps itself alive by passing energy around. Organisms feed on one another, passing energy along in a chainlike fashion. This relationship in a community is known as a *food chain*.

327

The concept of a food chain can be pictured as follows:

Green plant ⟶ Cricket ⟶ Frog ⟶ Snake

A food chain is more than a who-eats-whom relationship. A food chain is an *energy chain*. It shows the relationship that one organism has to another. It also shows the pathway through which energy moves in a community. This complex pathway of energy in a community is the subject of this Investigation.

A. PRODUCERS AND CONSUMERS

What does it take to put 1 kilogram of mass on your body? If you were fishing, it would take about 10 kilograms of trout. For those 10 kilograms, the trout would have to have eaten about 100 kilograms of insects. And those insects would have to have eaten about 1000 kilograms of green plants.

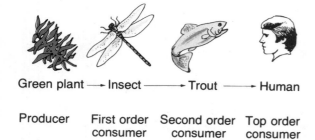

Green plant ⟶ Insect ⟶ Trout ⟶ Human

Producer | First order consumer | Second order consumer | Top order consumer

There are special names for each link in a food chain. The plants are the producers. The plant-eating animals, or herbivores, are called *first order consumers*. The animals that eat the herbivores are called *second order consumers*. The last animals in the chain are the *higher order consumers*. There may be several links within the higher order consumers.

This relationship can be shown as a pyramid. The pyramid shows how energy is transferred from one population to another. Food represents stored energy. The storage begins at the level of the producers. The

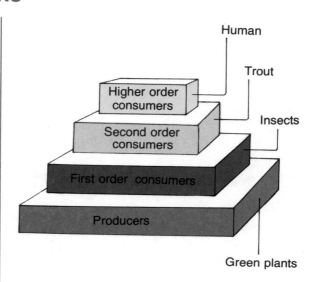

stored energy is the energy that remains after the producers have used what they need for themselves.

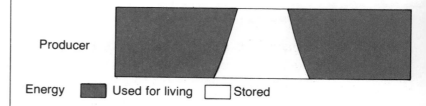

Energy ▪ Used for living ☐ Stored

Now the producers are eaten by the first order consumers. The consumers receive only the energy which remains stored by the producers. This is only a small part of the energy received by the producers from the sun.

First order consumer

Energy ■ Used for living □ Stored

Next, the second order consumer eats the first order consumer. The second order consumer receives the remaining energy stored in the first order consumer.

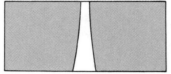

Second order consumer

Energy ▨ Used for living □ Stored

And finally, the higher order consumer eats the second order consumer. Again, only a small part of the energy is transferred.

Putting it together, the energy flow would look like this. The entire level represents the energy taken in by the organisms. The shaded area is the energy need for living. The clear area is the energy that remains.

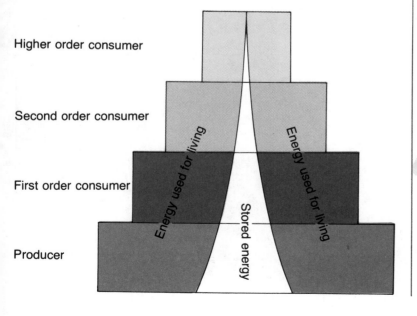

Higher order consumer

Second order consumer

First order consumer

Producer

1. What is a food chain relationship?
2. What is passed in a food chain?
3. What is a producer? Give an example of one.
4. What is a first order consumer? Give an example of one.
5. What is a second order consumer? Give an example of one.
6. What is a higher order consumer? Give an example of one.
7. When one organism eats another, how much energy is transferred?

B. MAKING FOOD WEBS

THINK ABOUT...
PEOPLE AND HAWKS EAT RABBITS, TOO.

AND MOSQUITOES BITE FOXES, RABBITS, AND COWS, TOO.

A FOX MIGHT EAT A MOUSE AND A SNAKE.

THERE IS NO LONGER A CHAIN.

The concept of a food chain has a limitation. Most organisms do not eat only one other organism. They eat many kinds of organisms. In turn, they may be eaten by several kinds of organisms. Food chains are really part of a bigger picture.

This is what your picture would look like.

8. Look at page D201. Cut out the pictures of the worm, fish, and person.

9. Paste the three pictures in Space A on page D198. Draw an arrow from the worm to the fish. Draw another arrow from the fish to the person.

You have just put together a simple food chain.

10. Cut out the pictures of the rabbit, carrot, and cow.

11. Add these pictures to Space A. Draw all the new arrows needed to show food relationships.

Now, you do not have a chain. You are beginning to get a picture that looks like a web.

12. Cut out the pictures of the cat, grass, and horse.

13. Add these pictures to Space A. Draw all the new arrows needed.

With all the arrows crossing back and forth, you have something that looks like a web. This is called a *food web*. A food web consists of many food chains put together. It shows the food relationships in a community.

14. What do you call many food chains put together?

15. What does a food web show?

C. IT KEEPS A COMMUNITY ALIVE

Here is a picture of a pond community.

Some of the living things in the community are:

(a) Bass   (d) Human   (g) Plants
(b) Frog   (e) Sunfish   (h) Snail
(c) Fly   (f) Minnows   (i) Turtle

16. Use words and arrows to draw a food web of these 9 organisms in Space B.

You have just drawn a food web of life in a pond. The pond is a community. Life continues as long as there is food.

17. What does a food web tell us about living things?

18. What does a food web tell us about a community?

19. What is a food web?

D. IT KEEPS US GOING

You have been doing very well. You have drawn two food webs. Let's see if you can make one up on your own.

20. Get an index card. Write the name of one living thing or part of a plant on the card. You may draw a picture too.

This is a class activity. Your task is to create a food web. Your teacher may ask you to use the chalkboard, bulletin board, or a large sheet of paper.

21. Your teacher will begin by sticking "Sun" to the board.

22. If you have something that needs the sun, raise your hand. Attach your card to the board. Draw the arrows that are needed.

23. See if your organism will eat the new organism just posted. If it does, raise your hand. Attach your card to the board. Draw the arrows.

24. **Draw new arrows as you see new relationships.**

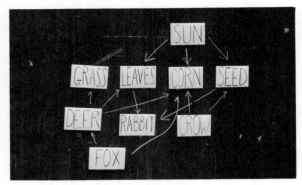

25. **Continue to add all the cards, if possible. Try not to get caught without a place in the food web for your organism.**

26. **If an organism does not get posted, what will happen to it?**

27. **What does a food web tell us about life?**

28. **What is a food web?**

E. WE'RE ALL PART OF A WEB

Energy is what it's all about. All living things need energy to live. Energy comes from food. Therefore, living things must live where they can get food. A community consists of many populations living together in a food relationship. You can't have one population without another. Populations are *dependent* on each other.

29. **Populations are dependent on each other. What does that mean?**

30. **What is a community?**

31. **How are a food web and a community related?**

32. **What is a food web?**

CONCEPT

ENRICHMENT

1. Construct a bulletin board display showing a food web relationship.

2. Look at the area where you live. Draw a food web showing the relationships in your community.

3. How does the sun fit into a food web?

4. How do bacteria and mushrooms fit into a food web?

5. Retrieve from the board the card that you used in Part D. Stand in class with your card in one hand. Run strings from your other hand to all the other organisms that have a food relationship with you. When this is finished, what does the class represent? The teacher will cut one or more strings. If this deprives you of food, what happens? What happens to the food web?

Investigation 7

This Is Our World

"This land is your land; this land is my land,
From California to the New York island,
From the redwood forest to the Gulf Stream waters;
This land was made for you and me."

Woody Guthrie

THIS LAND IS YOUR LAND
Words & music by Woody Guthrie
TRO — © copyright 1956 & 1958 Ludlow Music, Inc., New York, N.Y.
Used by permission.

New York Times

Public Housing Administration

Which one of these two communities will be your land? The decision is up to you. No organism lives alone. All living things interact with each other to make a community. But living things do more than just interact. They depend on each other for survival. The word for this relationship is *interdependent*.

333

A. THE COMMUNITY GAME

Jeff Foxx

To help you see how living things are interdependent upon each other, let's play a game. The game is *Community*. Your teacher will read the directions and help you play it.

Setting Up — Each Player

a. Sit facing one side of the game board.
b. Get 2 people pieces. Place them in apartment 4-A on your side of board. This is your family.
c. Get 8 resource pieces.
d. Get 8 money pieces.
e. Choose a player piece.
f. Roll the dice to see who goes first.

Setting Up the Board

g. Place 8 resources in the dump.
h. Place the extra resources in the resources circle on the board.
i. Place the extra people in the people circle on the board.
j. Place the extra money in the bank.

k. Shuffle and stack the decision cards on the board.
l. Place the player pieces at start.

To Play

m. Each player rolls the dice and moves his or her player piece forward the number of spaces indicated.
n. When you land on a space, do what it says:
   (a) Take resources from the resources circle.
   (b) To dump a resource, place it in the dump. Do not take resources out of the dump unless told to.
   (c) Take money from and pay it to the bank.
   (d) Add people pieces to your family from the board.
o. When you land on *decision*, another player will draw a decision card for you. He or she will read the top of the card to you. You must choose either A or B. Then he or she will read the result of your

decision from the bottom of the card. Do what the card says. Then replace it at the bottom of the stack.

p. When you add people to your family . . .
(a) Fill up apartment 4-A first.
(b) If your family outgrows 4-A, you will have to move them all to Apt. 6-B. But your rent will go up; you will have to pay the bank 1 money piece.
(c) If your family outgrows 6-B, you will have to move them all to 8-C. You will also have to pay the bank 2 money pieces.
(d) If your family outgrows 8-C, you lose the game.

q. You lose if you run out of resources or money.

r. When you pass start, take 1 money piece from the bank.

s. To win: stay in the game the longest.

The next five questions are related to the Community Game you have just played.

1. **What is a community?**

2. **What happens to the population when factors in the community are changed?**

3. **What happens to some communities as changes are made?**

4. **Explain the word interdependent.**

5. **How must living things live in a community?**

B. THERE'S MORE TO A COMMUNITY

The community is a living unit. The three major kinds of living things in a community are non-green plants, green plants, and animals. These living things are interdependent upon each other. They depend upon each other for survival.

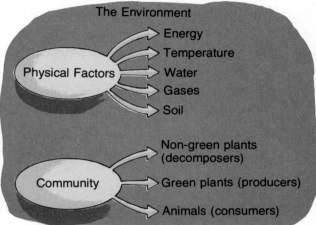

The Environment

Physical Factors → Energy, Temperature, Water, Gases, Soil

Community → Non-green plants (decomposers), Green plants (producers), Animals (consumers)

Living things depend upon proper conditions in the environment for survival too. You studied these conditions, called physical factors, in Idea 8. Some of these factors are energy, temperature, water, gases, and soil. The environment contains the physical factors that surround a community.

The study of the relationships of living things to each other and to their physical environment is called *ecology*.

Ecologists are people who study relationships between living things in their environment. They have a name for all of the relationships necessary for life in an area. It

Ecologist

is ecosystem. An *ecosystem* is the relationship between the community and the physical factors in the environment. An ecosystem may be an aquarium with fish, snails, plants, water, and sand. It may be an astronaut in a spaceship. Or it may be a forest, river, or pond.

Several kinds of relationships occur in an ecosystem:

(1) The relationships among living things in a community.

(2) The relationships among the physical factors in the environment.

(3) The relationships between the community and the environment.

These relationships can be seen as follows:

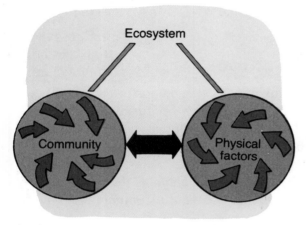

And now, a new level of relationships can be added.

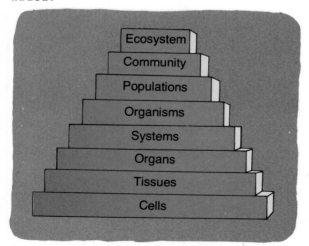

6. **Name the three major kinds of living things in a community.**

7. **Name five physical factors in the environment.**

8. **What is ecology?**

9 **What is an ecosystem?**

10. **What relationships occur in an ecosystem?**

C. WHAT IS AN AQUARIUM?

An aquarium can help you to understand an ecosystem.

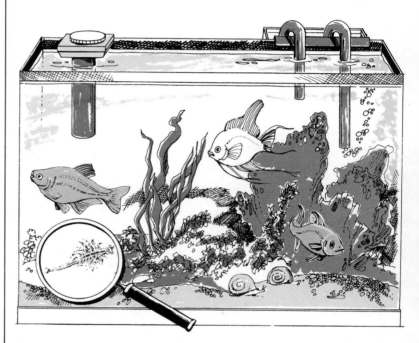

11. **Name the living things in the aquarium.**

12. **What do the fish eat?**

13. **What do the snails eat?**

14. **What do living things supply to each other?**

15. **What do you call the place where living things interact with each other?**

16. **What do green plants need for life?**

17. **How are the temperature and water important to the living things in an aquarium?**

18. What two gases are needed by the living things in the aquarium?

19. What is the function of the soil?

20. What do you call the physical factors that surround a community?

21. Re-read Questions 15 and 20. What relationship occurs in an ecosystem?

22. What is an aquarium?

23. What is an ecosystem?

D. GET THE RELATIONSHIPS TOGETHER

You have been studying relationships in this Idea. In the beginning Investigations, you studied relationships in a population. In the next few Investigations, you studied relationships in a community. And in this Investigation, you have studied relationships in an ecosystem.

Review Parts B and C. Re-read Questions 9 and 23.

24. What two parts make up an ecosystem?

25. How are these two parts related?

26. What is an ecosystem?

CONCEPT

WORDS TO KNOW

The following words have been used in this Idea. Carefully review the Idea and define each of them on your data sheet.

Biome	Food web
Commensalism	Interdependent
Community	Mutualism
Consumer	Parasitism
Density	Population
Ecologist	Predator
Ecology	Prey
Ecosystem	Producer
Fluctuation	Symbiosis
Food chain	

SUMMARY OF THE IDEA: THE RELATIONSHIPS OF LIFE

All living things are related to each other and to the physical factors in the environment. No living thing survives alone. No physical factor operates by itself, either. *Living things live in an interdependent relationship with each other and their environment.*

Organisms of the same kind tend to live together. Ducks migrate together; bees build colonies together; and tuna swim together. Groups of similar organisms are called populations. This relationship provides for reproduction of the species. Different populations, in turn, live together in a community. A community is a living unit because energy is constantly being transferred. Energy is transferred from producer to consumer. Sometimes one consumer eats another consumer. That is a predator-prey relationship. Sometimes they live together. That is symbiosis.

Living things in a community are affected by the environment. The relationship between the living things in a community and the physical factors in the environment is an ecosystem. The relationships in an ecosystem are interdependent.

In this Idea on relationships you have studied seven concepts.

1. State these seven concepts.

A forest is not just a place where trees grow. A forest is an ecosystem. All kinds of interdependent relationships can be seen in a forest.

Study the picture of the forest as you answer all of these questions.

2. Name or describe some populations in the picture of the forest.

3. What part of the forest is the community?

4. List or describe the producers you see in the picture.

5. What is the source of energy for the producers?

6. What other factors affect life in a forest?

7. List or describe some consumers.

8. There are some frogs in the picture. What does a frog need to stay alive?

9. What will the frog eat?

10. What do you call the animal that does the eating?

11. What do you call the animal that is eaten?

12. Name an animal that might eat the frog.

13. State the relationship when one animal eats another.

14. Describe one food chain.

15. Draw a simple food web.

16. What must all the organisms in a food web obtain to stay alive?

17. How are all the plants and animals in a forest related to each other?

18. What is a community?

19. What are water, light, temperature, and soil?

20. Review Questions 18 and 19. What must living things interact with?

21. What is an interdependent relationship?

Combine your answers to Questions 20 and 21 to summarize the Idea.

IDEA SUMMARY

ENRICHMENT

1. What are some careers available for someone interested in ecology?

2. Make a movie showing conditions in your community or ecosystem.

3. Prepare a bulletin board display explaining the concept of interdependence.

Investigation 1

Over and Over Again

Larry Berman/Leo deWys, Inc.

Skiing is fun. Especially on a long run. But skiing is not all downhill. You have to go up the hill before you can go down.

Skiing down a hill and going up the hill is a cycle that goes around and around.

Everett C. Johnson/Leo deWys, Inc.

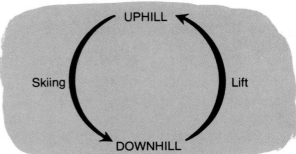

Life is full of cycles. For instance, you studied about photosynthesis and respiration. These two processes represent the cycle that furnishes energy to living things.

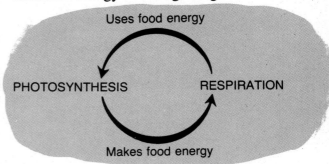

Directly or indirectly, all living things get their energy from the sun. But they get the materials of life from the earth. The food, water, and air that we use are all limited to the amounts present on earth. These materials must be used over and over again. Such a circulation of materials is known as a *cycle*. In this Idea you will study about three cycles: the water cycle, the oxygen-carbon dioxide cycle, and the nutrient cycle.

339

A. DO PLANTS PERSPIRE?

The **water cycle** is the movement of water from the atmosphere to the earth and then back again to the atmosphere. Water leaves the atmosphere mostly as rain or snow. Water returns to the atmosphere by evaporation. This is a cycle in itself.

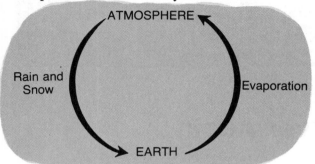

Living things also return water to the atmosphere. Animals do it through breathing and evaporation from the skin. In plants, water is lost mainly through the leaves. During the growing season a single corn plant can move 200 liters of water from the soil into the atmosphere. The passage of water out of the leaves of plants is called **transpiration**. Let's investigate this process.

1. Observe the transpiration device given to your team. Notice that both the tubing and the end of the cut stem are under water.

Your plant has many leaves. These leaves have thousands of stomates. Water will pass into the freshly cut stem, up the plant, and out through the stomates. As it does, the water level in the tubing will go down.

2. Mark the water level in the tubing.

3. Do not handle or touch the transpiration device any more than you have to. The heat or pressure of your hand can affect it.

4. **What time is it?**

5. Wait 8 minutes. After 8 minutes make a mark at the new water level.

6. Measure this distance and record it next to "Indoors" in Table 1.

7. Carefully place a plastic bag over your plant. Tie the bag at the bottom. Notice that the bag goes *only* over the plant and *not* the tubing.

8. **What time is it?**

9. Wait 8 minutes. While waiting, read the following paragraph and answer Question 10.

You have just measured the rate of transpiration for your plant in a normal indoor environment. Now you will see how a plant's transpiration rate changes when the amount of water vapor in its environment changes. The plastic bag increases the amount of water vapor surrounding the plant.

10. **Make a prediction. How will the amount of water vapor surrounding a plant affect its transpiration rate?**

11. After 8 minutes, mark the new water level.

12. Measure this distance and record it next to "Increased water vapor" in Table 1.

13. Remove the plastic bag. Place your transpiration device outdoors in the sunlight. If there is no sun, use a lamp in your classroom.

14. **What time is it?**

15. Wait 8 minutes.

16. **While waiting, predict whether the outdoor transpiration rate will increase or decrease compared to the indoor rate. Explain your prediction.**

17. After 8 minutes, mark the new water level.

18. Measure this distance and record it next to "Outdoors" in Table 1.

19. **What condition caused the most transpiration?**

20. **What condition caused the least transpiration?**

21. **Define transpiration.**

22. **What part do plants play in the water cycle?**

B. THE WATER CYCLE

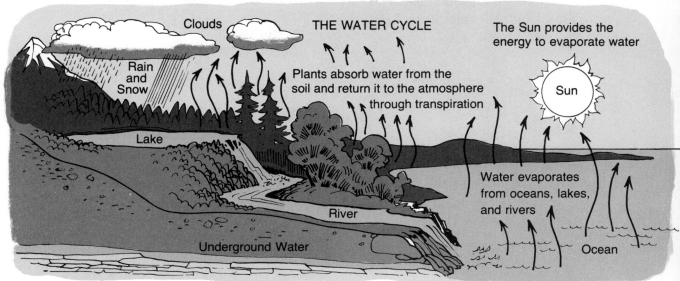

THE WATER CYCLE

Clouds

Rain and Snow

Lake

River

Underground Water

Plants absorb water from the soil and return it to the atmosphere through transpiration

The Sun provides the energy to evaporate water

Sun

Water evaporates from oceans, lakes, and rivers

Ocean

As water leaves the atmosphere, it may fall directly into the oceans. It may also fall on land, where it begins a journey through streams, rivers, lakes, and underground channels to reach the oceans. All along the way some of the water goes back into the atmosphere by evaporation.

Living things take in water at various points in this cycle. Animals get their water by drinking and eating. Plants get their water by absorbing it from the soil.

Eventually, all water taken in by living things returns to the atmosphere. Plants return water to the atmosphere by transpiration. Animals return water to the atmosphere through breathing and evaporation. And the water cycle keeps going around and around.

23. What provides the energy for evaporation?
24. Where does evaporated water come from?
25. How do plants return water to the atmosphere?
26. How do animals return water to the atmosphere?
27. What is the water cycle?
28. Explain why the movement of water on earth is called a cycle.
29. How does water move on the earth?

CONCEPT

ENRICHMENT

1. Place the transpiration device in front of a fan. How does wind affect the transpiration rate?
2. Set up a display showing the many ways people use water.
3. How much water does a dog or other pet use each day?

Investigation 2

Do We Drink This?

Through cycles, many materials necessary for life are continuously made available. You studied one cycle, the water cycle, in the last Investigation. A cycle must stay in **balance**. It is like a tire that needs balancing. When you buy a tire, it should be balanced before it is put on the car. Weights are put on the wheel to balance the tire. If the tire is not in balance, it will wear out faster on one side than on the other.

Like a tire, the water cycle must also stay in balance. Water pollution can upset the water cycle. **Water pollution** is the contamination of water, making it harmful for living things.

There are three major kinds of water pollution: chemical wastes, heat, and sewage. Chemical wastes can include all of the materials left over from manufacturing processes. They can be the detergents used by industries, businesses, and homes. Or they can be the tons of fertilizers and pesticides used by farmers. Many of these chemicals cannot be broken down. In fact, they may increase in concentration as the chemicals are passed along a food chain. You studied this in Idea 10.

Jay Hoops/Leo deWys, Inc.

Excess heat in water is called *thermal pollution*. It can come from power plants that use water to cool their generators. The water is then returned to the source; only now it is warmer than before. Warm water holds less oxygen, thus limiting the number and kind of organisms that can live in it.

Leo deWys, Inc.

Sewage is most dangerous in terms of health. It contains animal wastes, decaying matter, and disease-causing bacteria. Water polluted with sewage looks and smells foul.

Phiz Mezey/dpi

A. THE NATURAL WAY

Unlike chemical wastes, sewage can be broken down. This is done naturally by bacteria, and the process is called *decomposition*.

For decomposition to happen, there must not be too much sewage. There must be an adequate supply of oxygen. And the water temperature must be correct. If these conditions are present, the self-purification process takes place as follows:

Zone of pollution. This area lies at the source of pollution. The sewage can be seen floating in the water. The oxygen content is low. There are few large living things such as fish. Bacteria and stringy algae are in great number.

Zone of decomposition. In this area the oxygen is almost gone. There are no fish. The water is dark in color. There is a foul odor caused by decomposition of the sewage by the bacteria.

Zone of recovery. In this area, the amount of oxygen is higher. The amount of sewage is lower. The water looks better. Fish and other animals can survive.

Zone of clean water. The water has returned to its original appearance before being polluted. It is clear and free of floating sewage. The oxygen content is high. And fish and other living things are plentiful.

Nature has a way of purifying water if the balance is not upset too greatly.

1. How is a cycle in delicate balance?
2. What is pollution?
3. What are the three major kinds of pollution?
4. Explain chemical pollution.
5. Explain thermal pollution.
6. What is sewage?
7. What is decomposition?
8. How is water naturally purified?

B. HELPING NATURE

Nature does most of the job of purifying or recycling polluted water. Sometimes water is so polluted that people must give nature a hand. That's the only way we can obtain a clean, clear, tasty, odorless, and germ-free water supply. Let's investigate some of the ways we can help nature recycle water.

9. Obtain a sealed test tube of muddy water and a test tube rack.
10. Hold your finger over the seal. Shake the tube vigorously.

11. Place your tube in the rack. Do not touch it for 5 minutes.
12. After 5 minutes, observe your test tube. Do not touch it.
13. **Describe what you see.**

14. **The mud represents solid waste pollutants. What happened to the mud?**

What you have discovered is one method of purifing water. It is called *sedimentation.* During sedimentation the heavy, undissolved pollutants settle to the bottom.

15. **Why wouldn't you drink the relatively clear water at the top of the test tube?**

16. Obtain a funnel from your teacher. It has been prepared with a layer of paper covered with clean gravel.

17. Shake your sealed test tube again. The pollutant (mud) should be evenly distributed throughout the water.

18. *Slowly* pour the polluted water through the funnel into a clean test tube.

19. Observe the collected water.

20. **How does the water in the test tube compare to the original polluted water?**

21. **Where are most of the pollutants now?**

This method of purifying water is called *filtration*. Filltration means letting water pass through something that catches particles. The water passes through and the solid pollutants are trapped in the filter.

22. **Why wouldn't you drink the clear water passing through the filter?**

You're right in not wanting to drink the filtered water. Sedimentation and filtration remove most of the solid pollutants but can still leave water tasting and smelling bad. Your filtered water may still contain dissolved chemical poisons or even harmful bacteria.

23. **What are two ways of purifying water?**

24. **What is not removed from polluted water by sedimentation and filtration?**

The water cycle is nature's way of providing pure, clean water to living things.

25. **What can water pollution upset?**

C. THE UNSEEN POLLUTION

Many bacteria are helpful, such as the kind that cause decomposition of sewage. Some bacteria are harmful and can cause disease. A water technician tests water for its purity. One of the tests is for the presence of bacteria that can cause disease and death. Let's check water for bacteria.

26. **Obtain a petri dish with bacteria food.** *Keep the dish closed.*

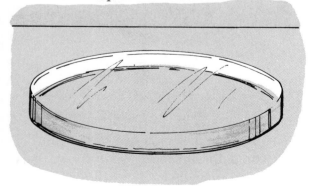

27. **Label the dish on the rim.**

28. **Draw a "Y" on the bottom of the dish. It should divide the dish into 3 roughly equal parts.**

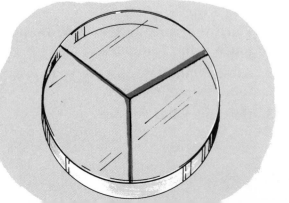

29. Mark "D" for drinking water in one section, "P" for polluted water in another, and "C" for chlorine in the last.

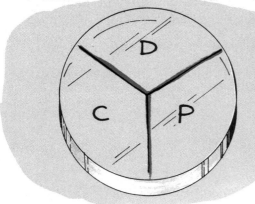

30. Place the petri dish on a table. The dish must be kept level through Step 35.

31. Now remove the lid. Place 1 drop of drinking water in section "D."

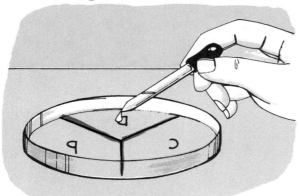

32. Place 1 drop of polluted water in section "P."

33. Place another drop of polluted water in section "C."

34. Your teacher will add a drop of chlorine to your "C" section right on top of the drop of polluted water.

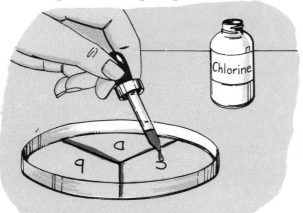

35. Your teacher will seal your dishes and collect them for storage.

36. Wait 2 or 3 days. Go on to Questions 37-40.

37. What two kinds of water did you use?

38. What do you predict will grow where the drinking water was placed?

39. What do you predict will grow where the polluted water was placed *without* chlorine?

40. What do you predict will grow where the polluted water was treated *with* chlorine?

41. After a few days, observe your petri dish. *Do not open it.*

CAUTION! DO NOT OPEN YOUR PETRI DISH

42. What do you observe in section "D"?

43. What do you observe in section "P"?

44. What do you observe in section "C"?

45. Which section has the *least* growth?

46. Which section has the *most* growth?

47. Where must these organisms have come from?

48. What can chlorine be used for?

49. What might happen to people or animals which drink water polluted with bacteria?

There may be many bacteria in every glass of water you drink. Most of these bacteria are harmless. However, if the water you drink comes from a source polluted by human or animal wastes, it must be treated. Untreated water can cause such diseases as hepatitis, typhoid, and amebic dysentery. These diseases are common killers in many places where the only water available is polluted.

50. What can water pollution upset?

CONCEPT

ENRICHMENT

1. You used paper and gravel as your filter. Experiment with other kinds of filters to find the best material.

2. What else can be used, besides chlorine, to kill the bacteria in polluted water? Set up a controlled experiment using different kinds of antiseptics.

3. Make a model of a water purification or sewage treatment plant.

4. Laundry detergents are a source of water pollution. Set up a controlled experiment with young seedlings. Grow some with pure water. Grow others with water polluted with detergents.

5. Research how sea water can be desalted. Report your findings back to the class.

6. Do a report on aeration, fluoridation, and ultra-violet light as methods of purifying water.

Living Dangerously

New York Public Library

During the early 1770's, Joseph Priestley, an English chemist, performed an interesting experiment. Using a magnifying glass, Priestley focused the sun's rays on a red powder. He noted that a substance was given off. Priestley called this substance ''air'' and claimed that it had unusual properties. Priestley placed a mouse in a sealed jar containing his ''air.'' He found that the mouse could live longer in his newly discovered ''air'' than in ordinary air. He also learned that his ''air'' caused a candle to burn with a brighter flame. Today, the ''air'' discovered by Priestley is known as oxygen.

The air we breathe is mostly nitrogen and oxygen. It also contains small amounts of carbon dioxide. These gases are part of the earth's resource cycles. Oxygen and carbon dioxide are used again and again.

You studied the water cycle in an earlier Investigation.

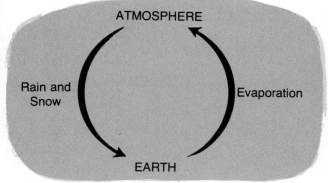

The air we breathe is also cycled. During respiration, animals take in and use oxygen. They give off carbon dioxide as a waste product. Green plants take in carbon dioxide during photosynthesis. They give off oxygen

349

as a waste product. The *oxygen-carbon dioxide cycle* can be illustrated in the following way.

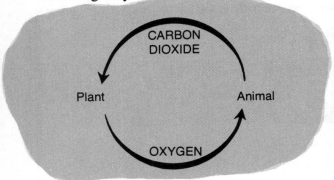

The Oxygen-Carbon Dioxide Cycle

Life depends on these cycles staying in balance. They are part of an ecosystem. An ecosystem includes all the living and non-living factors. These factors must interact with each other to keep the system in balance. What happens if the resource runs out? What happens if the balance is upset?

A. TRAPPED IN JELLY

Do you know that you breathe more than 15,000 liters of air each day? You need the air because of the oxygen. Your body uses oxygen to get energy from foods. But there are other substances in the air besides oxygen, nitrogen, and carbon dioxide. Many of these things are harmful. Some may cause disease and even death.

1. Get 4 microscope slides, 3 punched cards, petroleum jelly, tape, and an envelope.

2. Label all 3 cards.

3. Print "Inside" on the first card, "Outside" on the second, and "Home" on the third.

4. Place a small amount of petroleum jelly in the center of 3 glass slides. Do not place jelly on the fourth slide.

5. Use the end of the fourth slide to spread the jelly. It should be even and smooth. Cover only the center of each slide.

6. Tape a card onto each of the 3 jellied slides. The tape should be only on the ends of the slides.

7. Check the jelly inside the punched hole. It should be smooth. If there isn't a smooth layer, make a new slide.

8. Place the "Home" slide in the envelope and take it home. Put it where you think it will collect some dust.

9. Give your teacher the other 2 slides. They will be placed inside and outside of your classroom.

10. After 2 days, examine each of your slides with the microscope. Use low power. Move each slide around slowly to see all the particles inside the punched hole.

You will probably see many particles. A particle is a small speck of solid or liquid material in the air. Some are large and some are very small. Count the number of medium to large particles. Do not count the very small particles.

11. Count the number of particles on the "Inside" slide. Record your count in Table 1 on your data sheet.

12. Count the number of particles on the "Outside" slide. Record your count in Table 1.

13. Count the number of particles on the "Home" slide. Record your count in Table 1.

14. **Which of your 3 slides had the most particles?**

15. **Where was this slide placed?**

16. **Which of your 3 slides had the fewest particles?**

17. **Where was this slide placed?**

18. **Compare results with your classmates. Find out who had the slide with the highest particle count. Where was it placed?**

19. **Find out who had the slide with the lowest particle count. Where was it placed?**

20. **Besides gases, what else is in the air you breathe?**

B. THE LAST GASP

"ON A CLEAR DAY YOU CAN SEE THE SMOG IN THREE STATES."

Anything in the air that may be harmful to living things is a *pollutant*. The particles you saw under the microscope may make up *air pollution*.

Sometimes you can see air pollutants, such as soot and smoke. We call it smog. Most pollutants are too small to see except with a microscope. Some are poisonous gases; you can't see them at all. But they add up. In one way or another they destroy parts of the environment.

How destructive is polluted air? Here are some examples.

Polluted air can kill plants. Nearly 200,000 acres of evergreens in Southern California have already been affected.

Pollution like this killed people in Donora, Pennsylvania, and London, England.

In 1900 a copper refinery in Tennessee poured out clouds of poisonous gas. The gas killed all of the plant life in the area. It also poisoned the soil so badly that it is impossible to grow plants there even today.

21. **Why do you think these children in Tokyo wear masks on smoggy days?**

22. **Why do you think children in Los Angeles are excused from physical education on smoggy days?**

C. KEEP THE AIR CLEAN

Air is a resource. As with other resources, there is a limited supply. Factories, automobiles, and even cigarettes all add pollutants to the air.

23. **What is air pollution?**

24. **How can air pollution affect plants?**

25. **How can air pollution affect people?**

26. **What effect does air pollution have on the environment?**

Re-read your answer to Question 26. Write the concept.

CONCEPT

ENRICHMENT

1. Prepare a collage on air pollution.
2. Organize a panel to discover ways to improve the quality of the air.
3. Write to the Environmental Protection Agency office nearest your community. What is being done to improve the quality of air in your community?
4. How do pollutant particles affect plants? Cover the bottom surface of several leaves on a plant with petroleum jelly. After several days, examine the plant leaves. Report your observations and conclusions.
5. Why is pollen considered a natural pollutant?

Investigation 4

The Cycle Goes On

Mimi Forsyth/Monkmeyer

Recycling has become a popular household word. Everyone's recycling today. We see more and more paper products made of recycled paper. Most aluminum cans have the word ''RECYCLE'' clearly printed on them. Even iron, rubber, and glass have joined the recycling craze.

Crow/Monkmeyer

355

We use enormous amounts of paper, aluminum, iron, rubber, and glass in our everyday lives. In the past, once these materials were used, most were thrown away and left to rot. People have paid a high price for this waste. It has cost pollution and ugliness. But there is another aspect to recycling. As with water and air, all resources are limited. In some way, we have to put them back into the system. In this way, a balance in the ecosystem can be maintained.

Let's take a look at another cycle needed to keep the ecosystem in balance.

A. CHEESE AND BACTERIA

Have you ever stopped to think about how much garbage is produced in the United States each day? The thought may not be pleasant, but it is important. It is estimated that the average person produces more than two kilograms of garbage each day. Multiply this by the population of the United States and the figure is staggering. More than 400 million kilograms of garbage are produced daily.

Leaves fall off trees by the million. Plants and animals die. What happens to all of these waste products?

1. **Label half of a petri dish.**

2. **Spread some blue cheese onto a piece of bread.**

3. **Put the bread in the dish. Do not cover.**

4. **Store in a warm, dark place for several days.**

5. Observe the bread and cheese each
   day. Record your observations in
   Table 1 on your data sheet.

There are thousands of different kinds of
bacteria. Only a small number of these are
harmful. Actually, most are helpful and very
important, as you have seen. For example,

bacteria are used to make sauerkraut,
vinegar, leather, and linen. Bacteria are also
used to give flavor to butter and cheese; one
kind is used to make blue cheese.

6. What happened to the bread?
7. What do you think caused this to
   happen?

B. THE NUTRIENT CYCLE

Lopez/N.Y.C. Department of Water Resources

This is a part of a sewage treatment plant.
The round tanks contain stored waste
materials. Bacteria are added to the tanks to
speed up decay. Once the waste materials
decay, they are used as fertilizer. This is an
example of just one of the ways that plant
and animal wastes are recycled. Through
decay, they are returned to the soil and are
thus put back into the *nutrient cycle*.

Nitrogen is the key to the nutrient cycle.
Plants must have nitrogen for the

manufacture of protein. These plant proteins
serve as food for all animals through the
links in a food chain. But there is a problem.
Plants cannot use the nitrogen directly from
the air. Nitrogen must be supplied to plants
in another form. It must be combined with
other substances. How does it happen?
Where does it take place? The answer is
bacteria. Bacteria in the soil and in the roots
of some plants change nitrogen into a usable
form. This usable nitrogen is then taken in

by plants and changed to make proteins which are the foods for animals.

8. **Why must plants have nitrogen?**

9. **What do plant proteins serve as?**

10. **What must be done to the nitrogen in the air before it can be used by plants?**

11. **How does this change come about?**

This is only one example of the role of nitrogen in the nutrient cycle. Here is another.

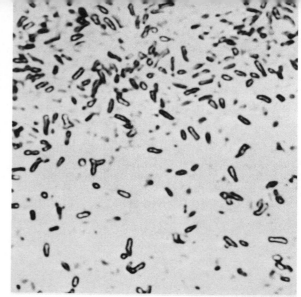

Walter Dawn

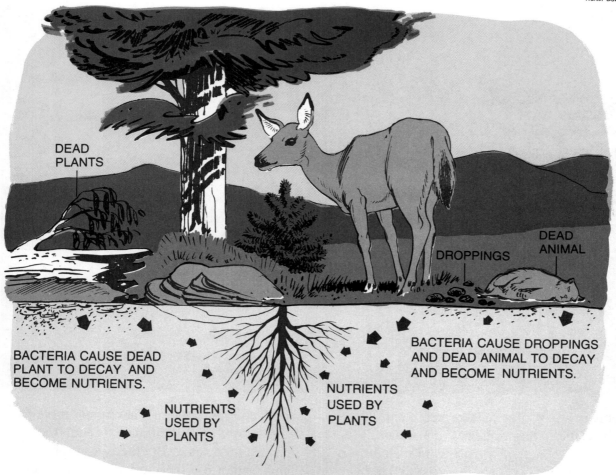

DEAD PLANTS

DROPPINGS

DEAD ANIMAL

BACTERIA CAUSE DEAD PLANT TO DECAY AND BECOME NUTRIENTS.

NUTRIENTS USED BY PLANTS

NUTRIENTS USED BY PLANTS

BACTERIA CAUSE DROPPINGS AND DEAD ANIMAL TO DECAY AND BECOME NUTRIENTS.

Study the drawing carefully.

12. **When plants or parts of plants die, what happens to them?**

13. **What happens to animals that die?**

14. **What happens to animal droppings?**

15. **What causes materials to decay?**

16. **What living things use the nutrients in the decayed materials?**

17. **Who eats the plants?**

18. **What is going around in this cycle?**

C. ROUND AND ROUND

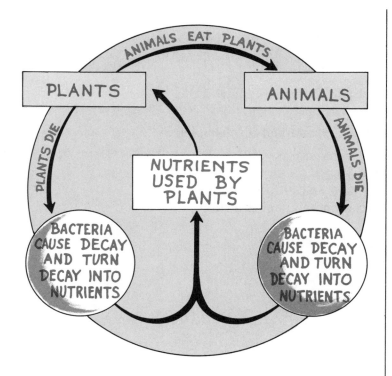

Animals and plants are part of the nutrient cycle. Nutrients are foods, minerals, and other materials needed by plants and animals to stay alive. Nutrients move in a cycle. They move from plants and animals to the soil. In the soil, they decay. As they decay, bacteria change the nitrogen in them into a usable form. Once this happens, the nutrients are again able to move back to plants. From the plants, nutrients move to animals once more as the cycle is repeated.

19. **What causes plants and animals to decay?**

20. **The decayed materials are changed into nutrients and dissolved in soil water. What takes in the dissolved nutrients?**

21. **How do animals take in nutrients?**

22. **How do animals put nutrients back into the cycle?**

23. **How do plants put nutrients back into the cycle?**

24. **How do living things put nutrients back into the cycle?**

25. **What is constantly happening to nutrients?**

Re-read your answer to Question 25. Write the concept.

CONCEPT

Grant Heilman

ENRICHMENT

1. Prepare a discussion on the need for more protein in the world's diet and on how this protein may be obtained.
2. Design another experiment that will also show mold or bacterial growth and decomposition.
3. What is the nitrogen cycle? What part do bacteria play in this cycle?
4. What are legumes? Report on these plants and discuss their importance in the nutrient cycle.
5. Additional reports can be written on:
   (a) the processes of ammonification and nitrification.
   (b) the processes of nitrogen fixation and denitrification.
   (c) bacterial decomposition.
   (d) the operations of a sewage disposal plant.

Investigation 5

Our Greatest Resource

Leo deWys, Inc.

Mimi Forsyth/Monkmeyer

Water is an important resource. Air is an important resource. Most of the time water and air can be recycled and used again. But there is one resource that cannot be recycled. That is the life of an individual. Indeed, our greatest resource is life itself.

Leo deWys, Inc.

Steve Eagle/Nancy Palmer

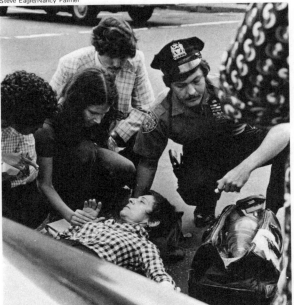

361

Most everyone values life. You can see it in the faces of those who worry about someone else's life. You can also see it in the faces of those who have created a new life.

At the San Francisco airport, this mobile unit rushes out to an airplane. It's function is to help maintain the life of a passenger as it moves through the airport.

We value life so much that we have all kinds of devices and machines that sustain life. It may be a device placed inside the body that keeps the heart beating. This device is called a *pacemaker*.

Some people make a commitment to protect the lives of other living things. Would you make the same commitment?

A. LIFE IS FOR LIVING

This book has been about life. The first seven Ideas were about the life of an organism.

Silberstein/Monkmeyer

Why is this lamb a living thing?

1. In Idea 2 you studied the characteristics of living things. What are these characteristics?

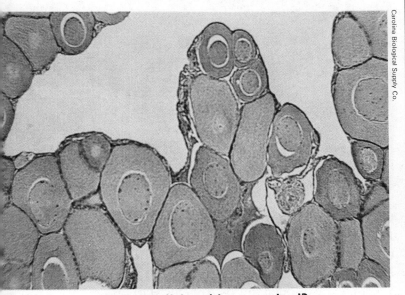

Carolina Biological Supply Co.

How is a living thing organized?

2. Idea 3 was about cells. Starting with cells, explain how a living thing is organized.

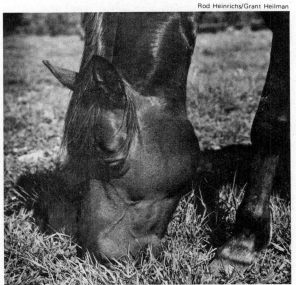

Rod Heinrichs/Grant Heilman

How do plants and animals obtain energy?

3. Ideas 4 and 5 were about energy. Explain the process by which plants obtain energy.

4. Explain how animals break down food to get energy.

United Nations

What are the systems of the human body?

5. You studied some human systems in Idea 6. What are these systems?

6. Idea 7 was about reproduction. Explain the difference between asexual and sexual reproduction.

The last four Ideas have been about the environment. The environment consists of physical and biological factors. Living things survive by adjusting to the physical and biological factors.

7. **Name the physical factors of the environment.**

8. **Name the three major kinds of living things in the environment.**

9. **Explain the concept of an ecosystem.**

10. **Draw a diagram that shows how living things are organized from cell to ecosystem.**

11. **What has this entire book been about?**

B. THE QUALITY OF LIFE

That's a quick review of what you have studied. This book has been about life, living things and their environment. Where do you proceed from here? Do you have any opinions? Have you made some decisions? What are your commitments?

A student in Kansas wrote:

> Apathy
> It never fed a hungry child
>   nor housed an outcast.
> It never cured disease
>   nor ended war.
> Instead it helped pollute our skies,
>   separate brothers.
> It drove some to seek help from drugs,
>   lesser numbers turn to God
> Conquer it. . .your life depends on it.
>
> Vicki Brooks, student

Here are some situations about life and the environment for you to think about. Your decisions may affect the quality of your future life.

On December 15, 1976, the tanker *Argo Merchant* ran aground near Cape Cod. It broke up and spilled oil 160 km across the Atlantic. On December 17, 1976, the tanker *Sansinema* exploded in Los Angeles Harbor. On December 27, 1976, the tanker *Olympic Games* ran aground in the Delaware River, spilling oil into the marshes. Tens of thousands of birds were endangered. The same thing happened in Puerto Rico on January 5, 1977, and in the Pacific Ocean on January 17, 1977. All of this happened within a month. All five tankers carried the flag of another country, where it is easy to register. Most other nations require higher standards for registration.

Can the United States forbid certain ships from entering its ports? Can one nation tell another nation what standards it must maintain?

12. What is your opinion?

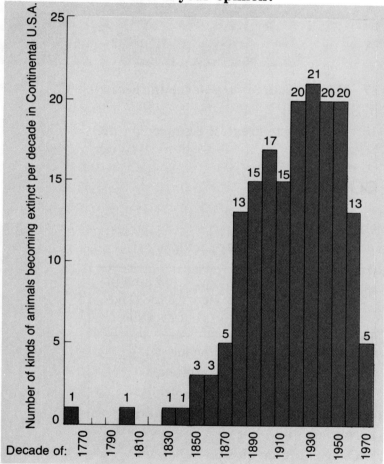

There are no more passenger pigeons, plains wolves, or Hawaiian land snails. They are _extinct_. For thousands of years, North America lost about three kinds of living things every 100 years. Since the arrival of the Puritans at Plymouth Rock in 1620, hundreds of plants and animals have become extinct. At present there are 170 endangered species in the United States.

Imagine that you are the owner of a beautiful, wooded lot. You paid a great deal of money for this lot. And now you are ready to build a home. Suddenly, someone discovers some rare salamanders on your land. They cannot be moved. If you build, you will disturb the environment and the salamanders will die.

13. What would you do?

Michael D. Sullivan

Each year over 200,000 cases of child abuse are reported. Over 1 million other cases are not reported. People don't like to talk about children being beaten and battered by parents and other adults. There was a Society for the Prevention of Cruelty to Animals 50 years before there was one for the prevention of cruelty to children.

14. How do you feel about these two rights? 1) The right of parents to bring up their children as they see fit. 2) The right of children to be free from bodily harm.

Child abuse is a crime. Now, a new California law makes it a crime also if you do not report a case of child abuse to the authorities.

15. Do you feel this is a good law? Why?

16. Would you report a case of child abuse and become involved in someone else's life?

Nancy Palmer

Armstrong/Rapho-Guillumette

Fitch/Black Star

17. What resource do you see in these pictures?

18. What is the greatest resource on the earth?

CONCEPT

WORDS TO KNOW

The following words have been used in this Idea. Carefully review the Idea and define each of them on your data sheet.

Air pollution	Pollutant
Balance	Transpiration
Cycle	Water cycle
Extinct	Water pollution
Nutrient cycle	
Oxygen-carbon dioxide cycle	

SUMMARY OF THE IDEA: BALANCE IN THE ENVIRONMENT

Early in this course you used an instrument called a *balance*. The balance is like a see-saw. There are two sides to it. On one side you place what you want to measure. On the other side you place masses until the two sides are in balance. Too much or too little on either side and you do not have balance.

The key word in this Idea has been *balance*. There is a delicate balance in the environment of the three resources necessary for life: air, water, and food. Too much or too little of a resource can affect life.

Animals remove oxygen from the air. Plants remove oxygen, too, and also carbon dioxide. Yet, the air does not lose all of its oxygen and carbon dioxide. This is because animals borrow oxygen from the air and return carbon dioxide. The plants borrow carbon dioxide and return more oxygen than they use. This oxygen-carbon dioxide cycle keeps everything in balance. That is, everything remains in balance if the air is not polluted too greatly.

A person needs to take in about two liters of water every day. That was fine a hundred years ago. But there are nearly five times as many people today. In addition, each person needs up to 300 liters of water each day to live in the style we are used to. Much of that water goes into irrigating or manufacturing the products we use. When living things use water, the water may become polluted. The major sources of pollution are: 1) chemical wastes, 2) decay of dead materials, 3) pesticides, 4) heat or thermal pollution, and 5) sewage.

Polluted water can be recycled to pure water again. If the pollution is not too great, nature can recycle and purify the water. Microorganisms can break down the waste materials, and running water can carry the waste away. The processes used in sewage plants are very similar to those used in nature. Centuries ago rain water was enough to sustain life. Living things lived in balance with the water cycle. Now we need more and larger sewage treatment plants to keep up with our needs. How much more can the water balance in nature take?

People seldom die from lack of air or water. But millions have died from starvation. Food has always been the resource in shortest supply. The rate at which our population is increasing is alarming. It may be too much for the natural cycles to provide us with the renewable resources necessary for life.

Animals eat plants, but the plants that survive reproduce. Predators consume their prey, but the prey that survive reproduce, too. Thus, there is a balance between plants and animals.

In nature there is no such thing as waste. Dead materials decay and become food for other living things. Thus, food grows, is consumed, or decays and becomes food again. This is the nutrient cycle, the process that supplies food to living things. The balance in the nutrient cycle can be upset when: 1) not enough food is grown, 2) too much is consumed, or 3) decayed nutrients are not returned to the ground.

All the resources necessary for life are parts of natural cycles. These cycles have no beginnings and no ends. The driving force behind all of these cycles is the sun. Apart from the sun, the earth is a self-contained unit. We are our own space ship. There is no chance of bringing in more resources. We have to use what we have wisely.

Is there a danger that we will destroy the ecosystem that is so necessary for us? That answer lies in the greatest resource on earth—people!

In this Idea on balance, you have studied five concepts.

1. State these five concepts.
2. What are the three major resources necessary for life?
3. Briefly explain or diagram the water cycle.
4. Briefly explain or diagram the oxygen-carbon dioxide cycle.
5. Briefly explain or diagram the nutrient cycle.
6. What organism has upset the natural cycles in the environment?
7. Explain balance in the environment.
8. What must living things live in balance with?

IDEA SUMMARY

ENRICHMENT

1. Prepare a display or collage showing the beauty of life.
2. Paint a mural showing how the natural cycles in the environment are related to each other.
3. Collect quotations on the dignity of people.

Aaron, Henry, 30
Acids, 170, 221
Acorn, growth of, 48
Active cells, 226
Acupuncture, 51
Adams, Alvin, 41
Adaptation, 289, 295-296
    of animals, 292-295
    of birds, 293
    of cacti, 289-292
Adrenal gland, 197
Adrenalin, 197, 282
African mantis, camouflage of, 293
Air:
    composition of, 61, 139, 142, 349
    and oxygen-carbon dioxide cycle,
        350, 367
    polluted, 62, 145, 177, 352-353
    and the respiratory system,
        174-175
Air sacs (see Alveoli)
Alaska, changing climate of, 259-260
Albino corn, 122
Alcohol:
    as a drug, 206
    effect on coordination, 206-207
    effect on drivers, 207
Alcoholism, 206-207
Alfalfa roots, 114
Algae, 316-318
    and formation of lichens, 318
    in zone of pollution, 344
Alice in Wonderland, 324
Alka-Seltzer, 145-152
Alveoli, 175, 188
    effect of smoking on, 178
Amber, formation of, 287
Ameba, 97, 105
    binary fission of, 219
Anaerobic bacteria, 142
Anemone, 319
Animals (see also specific type):
    adaptations of, 292-295
    camouflage of, 292-293
    cold-blooded, 243-244, 278
    heartbeat, rates of, 181
    in major land biomes, 307
    nocturnal, 251
    oxygen requirements of, 143, 152
    sexual reproduction of, 227-229
    temperature range for, 243
    traits in, 232
    warm-blooded, 243-244, 249
    and the water cycle, 340

Antarctic, temperature in the, 243
Ants, preservation of, 287
Anus, 169
Aquarium, example of an ecosystem,
    336
Argon, 61, 142
Arteries, 181-183
Asexual reproduction, 220, 225
Athelete's foot, 317
Atmosphere, and the water cycle,
    340-341
Atomic radiation, effect on
    Tardigrades, 268
Atria, 180
Automobile combustion, 160
    and air pollution, 353

Babies (human), 47
    footprints of, 73
    placed in incubators, 282
    size of, 45
Backbone, 204
Bacteria:
    anaerobic, 142
    colonies of, 255
    and decomposition of sewage,
        344, 357
    effect of temperature on, 243,
        285, 344
    found above biosphere, 264
    helpful, 357
    killed by penicillin, 9
    new forms of, 289, 295
    and the nutrient cycle, 357-359
    pathogenic, 255
    in polluted water, 344-346, 348
    reproduction of, 255
    resistant, 295
    role in decay, 217, 255, 285, 344,
        357
    shapes of, 255
    in water, 344-346, 348
Balance, 366-367
    of cycle, 343
    of ecosystem, 356
    Egyptian, 17
    laboratory, 18
    of plants and animals, 367
    precision, 22
    rules for using, 18-19
    zeroing of, 18
Banting, Dr., 160
Bear, fat reserve of, 246

Bedouins, 265
Benedict's solution, 163-164
Best, Dr., 160
Bichat, M., 101
Binary fission, 219
Biology:
    cell, 95
    history of, 85
Biomes, 306-307
    fresh water, 307
    land, 306-307
    ocean, 307
Biosphere, 263-266, 268
Birds (see also specific type):
    adaptation of, 293
    beak structure of, 293
    classification of, 42
    endangered by oil spills, 364-365
    found above biosphere, 264
    warm-blooded, 244, 249
Birth rate of humans, 254
Blepharisma, 221
Blinking, 54-55
Blood:
    circulation of, 180-184, 186
    considered a tissue, 183
    hormones in the, 194
    iron in the, 139
    oxygen-containing, 181
    waste-containing blood, 182
Blood cells:
    red, 92, 139, 183
    white, 183-184
Blood vessels, 179
    types of, 181
Box scores, 30
Brain, the, 200, 202-204
    complexity of, 273
    effect of alcohol on, 207
    parts of, 203
    size of, 203
Breathing, 61-64, 176-178, 202 (see
    also Respiration)
    animals that don't breathe, 177
    and average air intake, 63
    defined, 174
    and exercise, 63-64
Breathing rate:
    adult, 178
    of fish, 244
Brine shrimp, 270
Bromthymol blue and yellow, 117,
    143, 187
Bronchi, 174

Bronchioles, 174
Brooks, Vicki, 364
Brown, Robert, 105
Brown pelican, 326
Bud, 218
Budding, 218
Bumblebee moth, mimicry of, 293
Butterfly, development of, 48

Cactus, 289-292, 307
    environment of, 237
California kangaroo rat, 159
Calories, 161-162
Calvin, Melvin, 130
Camels, 265, 307
Camouflage, of animals, 292-293
Capillaries, 181-182, 188
    in the villi, 189
Carbohydrates:
    in foods, 161-162, 169
    manufactured by plants, 128,
        132, 136
    a source of energy, 165
Carbon, 67, 128
    in human body, 153
Carbon dioxide:
    in air, 61, 139, 349-350, 367
    in Alka-Seltzer, 145
    carried by red blood cells, 183
    diffusion of, 188
    and plants, 117, 124, 127, 132,
        135
    produced by yeast, 154
    and respiration, 137, 144-145,
        152, 159-160, 165, 177, 186,
        211
    sugar and the formation of, 155
    testing for, 117, 143-144
    and yeast, 145
Carbon monoxide, 145
Carburetor, 195
Carnivores, 69, 310
Carroll, Lewis, 324
Carrot, taproot of, 108
Cat dancing disease, 324
Caterpillar, metamorphosis of, 48
Celery, spots on, 110
Cell biology, 95
Cell membrane, 92, 191, 245, 255
Cell Theory, the, 91, 99-100, 105
    modern, 100
Cell wall, 92, 96
    of bacteria, 255
    of plants, 94, 96-97
    of spores, 239
Cells, 82-83
    active, 226
    binary fission of, 219
    budding of, 218
    and conduction of water, 111,
        115
    daughter, 219, 233
    dead, 115
    division of, 218-220, 225, 233,
        235
    egg, 228

and enzymes, 160
guard, 89, 116, 135
layer of, 101
in lilac, 100
liver, 157
mitochondria in, 157
nerve, 89, 102, 200
in nose and tongue, 274
nucleus of, 92, 226, 228, 239
oxidation in, 160
palisade, 101
parts, 92
passive, 226
plant, 82-83, 94, 96-97, 100-101
red blood, 92, 139, 183
reproduction of, 218-220
and respiration, 159-160, 165, 196
size and shape of, 86-87
skin, regeneration of, 223
sperm, 228
spongy, 102
staining of, 87
storage, 102
in tissues, 103, 105, 211, 298
water in, 96-97, 241
white blood, 183-184
yeast, 218, 245, 317
Cellulose, 92
Celsius degrees, 34
Centimeters, introduced, 12
Cereals, experiments with, 71
Cerebellum, 203
Cerebrum, 203
Changes in environment, 259-262,
    266
    and adaptation, 289
    adjustments to, 269-270, 281
    of United States, 287-288
Chemical control of systems,
    194-198
Chemical digestion, 169
Chemical energy, 132
Chemical indicator, 187
Chemical wastes causing water
    pollution, 343, 367
Chicago, temperatures in, 261
Child abuse, 365-366
Chlorophyll, 93, 120-122, 124-126,
    132, 135, 317
Chloroplasts, 93, 121, 135
Chromatography, 120-121
Chromosomes, 233-235
Cigarette smoking:
    and air pollution, 353
    effect on lungs, 177
    and respiration, 141, 177-178
Cigarette smoking machine, 28
Circulation, 179, 211, 241
Circulatory system, 179-184, 186,
    211
Classification, 42
Climate, 259-260
    of biomes, 306
    of earth, changes in, 290
Clown fish, 319
Coal, 153, 247

Coal dust, effect on lungs, 177
Coarse adjustment knob, 76
Cocaine, 209
Cockerals, 198
Cold-blooded animals, 243-244, 278
Colony, of bacteria, 255
Columbus, Christopher, 29
Comaneci, Nadia, 72
Commensalism, 319
Community:
    description of a, 308, 321, 327
    energy transfer in, 337
    food relationships in, 330, 332
    function of, 309-313
    pond, 330-331
    populations in a, 304, 332
    relationship to environment,
        335-336
Community game, 334-335
Compound microscopes, 74
Computers, 32
Concentration of molecules, 186
Conduction systems, 108
Conduction tissue, 111, 115, 132
Coniferous forests, 306
Conjugation tube, 226
Connective tissue, 102
Consumers, food, 309, 322, 337
    orders of, 328-329
Contractile vacuoles, 97
Control, 26
Coordination, 200-204, 206, 211
    effect of alcohol on, 206-207
Corn:
    albino, 122
    effect of temperature on, 243
    transpiration in, 340
Corn seedlings, 122, 126
Cotyledon, 58-59
Cowpox, 9
Cows, 69
Crabs, 57
Cricket, effect of temperature on,
    246
Crocodile, 315
Crocodile bird, 315
Cuts, healing of, 219, 223
Cycles, 339, 367
    balance of, 343
    nutrient, 357-359, 367
    oxygen-carbon dioxide, 350, 367
    predator-prey, 313, 337
    water, 340-342
Cylinder, graduated, 24
Cytology, 87
Cytoplasm, 92, 226, 228
    shrinking of, 96

Daphnia, 279-281, 310-311
Data, 29
Data tables, 29
Daughter cells, 219, 233
DDT, 325
Death rate of humans, 254
Death Valley, rainfall in, 260
DeBary, Heinrich, 318

Decay:
    caused by bacteria, 217, 255, 285, 344, 357
    of food, 285
    organisms that cause, 238
    study of, 217
Deciduous forests, 307
Decomposers, 238, 255
Decomposition, 344
    zone of, 344
Density, population, 300-301
    of selected areas, 301
Desert, 237, 243, 249, 260, 307
    cacti in, 289, 291
    Sahara, 265
    temperature range of, 278
Desert lizards, 278
Detergents, 343
Diabetes, 160, 197
Diaphragm:
    human, 175-176
    of microscope, 76
Diet:
    bad, 70-71
    balanced, 70
Diffusion, 186, 191, 211, 245
    in the intestines, 189
    through a membrane, 188
Digestion, 167-171, 202, 211
    chemical, 169
Digestive system, 168-169, 185, 211, 241
    water in, 169, 241
Dinosaur, fossils of, 287
Division, a form of reproduction, 218-220, 225, 233, 235
DNA, 236
Dogs, 319
Drug, 206
Drug abuse, 206-211
    defined, 206
Drugs, number of people using, 208
Dutrochet, Rene, 99, 101, 105

Earth:
    climate changes of, 290
    diversity of life on, 225
    origin of life on, 213-214, 235
    population of, 253, 257, 301
    space view of, 263
    sugar supply of, 131
    temperature range of, 243
Ecologists, 335-336
Ecology, 335
Ecosystems, 336-337, 350
Eggs, 233
    fish, 228
    human, 47, 227-228
    of penguins, 265
Egyptian balance, 17
Electron microscopes, 75, 231
Elodea, 92, 94
Embryo, 229
    human, 47
    in plant seed, 58-59

Endangered species:
    defined, 325
    number of, in United States, 365
Endocrine glands, 194, 196-197
Endocrine system, 194-198, 211
Energy:
    chemical, 132
    defined, 125
    heat, 157-159, 247-248
    light, 125-126, 132, 135-136, 157, 247-248
    obtained by plants, 124, 135, 247
    provided by plants, 131-132, 136
    provided by seeds, 134
    provided by sugar, 158-160, 196-197
    solar, 125-126, 135, 247-248, 258, 339
    stored in food, 161-162, 165, 167, 196, 211, 247-248, 328-329, 332
    stored and released by mitochondria, 157
Energy chains, 328
Energy flow in food chains, 328-329
Energy transfer in a community, 337
Environment, 237-268
    biological factors in, 237
    changes in, 259-262, 266, 269-270, 281, 289
    community relationship to, 335-336
    inside, steady, 276, 278
    on the moon, 267
    on other plants, 263
    physical factors in, 237, 241, 243, 268, 335
    studied by ecologists, 335-336
Environmental changes, caused by people, 262
Enzymes, 160, 165
    and conversion of starch, 162
Eohippus, 288
Epicotyl, 59
Epidermis, 101
Epiglottis, 174
Epithelial tissue, 102
Eskimos, 265
Esophagus, 168, 174
Evaporation, 340-342
Excretion, role of water in, 241
Exercise, effect on breathing rate, 63, 144
Exhaling, 176
Experiments, 38
    controlled, 26
Extinction, 292, 296, 365
Eyepiece, 75
Eyes, the, 274
    effect of marijuana on, 54
    limitations of, 73
    parts of, 53
    responses of, 54-55

Factories, and air pollution, 353
Farming, 132-134

Fatigue, 159
Fats, 153, 162, 165, 169, 265
Fertilization, 228
Fertilizers, soil, 123, 258, 343
    produced from sewage, 357
Fibrous roots, 108
Field mice, 313, 322
Filters in the respiratory system, 177
Filtration of water, 346
Fine adjustment knob, 78
Fingerprints, 73-74
Fish (see also specific type):
    breathing and respiration of, 62, 147, 151-152, 244
    cold-blooded, 244, 278
    depth of habitat, 264
    eggs of, 228
    gills of, 244
    growth rings on, 47
    and ingestion of mercury, 324
    in polluted water, 147, 344-345
    sexual reproduction in, 228-229
Fish protein concentrate (FPC), 258
Fission, binary, 219
Fleas, 319
Fleming, Sir Alexander, 9
Fluctuation of populations, 297
Fly:
    development of, 48, 214
    preservation of, 287
Food, 67-71
    absorbed by intestines, 189
    calorie content of, 161-162
    carbohydrates in, 161-162, 169
    carried in the capillaries, 182
    consumers of, 309, 322, 328-329, 337
    containing starch, 256
    decay of, 285
    digestion of, 167-169, 211
    effect of mold on, 238
    fatty, 265
    frozen, 285
    junk, 70
    and the nutrient cycle, 357-359, 367
    oxidation of, 165
    produced by halobacteria, 258
    producers of, 309, 316, 322, 328
    relationships, 310-311, 322, 330, 332
    seeds as a source of, 134
    as a source of energy, 161-162, 165, 167, 196, 211, 247-248, 328-329, 332
Food chain game, 325-326
Food chains, 322-323, 327-328, 343
    energy flow in, 328-329
    and passing of poisons, 324-325
Food supply, and human population, 254, 257-258
Food web, 329-330
Forests, 337
    types of, 306-307
Fossils, 284-287, 295
    dinosaur, 287

Fossils (*cont.*)
of horse, 287
preserved in amber, 287
preserved in tar, 285
rabbit, 285
of wooly mammoth, 285
Freezing point of water, 34
Fresh water biome, 307
subtypes of, 308
Frog:
cold-blooded, 278
development of, 48
Frozen food, 285
Fungi, 238, 317-318
and formation of lichens, 318

Gall bladder, 168
Gametes, 226
female and male, 227
Garbage, daily amount of, 356
Gasoline, 247
Gastric juice, 168, 170
Geese, Canadian, 251
Generations, 313
Genes, 234-235
Genetics, 233, 235
Gills, fish, 244
Glands:
adrenal, 197
endocrine, 194, 196-197
pancreas, 197
pituitary, 196
salivary, 194
Glucose, 165
Goldberger, Dr. Joseph, 70
Goldstein, Dr. Dora B., 206
Gonads, 197
Goose tree, 213
Graduate, 24
Grams, introduced, 18
Grass:
fibrous roots of, 108
of the sea, 136
Grasslands, 307
Growth:
of humans, 193
as a sign of life, 45-50
of trees, 46
Growth rings, 46-47
Guard cells, 89, 116, 135

Halobacteria, 258
Hamburger, food content of, 169
Harvey, William, 179
Hatchet fish, 264
Hawaii, rainfall in, 260
Hawaiian land snails, 365
Hawk and field mice cards, 311-312
Hawks, 313-322
Healing of cuts, 219, 223
Heart, 179, 273, 362
chambers of, 180
effect of adrenalin on, 197
size of, 180
valves of, 180

Heartbeat:
of daphnia, 280
rates of, 181
Heat energy, 157-159, 247-248
Helium, 61, 142
Hemoglobin, 139, 183
Herbivores, 69, 310, 328
Heredity, 232-233
Heroin, 209
Hibernation, 246
of Tardigrade, 268
Histology, 101
Homunculus, 227
Hooke, Robert, 81-83, 85, 91, 99,
105
Hormones:
carried in the blood, 194
defined, 194
game of, 197-198
growth, 196
as regulators, 195-196
sex, 197
types of, 196-197
Horse:
fossils of, 287
prehistoric (Eohippus), 288
telling age of, 47
Hosts for parasites, 319
Human body:
adjustment to temperature, 272
carbon in, 153
circulatory system in, 179-184,
186, 211
digestive system in, 168-169, 185,
211, 241
endocrine system in, 194-198, 211
nervous sytem in, 200-204, 211
organs in the, 103, 108
oxygen in the, 139, 181-183, 350
regeneration in, 223
respiratory system in, 174-175,
185-186, 211
sugar in, 158
temperature of, 195, 243, 274,
278
water in, 59-60
Humans, traits in, 232
Hydra, 310
budding of, 218, 225
Hydrochloric acid, 170
Hydrogen, 67
Hydrogen peroxide, 148
Hypocotyl, 59

Illusions, optical, 5
Indicator, chemical, 187
Inhaling, 176
Insects (*see also* specific types):
breathing of, 62
and DDT, 325
and mutualism, 318
Inside environments, steady, 276,
278
Insulin, 160, 197
Interdependent relationships, 333,
335, 337

Intestine, 189
difussion in, 189
large, 169
small, 168, 171
Intravenous feeding, 195
Iodine:
use of in cytology, 87
used to test for starch, 128, 190
Iris, of eye, 53
Iron:
in blood, 139
rusting of, 139

Jefferson, Thomas, 23
Jellyfish, 177
Jenner, Dr. Edward, 9

Keller, Helen, 6
Kilogram, introduced, 18
Kilometers, introduced, 15
Krypton, 61, 142

Laboratory balance, 18
Lake St. Clair, 324
Large intestine, 169
Larynx, 174
Lavoisier, Antoine Laurent, 145
Leaf:
characteristics of, 40, 42-43
cut-away drawing of, 121
Leeuwenhoek, Anthony van, 80-81,
85, 91, 99, 105, 227
Lens:
of electron microscope, 75
of eye, 53
of magnifying glass, 74
Lichens, 318
Life:
characteristics of, 39-72
diversity of, on earth, 225
origin of, on earth, 213-214, 235
on other planets, 263
our most valuable resource,
361-362
Light:
attraction to moth, 250-251
energy, 125-126, 132, 135-136,
157, 247-248
received by the eyes, 53
Lilac, cells in, 100
Liters, introduced, 24
Liver, 168
cells, 157
effect of adrenalin on, 197
effect of alcohol on, 207
Lizards, 57
cold-blooded, 244, 278
desert, 278
regeneration of tail of, 222
Lobsters, 57
Los Angeles, temperatures in, 261
"Lub-dub" sounds, 180
Lungs, 174-175, 244
diffusion of gases in, 188
effect of coal dust on, 177

effect of smoking on, 177-178
and respiration, 139, 141
role in breathing, 176

Maggot, metamorphosis of, 48, 214
Magnification, 74
Mammals, warm-blooded, 244
Mammoth, wooly, 285
Marijuana:
    effect on human responses, 54
    reasons for using, 208
Mars, life on, 39, 156
Mass:
    defined, 18
    measurement of, 18
Mealworms, metamorphosis of, 51
Measurements, 10-15
    eighteenth century, 23
    human, 11
    of mass, 18-22
    metric, 11-23
Meat, imitation, 257
Medulla, 203
Membrane:
    cell, 92, 191, 245, 255
    difusion through, 188
    plasma, 92
Mendel, Gregor, 232-233
Mercury poisoning, 324
Metamorphosis, 51, 214
    defined, 48
Methamphetamine, 209
Metric measurements, 11-23
Microorganisms in water, 147
Microscopes, 74-79, 95, 235
    compound, 74
    early, 79-83
    electron, 75, 231
    Hooke's, 82
    inversion of objects by, 100
    Leeuwenhoek's, 80, 227
    parts of, 75-76
Microscopic animals ("Beasties"),
    80-81, 85
Migration of geese, 251
Milliliters, introduced, 24
Millimeters, introduced, 11
Mimicry, 292
Mimosa, 56
Minamata, Japan, 324
Minerals (see also specific type):
    absorbed by plants, 108, 114, 123
    defined, 123
Mirror, of microscope, 75
Mistletoe, 319
Mitochondria, 157
Mitosis, 219
Mold, 238
    colonies of, 255
    reproduction of, 239
    as source of penicillin, 9, 238
    a type of fungus, 317
Molecules, 97
    concentration of, 186
    random movement of, 186
Moon, environment on the, 267
Moth, attraction to light, 250-251

Motor nerves, 203-204
Mountain tops, plant life on, 264
Mouth, 168, 174
Muscle tissue, 102
Muscles, 274
    effect of adrenalin on, 197
    motor nerves and, 203
Mushrooms, 317
Mutualism, 318
Mycelium, 239, 255

Neon, 61, 142
Nerve, optic, 53
Nerve cells, 89, 102, 200
Nerve tissue, 102, 202
Nerves:
    motor, 203-204
    sensory, 203-204
Nervous control of systems, 194,
    199
Nervous system, 200-204, 211
    effect of alcohol on, 207
Neuron, 202
New York City, rainfall in, 260
Nitrates, 123
Nitrogen, 61, 67, 128, 139, 349
    and the nutrient cycle, 357-359
Nocturnal animals, 251
Nose, 174, 177
Nucleus of cells, 92, 227-228, 239
Nutrient cycle, 357-359, 367
Nutrients, 359
Nutritional relationship, 310-311,
    322, 330, 332

Obesity, 197
Objectives, high and low, 75
Observation:
    defined, 4
    and scientific learning, 231
Ocean biome, 307
    zones of, 308
Oceans:
    pollution of, 324, 364-365
    tides of, 259
Oil spills, 364-365
Oils, 153, 247, 259-260
Omnivores, 69, 310
Optic nerve, 53
Optical illusions, 5
Organ systems, 104, 298
Organic materials, 153
Organisms:
    adjustments in, 270
    defined, 211
    in a population, 298, 303
    reproduction of, 218-220
Organs, 103-104, 211
    in human body, 103, 108
    in plants, 103, 108
    in a system, 298
    tissues in, 103, 298
Ovaries, 197
Owl, 251
Oxidation, 139
    in cells, 160
    of food, 165

Oxygen, 61, 67, 128, 137, 139
    animals' need for, 143, 152
    in the blood, 181
    carried in the capillaries, 182
    carried by red blood cells, 183
    diffusion of, 188
    discovery of, 349
    in human body, 139, 181-183,
        350
    needed for decomposition, 344
    in polluted water, 344-345
    and respiration, 141, 152, 159,
        177, 185-186, 211
    Tardigrade's survival without, 268
    testing for, 147-149
    in water, 147-151, 344-345
Oxygen booster, 148
Oxygen-carbon dioxide cycle, 350,
    367

Pacemaker, 362
Palisade cells, 101
Pancreas, 168
Pancreas gland, 197
Paper chromatography, 120
Paramecium, 97, 105, 177
    binary fission of, 219
Parasites, 319
Parasitism, 319
Passenger pigeons, extinction of,
    262, 365
Passive cells, 226
Pasteur, Louis, 217
Pathogenic bacteria, 255
Pavlov, Ivan, 55
Pea plant, 48
Pelican, brown, 326
Penguins, 265
Penicillin, 9, 238
Pepsin, 170
Peregrine falcon, 325
Perspiration, 272
Petersen, Dr. Robert, 206
Pharynx, 174
Phenolphthalein, 187
Phosphates, 123
Photoperiodism, 252
Photosynthesis, 339, 349
    compared to respiration, 137, 152
    defined, 127, 136
    equation for, 130
    and the making of carbohydrates,
        128
    raw materials of, 127, 130
    role of sunlight in, 247-248
    role of water in, 127, 132, 137,
        241
    of water plants, 151, 249
Phototropism, 56, 251
Physical factors in an environment,
    237, 241, 243, 268, 335
Pigeons, passenger, 262, 265
Pigments:
    defined, 119
    of plants, 119-120
Pine trees, effect of temperature on,
    243

Pituitary gland, 196
Plains wolf, 365
Planarians, regeneration of, 222
Plankton, 136
Plants (*see also* specific type):
    blooming of, and sunlight, 251
    breathing of, 62
    carbohydrates produced by, 128, 132, 136
    and carbon dioxide, 117, 124, 127, 132, 135
    cells of, 82-83, 94, 96-97, 100, 101
    and changes in earth's climate, 290
    dead, 136
    effect of temperature on, 243
    energy obtained, 124, 135, 247
    energy provided by, 131-132, 136
    flowering and mutualism, 318
    food intake of, 69
    green, as food producers, 309, 316, 322, 328
    green pigment of, 119-120
    growth of, 48
    historical importance of, 145
    killed by polluted air, 352
    minerals absorbed by, 108, 114, 123
    organs in, 103, 108
    photosynthesis in, 127-130, 132, 136-137, 152, 241, 247, 249, 339, 349
    phototropism in, 56, 251
    pigments of, 119-120
    protein produced by, 357-358
    and rain, 113
    responses of, 56
    seeds of, 48, 58-59, 130
    sexual reproduction in, 225-227
    starch produced by, 128, 132
    sugar produced by, 128, 131-132, 135
    sunlight energy trapped by, 247-248
    symbiosis in, 316-318
    systems in, 108, 117
    traits in, 232
    transpiration in, 240
    transportation system in, 117
    water in, 92, 108, 113-114, 117, 127, 132, 135, 137, 241, 340
Plasma, blood, 183
Plasma membrane, 192
    of Blepharisma, 221
    pores of, 94
shrinking of, 96
Plasmolysis, 96
Plastics, 153
Pollutants, 352
Polution:
    air, 62, 145, 177, 352-353
    ocean, 342, 364-365
    thermal, 343-344, 367
    water, 147, 324, 343-345, 367
    zone of, 344

Population:
    defined, 253, 298, 321, 357
    density, 300-301
    derivation of word, 298
    of earth, 253, 257, 301
    and food supply, 254, 257-258
    fluctuation of, 297
    of major land biomes, 306-307
    part of a community, 304, 332
    of predator, 313
    of prey, 313
    salmon, 297
    world, 253, 257, 301
Population growth curve, 302
Pores, in plasma membrane, 94
Precision balance, 22
Predator-prey cycles, 313, 337
Predators, 310-313, 322
    defined, 310
    number of, 213
Prediction, 20, 38, 115
Prey, 322
    defined, 310
    number of, 313
Priestley, Joseph, 349
Producers, food, 309, 316, 322, 328
Proteins, 153, 160, 165, 169, 256
    manufacture of, 357-358
    testing for, 256
Protoplasm, 67, 239, 241
Pulse, 183
Pupil, of eye, 53

Quail feathers, signs of growth, 47

Rabbits:
    preserved as fossils, 285
    snowshoe, 259, 306
Radicle, 59
Rain, and plant life, 113
Rainfall, amount of, 260
Raw materials, of photosynthesis, 127, 130
Receptors, on neurons, 202
Recycling:
    of waste, 356
    of water, 345-346, 367
Red blood cells, 92, 183
    iron in, 139
Redi, Francesco, 214, 216-217, 235
Redwood tree, size of, 45
Refrigeration of food, 285
Regeneration, 57, 221-223, 235
Regulate, 195
Regulation, 211
    examples of, 195
Relationships, 297-298
    and ecosystems, 336
    food, 310, 322, 330, 332
    interdependent, 333, 335, 337
    nutritional, 310, 322, 330, 332
    predator-prey, 313, 337
    symbiotic, 316-319, 322, 337
Remoras, 319

Reproduction, 218-220, 235
    asexual, 220, 225
    of bacteria, 255
    of cells, 218-220
    of mold, 239
    sexual, 225-229, 233
Reptiles, regeneration and, 222
Resistant bacteria, 295
Respiration, 61-64, 137-166, 211, 239, 349 (*see also* Breathing)
    and carbon dioxide, 137, 144-145, 152, 159-160, 165, 167, 186, 211
    cellular, 159-160, 165, 196
    cigarette smoking and, 141
    compared to photosynthesis, 137, 152
    defined, 174, 211
    of fish, 62, 147, 151-152, 244
    and formation of water vapor, 159-160
    and the lungs, 139, 141
    and mitochondria, 157
    and oxygen, 141, 152, 159, 177, 185-186, 211
    role of sugar in, 155, 159, 165
    and water, 137, 165, 241
Respiratory system, 174-175, 185-186, 211
    air and the, 174-175
    filters in, 177
    moisture in, 177
Respiratory therapy technician, 64
Response, 52
Retina, 53
Rhinoceros, 315
Ribs, 175-176
Rice, new variety of, 257
Rings, growth, 46-47
Ringworm, 317
Roadrunner, the, 249
Root hairs, 114, 135
Roots, 114
    types of, 108
Rusting, 139
Ruth, Babe, 29
Rye plants, roots of, 114

Saber-tooth tiger, fossils of, 285
Sahara desert, 265
Saliva, 162, 168, 170
Salivary glands, 194
Salmon, 297
Salt, dissolved in water, 97
Salt water, 96
Schleiden, Matthias, 99-100, 105
Schwann, Theodor, 99-100, 105
Science, discussion of, 39
Scientific method, 33, 37-38
Seaweed, 316
Sedimentation, 346
Sediments, 345
Seed coat, 59
Seeds:
    lima bean, 58
    need for water, 58

parts of, 58-59
pea plant, 48
as a source of energy, 134
as a source of food, 137
Senses, the, 4-6, 202
Sensory nerves, 203, 204
Sewage:
   decomposition of, 344
   and water pollution, 147,
      344-345, 367
Sewage treatment plant, 357, 367
Sexual reproduction, 225-229, 233
   of animals, 227-229
   in fish, 228-229
   in plants, 225-227
Shape, of living things, 41
Sharks, 68, 319
Sheep, growth rings on, 47
Shivering, 272
Shrimp, brine, 270
Size:
   of babies (human), 45
   of living things, 40-41
   of redwood tree, 45
   of whale, 45
Skin cells, 223
Small intestines, 168, 171
Smallpox, 9
Smog, 352
Smoker's cough, 178
Snakes, shedding of skin, 222
Snowshoe rabbit, 259
Soil fertilizers, 123, 258, 343
Soy beans, 257
Spallanzani, Lazaro, 217
Sperm, 227-228, 233
Spiders, 264
Spinal cord, 200, 204
Spiracles, 62
Spirogyra, 225-227
Sponges, regeneration in, 223
Spongy cells, 102
Spontaneous generation, theories of,
   213-217, 235
Spores, 239
Staining of cells, 87
Starch:
   composition of, 153
   conversion to sugar, 162, 165, 170
   effect of enzymes on, 162
   foods containing, 256
   manufactured by plants, 128, 132
   testing for, 128, 190
Starfish, regeneration of, 57, 223
Starvation, 367
Steel wool, 139
Stethoscope, 180
Stimulus, 52
Stomach, 168, 171
Stomates, 62, 115, 124, 340
   of cacti, 292
Storage cells, 102
Sugar, 153
   effect of insulin, 160, 197
   energy produced from, 158-160,
      196-197

and formation of carbon dioxide,
   155
glucose, 165
in the human body, 158
human intake of, 71
manufactured by plants, 128,
   131-132, 135
produced from starch, 162, 165,
   170
and respiration, 155, 159, 165
testing for, 163-164
and testing of Martian soil, 156
world supply of, 131
Sulfates, 123
Sundew plant, 69
Sunflower leaf, 116, 251
Sunlight, as a source of energy, 125-
   126, 135, 247-248, 258, 339
Sutton, Walter, 233
Symbiosis, 316, 332, 337
   of lichens, 318
   origin of word, 318
   types of, 318-319
Systems, 211
   circulatory, 179-184, 186, 211
   conduction, 108
   control of, 194-198, 200-204
   digestive, 168-169, 185, 211, 241
   endocrine, 194-198, 211
   nervous, 200-204, 207-211
   organ, 104, 298
   in plants, 108, 117
   respiratory, 174-175, 185-186,
      211
   transportation, 117

Tadpole, metamorphosis of, 48
Tankers, 365
Tapeworms, 319-320
Taproots, 108
Tar, and preservation of fossils, 285
Tardigrade, 71, 268
Taxonomer, 42
Teeth, 168
   regeneration of, 222-223
Temperature, 34, 243
   and adjustment of human body,
      272
   in the Antarctic, 243
   body, 195, 243, 274, 278
   in the desert, 278
   on earth, 243
   effect on bacteria, 243, 285, 344
   effect on corn, 243
   effect on crickets, 246
   effect on pine trees, 243
   effect on plants, 243
   effect on Tardigrades, 268
   recorded in Chicago and
      Los Angeles, 261
   of water, and cold-blooded
      animals, 278
Termites, 319
Test paper, 59-60
Testes, 197
Testosterone, 198

Thermal pollution, 343-344, 367
Thermometer, 34
Thermostat, 195
Thyroid gland, 196
Thyroxin, 196-197
Tick bird, 315
Tides, ocean, 259
Tissues, 101, 105, 211, 298
   conduction, 111, 115, 132
   connective, 102
   muscle, 102
   nerve, 102, 202
   in organs, 103, 298
   types of, 102
Tongue, 168
Trachea, 174
Traits, 232
   inherited, 234-235
Transpiration, 340-342
Transportation systems, in plants,
   117
Trees:
   goose, 213
   growth of, 46
   oak, 319
   phototropism in, 251
   redwood, 45
Tropical rain forests, 307
Tropism, 56
Tundra, 306

Vacuoles, 93
   contactile, 97
Valves:
   of the heart, 180
   in the veins, 182
van Helmont, Jan Baptista, 127
Veins, 181-183
Ventricles, 180
Venus fly trap, 56
Viking lander, 156
Villi, 189
Virchow, Rudolph, 220
Vocal cords, 174
Volume:
   defined, 24
   measurement of, 24-28

Walker, John, 64
Warm-blooded animals, 243-244,
   249
Waste:
   in blood, 182
   recycling of, 356
Water:
   in the atmosphere, 340-342
   bacteria in, 344-346
   in cells, 96-97, 241
   conduction of, 108, 111, 115
   in the digestive system, 169, 241
   and excretion, 241
   filtration of, 346
   flowing, 308
   freezing point of, 34
   and growth of seeds, 58
   in the human body, 59-60

Water (cont.)
  microorganisms in, 147
  oxygen content of, 147, 151,
    344-345
  and photosynthesis, 127, 132,
    137, 241
  and plant life, 92, 108, 113-114,
    117, 127, 132, 135, 137, 241,
    340
  and plasmolysis, 96
  pollution of, 147, 324, 343-345,
    367
  recycling of, 345-346, 367
  and respiration, 137, 165, 241
  salt dissolved in, 97
  sedimentation of, 346
  self-purification of, 344
  standing, 308

  temperature, and cold-blooded
    animals, 278
  warm, 344
Water cycle, 340-342
Water plants:
  depth of, 264
  photosynthesis of, 151, 249
Water vapor, 61, 117
  formed in respiration, 159-160
Whales:
  breathing of, 65
  size of, 45
Wheat, new varieties, 257
White blood cells, 183-184
Wooly mammoth, 285
Work, 158
World (see Earth)
Worms, 177

Wyoming, fossils found in, 287

Xenon, 61, 142

Yeast, 153-154
  and carbon dioxide, 145
Yeast cells, 317
  cell membrane of, 245
  reproduction of, 218
Yeast plants, 64-65, 67
Yolk, 228

Zeroing of balance, 18
Zone of clear water, 345
Zone of decomposition, 344
Zone of pollution, 344
Zone of recovery, 345
Zygote, 226-229